Polychaetes

Oligochaetes

Leeches

Echiurids

Sipunculids

ANNELIDS

ARTHROPODS

Myriapodous arthropods

Crustaceans

Insects

Cephalopods

Tooth shells

Bivalves

Gastropods

Chitons

MOLLUSKS

Protostomes

Lamp shells

Moss animals

LOPHOPHORATES

Nemerteans

Flatworms

LOWER WORMS

Glass sponges

Calcareous sponges

Fibrous sponges

SPONGES

The
Animal
Kingdom

The
Animal
Kingdom

ROBERT T. ORR

THE MACMILLAN COMPANY, NEW YORK

DEDICATED TO MY WIFE

DOROTHY

WHO NOT ONLY PROVIDED GREAT MATERIAL ASSISTANCE
BUT ALSO SHARED WITH ME MANY OF THE EXPERIENCES
RELATED IN THIS BOOK.

CONTENTS

ILLUSTRATIONS

COLOR PLATES

(Following page 96)

INTRODUCTION

To become acquainted with other living creatures that share the world with us is one of the most satisfying and intellectually stimulating things that man can do. Whether we travel far or just explore our own back yard, it gives us pleasure to be able to name the things that we see. Apart from the pure satisfaction of being able to identify objects, whether they be animate or inanimate, there is a great deal that can be learned from studying the habits of the living things that eat, sleep, fight, or even make love much like man himself.

A child who observes nature often makes a better citizen than one who does not. This does not necessarily imply greater mental powers on the part of the farmer or hunter or zoologist, but perhaps reflects a broader background that results from an awareness of animal behavior. Many of the lower organisms have rather highly developed social systems, and in these we can perceive resemblances to our own human society.

Apart from the possible social and cultural benefits that may result from an acquaintance with animals, there is also the pleasure derived from it. No one can observe a tide pool along a seacoast without being overwhelmed by the beauty and diversity of the animals that inhabit it. The throngs that daily visit the zoos throughout the world bear witness to the enormous attraction that other animals have to our own kind.

There are estimated to be close to one million different species of animals living in the world today. No one person could possibly hope to see or know every one of these, nor could all the names be contained within the covers of a single volume. Even the expert is usually a specialist in one small group of animals and has only a general knowledge of the rest.

In this book an attempt has been made to describe the major groups of animals and give some examples of the better-known species as well as some facts regarding their life history and behavior. It is slanted primarily toward the nontechnical reader, but some technical terms are used. This has been necessary where no common names or terms are available.

I

CLASSIFICATION

When one is dealing with large numbers of entities, a system of arrangement is necessary so that any one item can be located with a minimum of effort. In a library, books are catalogued and arranged on shelves in a definite order. Those pertaining to similar subjects are grouped together. Such a system not only facilitates the quick location of a particular volume but gives some sort of indication of its relationship to other works.

Zoologists, or students of animal life, have developed a somewhat comparable system for classifying the organisms with which they are concerned. This system was started by a great Swedish scientist named Karl von Linné, but better known as Linnaeus, back in the middle of the eighteenth century. Linnaeus proposed that each kind of organism be given two names and that these names be in the universal language of Latin so that no confusion could arise as a result of translation. The first given name is the generic name and the second is the specific name. For example, he named man *Homo sapiens*.

Within a single genus there may be a number of species. Such a grouping shows a close relationship yet indicates differences. In North America there are a number of different kinds of tree squirrels classified under the genus *Sciurus*. These include such species as the eastern gray squirrel (*Sciurus carolinensis*), the western gray squirrel (*Sciurus griseus*), the Kaibab squirrel (*Sciurus aberti*), and the fox squirrel (*Sciurus niger*), to mention a few. However, there are other tree squirrels in North America that are sufficiently distinct from the genus *Sciurus* that they are placed in another genus called *Tamiasciurus*. This includes the several species of red squirrels. In other parts of the world there are other genera of tree squirrels.

Genera, in turn, are grouped together in families. All the squirrel-like animals, including the woodchucks, marmots, and chipmunks, are in a family called the Sciuridae. Squirrels are rodents, and all the families of rodents are placed in a higher category known as an order. In this instance, the order is called Rodentia. Orders are then grouped under classes. The Rodentia represent one of the nineteen orders of living mammals, or members of the class Mammalia. Classes are large categories, but they are grouped into even larger divisions known as phyla. The Mammalia belong to the phylum Chordata—animals that have an internal axial skeleton.

The chordates, or members of the phylum Chordata, represent the highest group of living animals. The lowest are placed in the phylum Protozoa, which includes those animals whose bodies consist of but a single cell.

From the lowest to the highest forms of animal life, it is evident that there is an orderly sequence of increasing complexity. It is the belief of biologists that the simplest multicellular organisms arose from unicellular forms of life as a result of certain cells aggregating and then specializing in different functions, each of which contributed to the welfare of the community of cells. This led to the development of tissues and, later, organ systems. Once the organ systems were well established, the higher animals branched into two main stems. One of these led to the development of mollusks, segmented worms, and arthropods. The other branch led to the echinoderms and backboned animals, or vertebrates.

Since man is a vertebrate, he too can assume that his lineage goes back to unicellular forms of life. In the modern system of classification, man is placed in the family Hominidae, which is very close to the family containing the great apes. Paleontologists and anthropologists believe that both families developed from a common ancestor. The order Primates to which man, the apes, and monkeys belong arose from a primitive insectivorous group of animals which is represented in the world today by shrews, moles, hedgehogs, and their relatives.

Despite his advanced brain and upright posture, man is in many respects a rather primitive mammal, lacking in many specializations. He still retains the basic terrestrial limb with five digits on each appendage. His teeth are unspecialized and suitable therefore for an omnivorous diet. Most of his organ systems are extremely close to those of other higher primates.

2

ANIMALS IN TIME

The science of paleontology has shown us that living things have been steadily undergoing changes in structure and distribution since life began. Indisputable evidence of this is found in the study of the earth's history.

We are familiar with many of the common animals about us in the world today and are aware in general of the present distribution of the better-known species. For example, we associate elephants with Africa and Asia. In the past, however, elephants were more widely distributed. A study of fossil deposits in the Northern Hemisphere shows that within the past million years a number of species of elephant-like animals inhabited both North America and Europe. They belonged to two groups. One of these consisted of the mastodons and the other the mammoths. There are no longer any close relatives of the mastodons left in the world, but the mammoths are represented by the modern elephants. (It is believed that some species of true mammoths were contemporary with man during the Stone Age. This contention is supported by the presence of ancient pictures of these animals found on the walls of caves in France.)

Paleontology shows us that the farther back we go into the history of the earth the more primitive were the various forms of plant and animal life. This is demonstrated both by the study of fossils and by geology.

Fossils are formed in several different ways. In most instances they result from the covering of a dead animal or plant either with sediment, as on the bottom of a lake or ocean, or by silt and sand on a flood plain or desert. In time the deposit, as a result of the action of water and various chemicals, may harden and encase some of the organic remains in rock. The original elements—such as bone, shell, or wood—are eventually replaced by minerals.

The age of a fossil is determined by the age of the rock in which it is found. Geologists determine the age of rocks in a number of ways, but the commonest method involves a study of the radioactive elements present. For example, in a period of four and a half billion years a pound of uranium will be reduced to one-half that amount plus half a pound of lead, irrespective of other forces such as pressure and heat to which it has been subjected. By determining the ratio of uranium to lead in a given deposit, its age may readily be computed.

The geological timetable is divided into five great eras on the basis of different strata of sedimentary rock found on the earth's crust. The latter, which formed as the earth began cooling from a molten mass, consists of basalt with a thin covering of granite.

The first era began a little over three and a half billion years ago, when the first mountains on the surface of the earth began to deteriorate as a consequence of erosion and the resulting sediments settled in adjacent basins. This era is known as the Archeozoic. Rock of this age may be seen in the bottom of the Grand Canyon in Arizona. Although no fossils have been found in Archeozoic deposits, they contain many examples of pure carbon, considered an indication of organic life.

The second era is the Proterozoic, which began about one and a half billion years ago. Deposits of this age contain remains of many kinds of invertebrates, such as sponges, corals, and worms. Before it terminated there were brachiopods, mollusks, and arthropods.

The third era, the Paleozoic, started six hundred million years ago. This was probably a time when all modern phyla were represented. At the beginning the dominant animals were trilobites, a group of ancient arthropods that became extinct long ago, and brachiopods, which are represented in the world today by but a small number of species. They were supplanted within one hundred million years by primitive back-boned animals—first the fishes, then the amphibians. By the end of the Paleozoic, some two hundred and twenty-five million years ago, all major modern groups of animals, except birds and mammals, had made their appearance.

The fourth era is the Mesozoic, commonly known as the Age of Reptiles, since these animals then dominated the world. It began two hundred and twenty-five million years ago with the appearance of the first dinosaurs, a group that rose to great dominance and then became extinct by the end of the Mesozoic, nearly one hundred and fifty-five million years later. While reptiles ruled the world, the first birds and mammals made their appearance.

The last era is the Cenozoic, or Age of Mammals. This began about seventy million years ago with the rise of warm-blooded animals and is still continuing.

For convenience, the Paleozoic, Mesozoic, and Cenozoic are divided

GEOLOGICAL TIME TABLE

Era	Period	Began (Years Ago)	Epoch	
	Quaternary	11,000	Recent	Age of man
		1 million	Pleistocene	
Cenozoic			Pliocene	
	Tertiary	65 million	Miocene Oligocene Eocene Paleocene	Age of mammals
Mesozoic	Cretaceous Jurassic Triassic	135 million 180 million 225 million		Age of reptiles
	Permian	270 million		Age of amphibians
	Carboniferous	350 million		
	Devonian	400 million		Age of fishes
	Silurian	425 million		
Paleozoic	Ordovician	500 million		First vertebrates
	Cambrian	600 million		Trilobites and brachiopods dominant
Proterozoic		1600 million		Protozoa to higher invertebrates
Archeozoic		3600 million		No fossils, but indirect evidence of beginning of life

into shorter segments of geological time called periods. The first sixty-nine million years of the Cenozoic Period is called the Tertiary, and the remaining million years constitute the Quaternary. The periods of the Cenozoic are further divided into epochs. The Quaternary, by way of example, has two epochs which are referred to as the Pleistocene and the Recent.

The Pleistocene Epoch, which lasted about one million years, is often called the Ice Age because there were four successive periods of glaciation during that time. The northern polar caps extended down over northern Europe, much of northern Asia, and, in North America, as far south as the northern United States. This is believed to have been responsible for the extinction of many kinds of animal life in the Northern Hemisphere.

Africa was unaffected by this glaciation, which did not extend that far south. This probably accounts for the abundance of big game on that continent in modern times, in contrast to the relative scarcity of animals on the more northern continents. No doubt North America nearly equalled Africa in numbers of species of animals before the Ice Age began.

3

THE ONE-CELLED ANIMALS

The phylum Protozoa represents the simplest and lowest group of organisms in the animal kingdom. While its members are often described as one-celled, they are actually composed of a mass of protoplasm which, for the most part, has not divided into cellular units, yet is so organized that it is capable of carrying on all necessary bodily functions. They might be considered as acellular, or without cells.

A good example of this phylum is the well-known *Amoeba proteus*, a species that is relatively large for these animals, although barely visible to the naked eye, and capable of slow locomotion on some kind of substratum in fresh water. The amoeba has a body that is essentially transparent and colorless, so that all parts of its anatomy can be seen easily under a low-power microscope. It moves by slowly pushing out portions of its anatomy to form what are called pseudopodia, or false feet, causing its protoplasm to flow by means of streaming movements into these extruded parts. An amoeba feeds by engulfing other microorganisms and taking them into its own body. Since *Amoeba proteus* is not free-swimming, it lives in ponds or slow-flowing streams, where it creeps along on rocks in shallow water or on the leaves of water plants and even debris.

There are five major groups or classes of protozoans: (1) the Sarcodina, which include the amoebas, the Foraminifera, and the Radiolaria; (2) the Mastigophora, or flagellates; (3) the Ciliata, or ciliates; (4) the Sporozoa, a group of parasitic protozoans lacking a well-developed power of locomotion; and (5) the Suctoria, which are free-swimming when young but become attached to a substratum by a stalk in the adult stage.

Sarcodina. Members of this class all move about by means of pseudopodia in the manner described for *Amoeba proteus*. However, they are not all soft-bodied like the amoebas. Some, like the Foraminifera and Radiolaria, are encased in hard shells that are either secreted by the body or formed from sand grains. These minute animals have openings, or foramina, in their shells through which they extend their pseudopodia so as to move about and secure food.

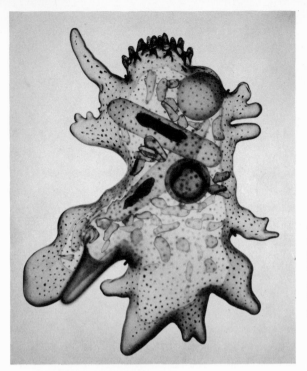

Although the amoeba is a one-celled animal, it is capable of movement, digestion, reproduction, and many other activities carried on by higher organisms. AMERICAN MUSEUM OF NATURAL HISTORY

One of the best-known unicellular organisms is *Amoeba proteus,* a common inhabitant of freshwater ponds. AMERICAN MUSEUM OF NATURAL HISTORY

Foraminifera are primarily marine and occur in vast numbers in the sea. As they die they sink to the bottom, where their tiny shells, which may be composed of calcium carbonate, accumulate and sometimes form huge chalk deposits. The Dover Cliffs, along the southeastern coast of England, are composed of white chalk derived from accumulations of "foram" shells of ages past that presently rise above the level of the ocean. Some of the world's oldest fossils, estimated by geologists to date back five hundred million years, are Foraminifera shells very much resembling various kinds existing today. The related Radiolaria and Actinopoda, which include the so-called "sun animalcules," are among the most beautiful of microorganisms.

Not all members of the class Sarcodina are free-living like *Amoeba proteus* or the Foraminifera. Some normally live within the digestive tract of man and other kinds of organisms. Certain species are harmless and cause no injury to their host. However, a very serious human disease known as amoebic dysentery is caused by a protozoan named *Endamoeba histolytica*. In areas where sanitation is poor these organisms may be ingested and become established in the large intestine, where they invade the mucosa, destroying tissue and producing ulcers. These lesions become infected and

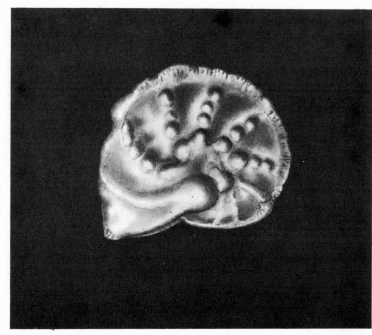

Fossil foraminifera are very abundant in the world. They are responsible for many chalk deposits and are often associated with oil deposits. Drawing of a Cretaceous species. MARGARET HANNA

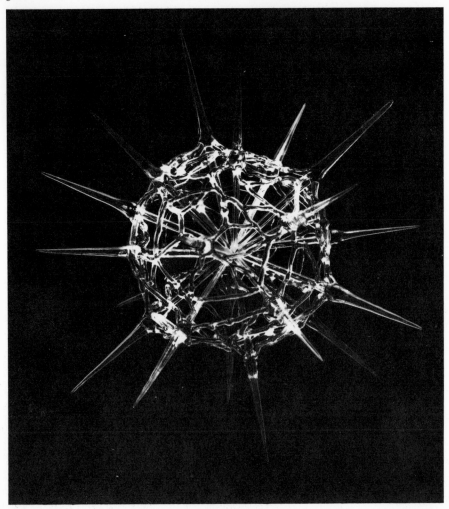

Radiolarians secrete beautiful and complicated skeletons such as seen in this model. AMERI-CAN MUSEUM OF NATURAL HISTORY

the body becomes weakened. The causative organisms may even get into the bloodstream and settle in other tissues in the body, where they cause lesions. Sanitary living conditions, adequate water purification, and the pasteurization of dairy products are the principal means of combating amoebic dysentery. In former days this was considered entirely a disease of the warmer parts of the world, particularly the tropics. However, modern transportation has caused a wider dispersion of the disease.

Mastigophora. These are freshwater and marine protozoans whose common feature is the possession of one or more flagella, or tiny whiplike structures, attached to the body. This accounts for the name Flagellata, by which the class is often known. Flagellates exhibit great diversity in shape and structure. Some even resemble plants in certain respects and possess chlorophyll. Botanists and zoologists for years have each laid claim to these organisms. Many flagellates are free-living, some are colonial, and others live within the bodies of various animals. This latter group may be either parasitic or symbiotic, a term that implies a mutual interdependence.

One of the common species of freshwater flagellates is *Euglena viridis,* which has a single, threadlike flagellum at the anterior end of its somewhat spindle-shaped body. It is the beating movement of this whiplike structure that propels the animal on its spiral course through the water. Within the body are tiny inclusions called chloroplasts, which contain chlorophyll and cause it to appear green.

In some parts of the world, especially near the Equator, the sea may be luminescent at night. Such luminescence is often caused by another member of the Mastigophora, belonging to the genus *Noctiluca,* which is one of the dinoflagellates, or protozoa with two flagella. One of these is situated anteriorly and the other encircles the body. These animals, which are capable of producing a faint light, occur in untold numbers in the sea at certain seasons of the year.

There are some marine flagellates that secrete a lethal toxin. Sometimes these organisms undergo marked seasonal changes in abundance, occurring in vast numbers in the summertime. So-called "red water," which occasionally appears on the Gulf coast of the southern United States and results in the death of large numbers of fishes, is caused by such flagellates. Mussel poisoning, which often occurs along the Pacific coast of North America, is likewise the result of a flagellate toxin. The protozoans accumulate, particularly during the summer months (those without "r" in them), in parts of the digestive system of the mussels. They do not harm their hosts but can produce death in human beings who consume the shellfish.

There are many truly parasitic flagellates. Perhaps the best known species is *Trypanosoma gambiense,* the causative organism of African sleeping sickness. There are many other kinds of trypanosomes in the world. Some occur in the bloodstream of backboned animals. Others live in the digestive system of invertebrate organisms. Although *Trypanosoma gambiense* lives in the circulatory system of various big-game animals, the latter seem to show no ill effects from this relationship. When transmitted to man by the bite of the bloodsucking tsetse fly, however, this trypanosome may in its final stages invade parts of the central nervous system, producing stupor and ultimately death.

There are many other kinds of flagellates that live in parts of the digestive system of different kinds of animals. Among the most interesting are those found in termites. These insects live on wood but are incapable of producing the enzymes necessary for the digestion of cellulose, of which wood is composed. This deficiency is made up by intestinal flagellates, so that the cellulose is converted into sugar on which both the protozoans and their host subsist.

Some flagellates are colonial. A well-known example is *Volvox*, a genus

During the summer months, some shellfish, like mussels (*Mytilus*), may be poisonous because of the presence of certain flagellates within their bodies. R. T. ORR

which possesses chlorophyll and is considered by some biologists to belong to the algae rather than the protozoa. Members of a *Volvox* colony form a hollow sphere, adhering to one another as a result of a sticky secretion. Like most plants the cells of a *Volvox* colony live on inorganic materials. There are, however, colonial flagellates that depend upon protein substances for food.

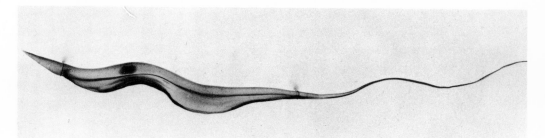

(Above) *Trypanosoma gambiense* is the protozoan flagellate responsible for the dreaded African sleeping sickness. AMERICAN MUSEUM OF NATURAL HISTORY

(Right) The assassin bug (*Triatoma*) is responsible for the transmission of *Trypanosoma cruzi*, the causative organism of Chagas' disease. EDWARD S. ROSS

The more advanced colonial flagellates exhibit certain characters that we attribute to higher multicellular organisms. There may be a division of labor, with certain cells concerned with securing food and others with locomotion.

Ciliata. These are protozoa that possess tiny hairlike projections called cilia, which are capable of movement. A drop of stagnant water examined under a microscope will usually reveal a preponderance of these minute animals propelling themselves by movements of the cilia, which are often

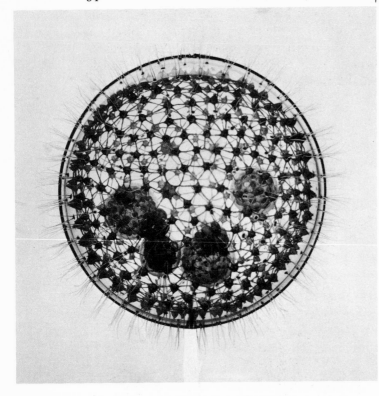

Some flagellates, like members of the genus *Volvox,* live in colonies, thereby resembling multicellular organisms. AMERICAN MUSEUM OF NATURAL HISTORY

arranged in bands around the body. A well-known example is the paramecium.

Some ciliates, while free-swimming early in the life cycle, become attached to the substratum by a stalk as they grow older. Such species are often bell- or trumpet-shaped. *Vorticella* is a common organism whose bell-shaped body is attached to rocks or water plants by means of a stalk which may be coiled.

Ciliates occur in both marine and fresh water, and certain species are even parasitic, living in the digestive system of various kinds of mammals and amphibians. Very few species have any covering or shell, but some are protected by a chitinous coat. Certain ciliates have specialized cells known as trichocysts, which serve for protection. These consist of sacs containing long, coiled, threadlike structures which may be discharged, much like the stinging cells, or nematocysts, of certain jellyfish, when the organism is sufficiently irritated.

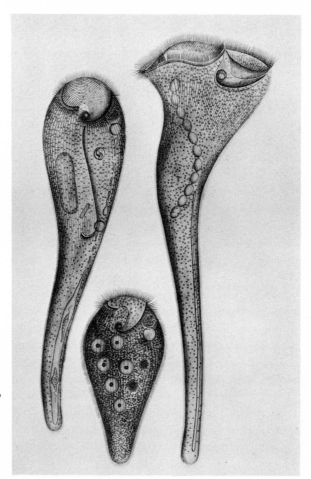

Stentor polymorphus is a stalked, sessile ciliate. AMERICAN MUSEUM OF NATURAL HISTORY

Sporozoa. These so-called "seed animals" are all parasitic. As their name implies, they multiply by spore formation. They are essentially lacking in locomotor power except for amoeboid movement in certain species. Sporozoans are found in the bloodstream, digestive system, and even muscle tissue of many kinds of vertebrate and invertebrate animals; hence they are of considerable economic importance.

The best-known sporozoan, the causative organism of malaria, is *Plasmodium.* Malaria has been one of the most serious pests with which the human race has had to contend. It was one of the scourges of ancient Greece and Rome and is still widespread in all the warmer parts of the world, although great advances have been made in effectual control. It is estimated that even today more than three hundred million persons in the world are infected with malaria and that it is responsible for more than three million deaths annually.

One of the interesting things in the history of malaria is the fact that its successful treatment was known to the Indians of South America for centuries. The early explorers found that these Indians cured their fever with the bark of a native tree. In 1638 this bark is said to have cured the Countess de Chinchón, who was the wife of the Viceroy of Peru. The tree was later named cinchona and, as we know, is the source of quinine, the principal cure for malaria until World War II. Since then new and more effective remedies as well as preventives have been developed.

The word malaria is a contraction of *mala aria,* meaning "bad air," because the disease was associated with air that presumably came from the swamps at night. It was not until the end of the nineteenth century that the disease was discovered to be the result of inoculation of a sporozoan protozoan into the bloodstream by the bite of a female mosquito of the genus *Anopheles.*

Suctoria.   This is the smallest protozoan group. These organisms swim freely by means of cilia, somewhat like a paramecium, during the early part of their life cycle. Later, however, they settle down and attach themselves to objects in the water by means of a stalk. The cilia are then replaced by tentacle-like structures. By means of these they are able to capture small organisms that come by. The tentacles also serve as tubes by which the body juices of the prey are sucked, hence the name Suctoria.

4

THE SPONGES

We have seen how the simplest forms of animal life, the Protozoa, consist of single cells that are capable of performing all the necessary body functions, such as the securing of food, reproduction, transportation, and protection. Some of these animals are colonial, but each cell still retains its independence and is self-sufficient when the colony breaks up.

As life became more advanced in the course of earth history, some of those colonial aggregations of individual cells developed permanency. This resulted in a specialization of different cells and a dependency of one cell upon another. In this way tissues were formed, which in turn led to the development of organ systems or large groups of cells resulting in a division of labor.

The most primitive of these truly multicellular organisms, or Metazoa, are the sponges, a very ancient group whose fossil remains are known from the Proterozoic era, which ended almost six hundred million years ago. The sponges are porous organisms, as we all know, and this is the reason why the phylum to which they belong is technically called Porifera, which is derived from two Latin words meaning "pore bearer."

The simplest kinds of sponges are usually shaped like tiny urns. The cylindrical body is penetrated by many pores, and the center of this cylinder is hollow. The top of the urn has an opening leading from the inner cavity, and the base of the urn is firmly attached to some object in the water, usually a rock or part of a reef.

At first appearance sponges seem to look like plants of some sort. They have even been mistaken in past ages for homes constructed by marine worms. Aristotle, however, correctly recognized them as animals more than two thousand years ago. If a simple living sponge is brought into the laboratory and examined carefully, it will be seen that currents of water are constantly entering the large central cavity through the small pores in the body wall. The current then flows out of the opening at the top, the osculum.

This flow of water is possible because of the specialization and arrangement of various cells in the sponge's body. Those lining the inner cavity, or spongocoele, are called choanocytes; each possesses a long whip, or flagellum, which keeps moving and sets up a water current. This can be demonstrated by placing colored particles near the outer openings of the pores. These particles will be sucked into the pores and soon be seen emerging from the osculum at the top. This is the way a sponge obtains its

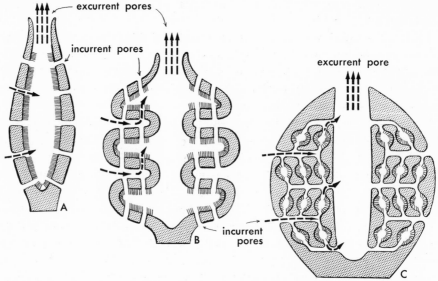

In a sponge, water enters through ostia, or incurrent pores, and passes out through a large excurrent pore known as the osculum. Here we see (A) a simple sponge, (B) a more advanced type and (C) a complex sponge.

food, consisting of small organisms or organic matter in the water. These enter the cavity and are ingested by the choanocyte cells. The nutrient material is then passed on to other wandering cells called amoebocytes, which can travel like an amoeba and, in so doing, distribute food to other cells in the body.

Sponges reproduce by both sexual and asexual means. Sex cells are produced within the body and liberated into the central cavity. Both types of sex cells can be produced by the same individual, but they are rarely produced at the same time. Since sponges are usually colonial, some are producing male sex cells and others female sex cells, thereby preventing self-fertilization.

The egg is fertilized by the sperm, which enters the spongocoele. The fertilized cell, known as a zygote, develops into a flagellated larva that leaves the parent by means of the osculum and swims freely in the water for a short while before it settles down and attaches itself in preparation for development into an adult sponge.

Budding is another method of reproduction, whereby a new individual starts to grow from the side or base of the parent in a somewhat plantlike manner. This may result in the formation of large colonies of sponges aggregated in a mass.

Not all sponges are as simple as those described here. Some of the higher groups may develop complicated systems of canals through which the water circulates. These sponges are able to regulate the flow of water by increasing or decreasing the size of the pore apertures. This, of course, necessitates some sort of coordination.

It has been shown recently that sponges have a very primitive nervous system. These nerves make connections between the choanocytes, whose tiny whips set up the water currents in the central chamber, and the cells lining the pores on the outer surface of the body. If too much water is entering, this information is transmitted to the cells lining the pores; then the pores contract, thereby reducing the flow of water.

This organization of cells in sponges represents a great advance over the independence of cells exhibited by the protozoa. The permanency of this type of organization in these lowly forms of multicellular life has been demonstrated by various experiments. It has been shown that when tissue from sponges is fragmented and strained through fine silk cloth and then permitted to stand in dishes of water the individual cells will immediately begin to aggregate into masses forming a sponge once again.

One of the most interesting and important parts of a sponge is its skeleton. We think of an internal skeleton as being characteristic of the backboned animals; and of an external skeleton, such as a crab's shell or a snail's shell, as representing the only type of invertebrate skeleton. Furthermore, among invertebrates we think of skeletons only in connection with the higher types. Yet the sponge has a skeleton, and it is an internal one. In fact, differences in the skeleton provide the major basis for the classification of sponges.

The skeleton of a sponge may be of lime or glass or it may be fibrous. In each type the basic elements are minute spicules. These spicules have very characteristic shapes, which vary with different families and genera and are therefore extremely useful in classification. Fossilized sponge skeletons are responsible for our knowing that these primitive animals lived more than half a billion years ago.

The once familiar bath sponge (largely replaced now by synthetic products) has a skeleton made of fibrous spicules. Commercial sponges are found in warm sea water, where they often occur in great beds. In the United States the principal sponge fisheries have long been along the Florida coast. Here divers or dredges are used to remove the living sponges from the ocean floor. All parts of the animal except the skeleton must be

The bath sponge is a well-known example of a fibrous sponge. AMERICAN MUSEUM OF NATURAL HISTORY

eliminated before the "sponge" becomes a finished product. This has usually been accomplished by placing the sponges in vats or tanks where they are allowed to decay. The decomposition does away with the organic parts, leaving only the skeleton. This is then washed, thoroughly dried, and finally sorted into various sizes for sale. Central America, Europe, and Africa also have extensive sponge fisheries.

The fibrous sponges are in a class known as the Desmospongiae. The other two groups of sponges are represented by the class Calcarea, or calcareous sponges, and the class Hexactinellida, or glass sponges. The spicules comprising the skeletons of the latter two classes are stiff and sharp and may cause considerable discomfort to one who inadvertently picks up one of these animals. These tiny spicules will penetrate the skin like slivers of glass and will feel just as painful. The spicules, whether they are calcareous or siliceous, last a long time and, like Foraminifera shells, sink to the bottom of the ocean, where many become fossilized.

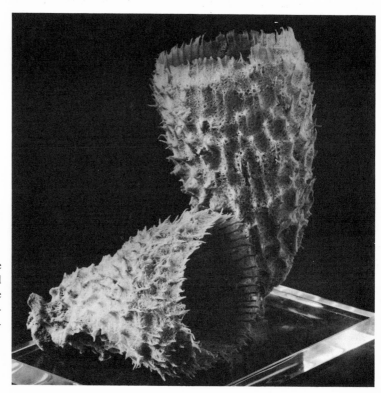

Some fibrous sponges, like *Stelospongia,* are urn-shaped and not unlike some of the calcareous sponges. AMERICAN MUSEUM OF NATURAL HISTORY

Most sponges are marine in occurrence, although there are some fresh-water species. In general, sponges are more abundant in warm ocean water than elsewhere, but they are by no means restricted to tropical seas. They rarely occur in deep water, being usually found close to shore, where the water is shallow, or even in the low intertidal area. Sometimes they occur in great abundance in particularly favorable localities. In the vicinity of Bermuda sponges have been reported to be so prolific in some places that the ocean water literally wells up from the currents set up by their internal body canals.

There are certain sponges that grow on rocks in the form of an incrustation. Sometimes they are very brightly colored—purple, orange, red, or green—and appear almost lichen-like when seen at a distance on rocks exposed at low tide.

Most clear freshwater streams and lakes are apt to possess sponges in small numbers. They are essentially like marine sponges and are very intolerant of turbid water heavy with sedimentation. Mud clogs their pores and results in the death of the sponge.

5

THE JELLYFISH, SEA ANEMONES, CORALS, AND THEIR RELATIVES

The phylum Coelenterata contains an old and diversified group of animals whose history goes back far beyond the earliest known fossil remains of most other multicellular organisms. Its best-known representatives are the corals, sea anemones, and jellyfish—organisms seemingly so different that one would hardly expect them to be related. The great majority of coelenterates are marine inhabitants, but there are a few freshwater kinds, such as the hydra, which is so well known in biology laboratories.

These animals are radially symmetrical. Their body plan is arranged somewhat like that of a wagon wheel. No matter how it is cut in half, the halves are essentially the same.

In addition to radial symmetry, coelenterates possess tentacles that are armed with tiny sting-cells called nematocysts. It is by means of these tentacles and sting-cells that they capture their food, which consists of living animals ranging from the young of other coelenterates up to fishes. The nematocysts are cells containing coiled threadlike structures that may be shot into a victim when the trigger mechanism on the edge of the nematocyst is touched. The projectile turns inside out as it emerges from the tentacle and assumes a barbed form as it penetrates. Poison is also released, which either incapacitates the prey or causes its death.

Most coelenterates are harmless to man. In fact, we often use such expressions as "spineless as a jellyfish" or "weak as a jellyfish." However, this is not true of all members of this group. The large free-swimming Portuguese man-of-war of tropical seas, which is really a floating colony of coelenterates, has tentacles forty to fifty feet long armed with nematocysts that not only can paralyze fish but are capable of inflicting serious injury to human swimmers who inadvertently contact them.

Coelenterates have a more advanced type of body organization than sponges. There is, for example, a digestive system with a single opening through which food is taken in and indigestible material ejected. The

43

digestive system is in the center of the body, with its opening surrounded by the tentacles. Between the digestive system and the outer wall there is a layer of jellylike material called mesoglea.

Some coelenterates, like the jellyfish, are free-swimming, while others, such as the sea anemones, attach themselves to the substratum. Certain kinds are solitary; others, like the corals, are colonial. One of the interesting

There are certain small reef fishes that live safely in close association with large sea anemones.
R. T. ORR

things about many coelenterates is that they have two phases to their life cycle. One of these is an asexual phase, in which the organism is referred to as a polyp. The polyp has tentacles surrounding the free end on which the mouth is located, and at the other end it is attached to some substratum. The polyp produces buds that in turn produce free-swimming medusae, which are more or less like simple jellyfish. These medusae produce sex cells that unite and once again form the asexual polyp generation.

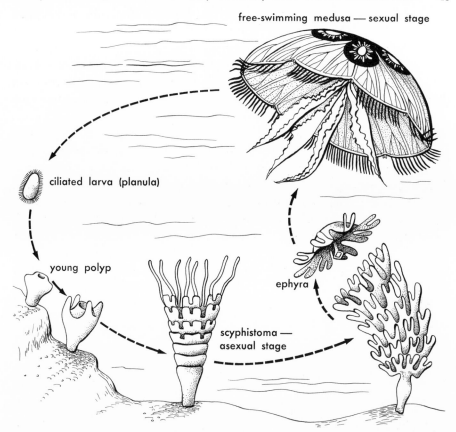

free-swimming medusa — sexual stage

ciliated larva (planula)

young polyp

scyphistoma — asexual stage

ephyra

Many species of jellyfish, like *Aurelia*, have two phases in their life cycle. One of these, the asexual polyp stage, is essentially sedentary. It in turn produces a free-swimming, sexually reproducing, medusa stage.

The importance of coelenterates in our earth's history must not be overlooked. Despite the delicacy and softness of some kinds, others are responsible for the formation of many of our oceanic islands. Most of these islands that are not volcanic in origin are basically made of coral. Many atolls dotting the waters of the tropical Pacific Ocean are little more than masses of coral, lime from lime-secreting algae or seaweed, and the shells or casings of microscopic foraminifera and diatoms, with a small amount of soil on top. Borings made into these coral islands have shown the same composition to occur down to depths of as much as one thousand feet. This, of course, indicates either changes in the sea level or a gradual depression of the island, since corals do not live at depths of more than about three hundred feet.

There are three major classes of coelenterates recognized in the world today: the Hydrozoa, containing the hydroids and medusae of various kinds; the Scyphozoa, or large advanced jellyfish; and the Anthozoa, comprising the sea anemones, sea fans, sea pens, and the true stony corals.

Hydrozoa. These are considered to be the simplest of the coelenterates, although they show great diversity in form and, unlike the two other groups in this phylum, occur in fresh water as well as in the sea. Most hydrozoans go through a polyp and medusa stage at some time during their lives, although this is not true of all of them. They are distinguished from the Scyphozoa and Anthozoa by these characters: nematocysts are lacking in the tissue lining the digestive cavity; the sex cells are generally produced on the outer surface of the body; and the mesoglea is entirely

Coral atolls, like Eniwetok in the Marshall Islands seen here, are built largely by marine coelenterates. JOHN KORANDA

noncellular. Sometimes, however, it is difficult to distinguish superficially between some of the large floating colonial hydrozoans and the true jellyfish.

Many of our hydrozoans are little known, even though abundant, because of their small size or their appearance. A very common freshwater type is the hydra, which is likely to be found attached to water plants or rocks in most lakes and ponds. These little animals have slender tubular bodies that are rarely much more than a quarter of an inch in length. The oral, or free, end is surrounded by four to six tentacles that contain a large number of nematocysts. The basal end attaches itself to the substratum. When moving about, however, a hydra may bend over so that its tentacles become attached to a surface, after which the basal end is released and the animal literally does a somersault, so that the basal end may again become attached. The process may be repeated a number of times. Occasionally a hydra will float freely in the water. Although hydras may possess sex cells that will unite and then undergo cell division to produce new individuals, reproduction is commonly asexual by means of budding. A bud containing an extension of the gastrovascular cavity grows out from the body stalk of the parent. It soon develops tentacles as well as an oral opening on its distal end and then pinches off at its base as a new free individual.

There are many hydrozoans that are colonial. In development they resemble the hydra, but the buds that form new individuals do not separate from the parent stalk. As a result, a many-branched mass of polyps attached to one another by stalks appears. These colonial coelenterates or hydroids are very common on marine pilings as well as on rocks exposed along the seacoast at low tide. Their animal nature is usually overlooked by the casual observer because of their resemblance to certain kinds of seaweed.

The gastrovascular cavities of colonial hydroids are connected together, but certain individuals are primarily concerned with capturing food while others function for reproduction. These animals produce free-swimming medusae, which are very small and resemble miniature jellyfish.

Not all Hydrozoa are tiny like the hydras or permanently attached to the substratum in the colonial form like the hydroids. Some remain in a medusa form very much resembling the more complicated jellyfish. Some medusae usually have a bell-shaped body bearing large numbers of tentacles often arranged in rows. Many species have a luminescent organ at the base of each tentacle, and these are capable of glowing after dark if the animal is jarred or otherwise disturbed.

Still other hydrozoans occur in the form of medium-sized or large floating colonies of polyps and medusae. They are found principally in tropical or semitropical waters. The best known of these is the Portuguese man-of-war, whose size has previously been mentioned.

These aberrant hydrozoans superficially look like jellyfish, but actually each floating mass consists of a large number of individuals. The polyp-like

The freshwater *Hydra* is one of the simplest of the coelenterates. AMERICAN MUSEUM OF NATURAL HISTORY

The medusa (*Geryonia pro-boscidalis*) is a typical scyphozoan coelenterate. AMERICAN MUSEUM OF NATURAL HISTORY

members may be specialized for the securing of food, for reproduction, or for protection. Some have single long tentacles heavily armed with nematocysts. The medusae-like individuals may be modified so that they form a pulsating umbrella that provides locomotion for the colony. There may even be a gas bag or float on top. In some species the amount of gas can be regulated so that the colony may float on the surface of the ocean or sink beneath.

A very interesting colonial hydrozoan, known as the purple sail (*Velella lata*), occurs widely over the warmer parts of the Pacific Ocean, from Japan and southern British Columbia south. This beautiful purple species has the members of the colony suspended from a gas-filled raft, on top of which there is a triangular sail. Wind striking the sail keeps the colony moving, at times rather rapidly. At certain seasons of the year the beaches along the Pacific coast are almost purple with the bodies of vast numbers of these coelenterates washed ashore.

Scyphozoa. Most of the large, free-floating, jellyfish-like coelenterates that are found in oceans and bays belong to this group. The medusa phase is the important one in the life of scyphozoans in contrast to the polyp stage so significant among most hydrozoans. Furthermore, in scyphozoans the sex cells are discharged into the digestive canal and then pass out through the mouth. The mesoglea, or intermediate body layer, is cellular, unlike the corresponding layer in the Hydrozoa.

Scyphozoans usually have a polyp or fixed stage that results from a fusion of the sex cells. These polyps, however, remain quite small and produce tiny medusae, one at a time, which grow into the large free-swimming forms that we often see.

Some true jellyfish attain a remarkable size. This is particularly true of members of the genus *Cyanea.* The so-called "sea blubber" of the Atlantic is said to attain a diameter of seven feet and to have tentacles that may be extended one hundred and twenty feet. These giants are a serious menace to swimmers. A few species of jellyfish occur in the Arctic, where they are reported to be able to withstand freezing.

Anthozoa. This class contains the best-known members of the phylum Coelenterata, such as the sea anemones, the corals, and the sea fans. They are also the most beautiful and most conspicuous coelenterates.

All anthozoans remain permanently in the polyp stage. They have a well-developed tubular pharynx, which extends into the stomach cavity. The latter is divided by means of radiating septa into a number of separate compartments, each of which opens into a central cavity. The edges of these septa contain nematocysts. As in the scyphozoans, the sex cells are discharged into the stomach cavity and the mesogleal layer is cellular. The tentacles are arranged around the free end.

In the temperate coastal waters of the world the best-known anthozoans are sea anemones. Those that inhabit the intertidal zone on rocky shores like the pounding surf. At low tide, especially if they are out of water rather than in a tide pool, they will retract their tentacles and appear very inconspicuous. You may be unaware of their presence until you place a foot on one and a squirt of water deluges your shoe. However, as soon as the rising tide brings water surging over these animals, they open up in a matter of seconds into their flower-like form, with the tentacles expanded and ready to trap some unwary small animal.

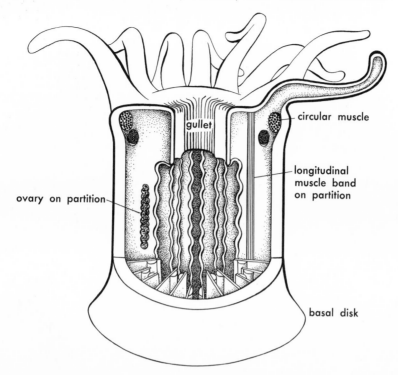

Diagram of a sea anemone showing its internal structure.

In tide pools sea anemones frequently remain open and, because of their form and often beautiful coloration, constitute the most attractive and conspicuous element to be seen. Many kinds of anemones also occur below the intertidal zone along continental shores. Here the skin diver has the pleasure of seeing species often much more brilliantly colored than their shore-dwelling relatives.

Sea anemones are even more abundant in tropical than in temperate waters, and there they exhibit great variation in color and size. One species, found on the Great Barrier Reef of Australia, is reported to reach a diameter of more than three feet.

We are apt to think of sea anemones as stationary animals, but most of them can move by gliding with the basal disk. Their locomotor ability can be easily demonstrated by keeping them in an aerated aquarium. They will be found to move at a speed somewhat less than that of a snail.

Corals, in contrast to sea anemones, are immobile. They range from the

Corynactus californicus is one of the more beautiful anthozoans along the Pacific coast of North America where it lives just below the intertidal zone. R. T. ORR

Arctic to the Antarctic but are predominantly animals of tropical waters, where they may occur in such numbers that they are primarily responsible for the formation of oceanic islands. One may search for a long time for an example of a coral along a coast in temperate parts of the world. On the other hand, there are tropical reefs where it is impossible to walk without stepping, often painfully, on one or more species of these anthozoans. It is said that more than two hundred kinds of corals occur on the Great Barrier Reef.

When closed at low tide, the giant green anemone (*Anthopleura xanthogrammica*) resembles a rock. R. T. ORR

The giant green anemone opens in flower-like beauty as it becomes submerged by the incoming tide. R. T. ORR

A few corals are solitary polyps, but the majority are decidedly colonial. Corals resemble sea anemones in structure but produce a hard skeleton of calcium carbonate around the outer surface of the lower part of the body and the basal disk. From the latter, calcareous radiating septa develop. These septa push into the chambers of the digestive system.

Corals secure food by means of their nematocyst-armed tentacles as well as through water currents set up by tiny cilia on the oral surface of the

The star coral, like most stony corals, is abundant in warm ocean waters. R. T. ORR

body. These currents direct small food particles to the tips of the tentacles, which capture them. This is the same way a sea anemone feeds. In colonial corals the upper portion of the stomach cavities of adjacent polyps are connected with one another.

On tropical reefs where corals abound there are many kinds of organisms associated with them. Some fishes live between their armlike branches, often resembling them in color and depending upon retreat between them for protection. Numerous invertebrates also make use of corals in one way or another for sanctuary. One of the most interesting of these is the gall or marsupial crab. The female of this crustacean invades certain types of branching corals when she is young and, by manipulating her body, influences the development of a large gall-like chamber in which she becomes imprisoned as she attains maturity. However, passages remain for food to enter her chamber, as well as for her tiny mate so that she may reproduce.

Corals have many beautiful colors and shapes, which are responsible for several of their common names, such as black, blue, brain, mushroom, staghorn, organ-pipe, and cup coral. The living polyp, whose tentacles and

Elkhorn coral. AMERICAN MUSEUM OF NATURAL HISTORY

oral end extend from its stony prison, is often differently colored from the calcareous skeleton.

There is another group of anthozoans closely related to the true corals, known as the Alcyonaria. These are the sea fans, pipe corals, sea pansies, and sea pens. They are colonial polyps, often with bizarre shapes that differ principally from the true corals in having only eight tentacles, each of which has feather-like branches.

6

THE COMB JELLIES OR SEA WALNUTS

The members of the phylum Ctenophora, which contains a small group of marine organisms related to the coelenterates and in former years often classified with them, include the comb jellies. Like the coelenterates and the sponges, the ctenophores possess radial symmetry. For this reason these three primitive phyla of animals are sometimes referred to as the Radiata, or radiate organisms.

The comb jellies, sometimes referred to as sea walnuts, although superficially resembling jellyfish or a medusa-like coelenterate, differ from them in many fundamental respects. The external surface of the body, which may vary from pear- to ribbon-shape, possess eight bands or rows of combs that are composed of fused cilia. These combs are responsible for locomotion in the few swimming species. They beat in waves, so that the comb jelly moves through the water with the mouth forward.

In addition to the eight rows of combs there are two long contractile tentacles, which possess special cells called colloblasts. These secrete a sticky substance that aids in the capture of small animals upon which they feed. The digestive system of ctenophores is more advanced than that of coelenterates and possessess two openings, one at each end of the body. These serve for the intake of food and the elimination of waste. A long pharynx leads into the stomach, and a complicated series of canals are connected with the central digestive system.

Between the outer and inner surfaces of the body, ctenophores have a mesoglea-like layer containing a network of true muscle cells that are not found in lower animals. Most ctenophores have luminescent organs situated beneath the bands of combs. These organs glow at night.

It is estimated that there are about eighty species of comb jellies living in the world today. A few of these have become adapted to life on the bottom of the sea and get about by creeping. The majority, however, are free-living and are occasionally found in coastal areas.

Although not numerous as far as species are concerned, comb jellies may be present in vast numbers in the sea at certain seasons of the year. They are said practically to choke the waters of the Great Barrier Reef during the midyear months. Their delicate bodies are transparent and often glitter like jewels as the iridescent bands of combs move rhythmically. A few comb jellies have a rosy tint to parts of the body.

7

THE LOWER WORMLIKE ORGANISMS

The animals that we have considered so far are either unicellular or radially symmetrical. The rest of the animal kingdom, with the exception of the echinoderms (the starfishes, sea urchins, and their relatives), have bilateral symmetry. By this we mean that the right and left sides of the body are essentially the same. The term Bilateria has sometimes been used to designate all these organisms, even the vertebrates.

One wonders how, if the more primitive organisms were radially symmetrical, bilateral symmetry arose. One of the theories is that this developed as a result of these animals creeping on the ocean floor, on rocks, and on other objects. This may ultimately have led to a difference between the upper and lower part of the organism. The upper part was in contact with water, light, and enemies, as well as food. The ventral part of the body made contact with the substratum. Once this differentiation occurred, bilateral symmetry was established.

Between the Radiata and the highest of the invertebrate animals (those without backbones), such as mollusks, arthropods, and echinoderms, are a number of distinct but little known phyla containing many thousands of species of organisms that can best be described as "wormlike." Some are marine inhabitants while others live in fresh water. Many are found in the soil. There are several kinds that are parasitic and responsible for various diseases in man and lower animals. A few of the less obscure groups are considered briefly in this chapter.

The flatworms. From the standpoint of disease, flatworms are a significant group of animals. Its members for the most part are rarely seen by anyone except the specialist or students. The group includes three classes. One of these comprises the free-living planarians and their relatives. The other two are parasitic—the flukes and the tapeworms. They all belong to the phylum Platyhelminthes.

There are few high school biology students who have not come in contact with planaria worms. These small, extremely flat animals creep about

59

feeding on microscopic plants and animals that are in the water or the underlying mud.

When I began graduate school, one of my occasional duties was to visit a lake not far from my home and secure fresh, living specimens of planaria for the zoology department. Since they were needed at eight o'clock in the

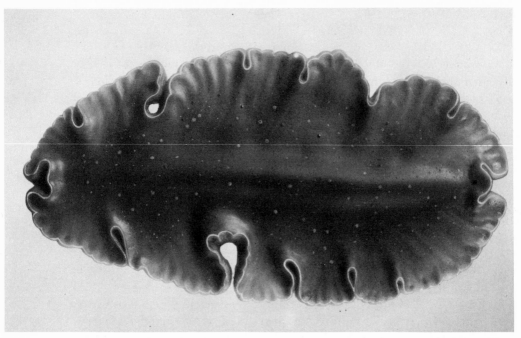

Some of the marine flat worms, like members of the genus *Yungia,* are quite large and colorful. They are capable of swimming by undulatory movements. AMERICAN MUSEUM OF NATURAL HISTORY

morning and it took me one and a half hours to commute to school, these little worms didn't make too favorable an impression on me at the time—and I've never seen too much reason to change my mind.

In the laboratory, planarians will glide along slowly on the side of a glass aquarium. Their bodies are so transparent that many of their organs can be seen by merely holding them up to the light. Planarians have been subject to many kinds of experiments. They are especially suited to demonstrate regeneration. If a piece of reasonable size is removed from a living animal, it is capable of regenerating a perfect individual. These worms have a fairly well developed nervous system with a simple brain, reproductive organs, digestive and excretory systems, and a pair of eyes that react very definitely to light.

The planarians are members of the class Turbellaria. Not all of them are restricted to fresh water. Many occur in salt water, and a few are terrestrial, living in the soil or on plants in tropical regions. Some of the marine species are beautifully colored and may be seen creeping along rocks in tide pools.

The flukes are also flatworms, but they are parasitic and placed in the class Trematoda. There are two major groups of flukeworms. One group has a relatively simple life history and consists of species that live either on the outer surface of the body of various animals or close to it, such as in the mouth cavity. These small, flat, wormlike parasites lay eggs that soon hatch and develop into young that very much resemble the adult form. The eggs may remain attached to the host, which is usually an aquatic vertebrate, or else they hatch in the water, after which the young soon find a host of their own.

The internal flukes, in contrast to those that live on the outside of the body, have some of the most complicated life histories to be found in the animal kingdom. Backboned animals constitute their final host, and there are a number of species that are very dangerous to man. Internal flukes usually live in various parts of the digestive system, the bile duct and liver, the lungs, the bladder, or the bloodstream.

The Chinese liver fluke is a very harmful parasite in the Orient. The adults live in the human bile duct, where they produce large numbers of eggs that pass into the small intestine and ultimately are voided. To continue the life cycle it is necessary that these eggs be consumed by certain kinds of snails belonging to a single family. If this occurs, the larval worm within the eggshell hatches. It then goes through several stages and ends up in the liver of the snail. Here a generation of tailed larval forms called cercaria is produced. The cercaria leave the body of the snail and pass into water, where they swim about freely for a while. Finally, if they are fortunate, they become attached to a fish and bore into the flesh of the new host. In the muscle they lose their tails and become encapsulated as a cyst. If a human being eats one of these parasitized fishes whose flesh has not been cooked sufficiently to kill the encysted larvae, these larvae soon emerge from their capsules in the intestine and make their way up into the liver. Here they mature into adults and soon start laying eggs, which pass down the bile duct just as did the eggs from which the larvae developed.

Other flukes have even more complicated life histories. Some require three intermediate hosts before they reach the fourth and final host. The very complexity of the lives of these dangerous parasites is, in a sense, one of their redeeming features. If one of the necessary hosts is missing or cannot be contacted, the life cycle cannot be completed. Furthermore, most of the flukes are restricted to rather specific host organisms, whose ranges are frequently limited. This prevents many fluke diseases from spreading widely over the world.

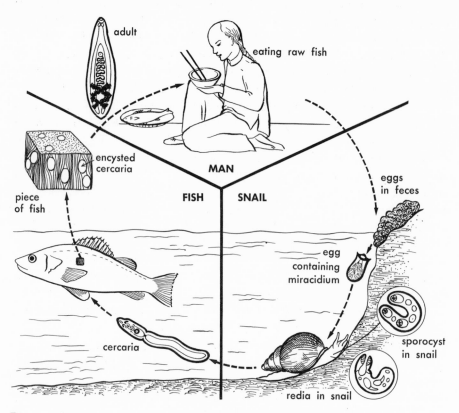

Diagram of the life cycle of the Chinese liver fluke (*Clonorchis sinensis*).

The third group of flatworms are the tapeworms, which are placed in the class Cestoda. The cestodes are all highly specialized parasitic worms. Most of them spend their adult life in the intestinal tract of backboned animals. A unique feature of the tapeworms is that they lack a digestive system. They absorb the digested food of their host. The body of a typical tapeworm consists of a head containing a number of hooklets by means of which the parasite attaches itself to the intestinal wall of its host. Behind the head in most cestodes is a series of repeated body segments, which are primarily reproductive. The number of segments in some species may be so numerous that the worm attains a length of as much as thirty feet.

The many eggs that a tapeworm produces pass out of the host's body by way of the intestine. These eggs then develop to a certain degree, after which further growth is dependent upon their being eaten by an inter-mediate host. The pork tapeworm, which parasitizes man and the pig, although each in a different way, must have its eggs consumed by a pig after they have left the human body. Inside the digestive system of the pig they emerge as a larval form, which bores its way through the intestinal tract and enters the circulatory or lymphatic system. This provides a means of getting into muscle tissue, where the larva encysts. Here it re-mains until the pig is eaten by man. If the pig is not consumed, no further larval development occurs. But if the larva is ingested by the proper host, it rapidly develops into an adult tapeworm in the human intestine and attaches itself by means of the hooks on its head. Tapeworms are long-lived and may survive for years unless removed by proper medication.

Nemerteans. Proboscis worms, which in some ways are related to the flatworms, are placed in the phylum Nemertina. It is estimated that there are between five and six hundred species of these animals, most of which are found in intertidal areas. Nemerteans live in mudflats, tide pools, and sandy beaches. A very few kinds are found in fresh water or on land. They resemble the flatworms in not having any cavity, or coelom, in the body. By this we mean a space between the digestive system and the body wall. In certain respects, however, they show advances over the planarians, flukes, and tapeworms. Their nervous system is more like that of higher animals, and they have a circulatory system.

Some of the proboscis worms are very colorful. Though slender, they may attain remarkable lengths. One species along the Pacific coast of North America is reported to be able to extend to a length of seventy-five feet. Under such circumstances, however, the diameter of the body is not much more than that of a thread. The name "proboscis worm" is applied to these animals because of the presence of an inverted structure associated with the mouth. This structure, under certain conditions, may be pro-truded and used as a weapon or to secure food. It is armed terminally with a stylet that can pierce other small organisms and inject a poisonous secre-tion.

Rotifers and roundworms. Two interesting groups of animals whose size is compensated for by their abundance and worldwide distribution are the rotifers, or wheel animalcules, and the roundworms. They are placed together in the phylum Aschelminthes because of certain characters they have in common, such as the absence of both a circulatory and respiratory system. The lack of these organ systems has been attributed to the small size of the animals and to the fact that they live either in water or in a moist environment. The absorption of oxygen and the elimination of waste products from the body is therefore accomplished in a very simple manner.

The rotifers are among the first of the small animals that were discovered early in the eighteenth century after the invention of the microscope. Their name is derived from what appears to the naked eye to be one or two wheels rotating on the head. When examined under a lens, such a "wheel" is seen to consist of a ciliated crown, or corona. The movement of the cilia, which serves to direct food into the mouth, gives the appearance of a revolving wheel. The largest of the so-called "wheel animalcules" are barely a tenth of an inch in length. Most of them are much smaller and can be seen only with a microscope.

My first experience with rotifers occurred when I was ten years old. One day while camping with my father in the high country east of the Yosemite Valley I was lying flat on my stomach drinking from a small pool when I suddenly saw some tiny, transparent creatures that seemed to have propellers attached to them in the water. They made a lasting impression on me, but my inquiries as to their identity were all in vain. No one seemed to know what I had seen. It was some years before I discovered what these animals really were.

The majority of the rotifers live in fresh water, where they are most abundant along the shores of lakes and ponds. There are also marine species and a few kinds that are even terrestrial. The latter may be found swimming in water that accumulates on lichens and mosses in damp situations. When conditions come to be dry, the rotifers become dormant. Under certain circumstances, they may survive in this state for several years. Some species are extremely resistant to heat, cold, and drought.

There are rotifers that swim freely throughout their lives. Certain of the larger kinds can be seen in pools of semistagnant water. They look like tiny, transparent, glass boats with propellers on the front end. Other species creep along the bottom in an inchworm-like manner, and still others are sessile. The latter usually attach themselves to certain parts of water plants and algae. A few species of rotifers are parasitic. Some live on the gills of crustaceans, while others are true endoparasites, occurring in the intestinal organs of certain invertebrates and even within the tissue of algae.

Although there are several other small groups in this phylum, the most important class is the Nematoda. The nematodes are commonly referred to as roundworms. Though small in size, they are probably more numerous than any other form of multicellular animal life. They occur in untold numbers in the soil as well as in fresh and salt water. Many species are parasitic, some being responsible for serious human diseases.

Nematodes have a tubular, wormlike body that is tapered at both ends. For the most part they are small. The majority are less than one-sixteenth of an inch in length, and many are microscopic. Some of the parasitic species may be several inches long.

My first encounter with these animals came when I was taking high school biology. Aware of my interest in the subject, my aunt bought a microscope for me to use at home. We were studying worms in class at the time, and my first use of this exciting new instrument was to verify the existence of vinegar eels. These are tiny nematodes that live in nonpasteurized vinegar, feeding on bacteria and fungi in the sediment. The discovery was enthusiastically communicated to the family, but it was far from catching. The following year, oil-and-vinegar salad dressing, which had always been a must, was conspicuously missing from the dinner table. These nematodes are perfectly harmless. They are capable of surviving in acetic acid, which is the principal ingredient in vinegar. Pasteurization nowadays eliminates such living organisms.

Roundworms, because of their great abundance (over a billion may be present in a single acre of soil), play an important role in consuming dead organic material and breaking it down to simpler products. Their action is much like that of many soil bacteria.

The parasitic nematodes may be harmful in varying degrees. Hookworm, which has been so prevalent in warmer countries, is an organism that attaches itself to the wall of the human intestine and lives on the tissue and blood of its host. Large infestations can cause serious loss of blood and result in anemia. Filarial worms, which are transmitted to man through the bite of a mosquito, the intermediate host, live in the lymphatic system. There they may block the lymph channels and cause swelling. Elephantiasis, which is the enormous lymphatic enlargement of certain parts of the body, is produced by filarial worms. Filariasis is another name for this disease.

One of the best known and most widespread nematode infections is trichinosis. This is produced by the trichina worm, which lives in the human intestine. The eggs may pass out of the body and be taken into the digestive system of pigs, in whose bodies they develop. The juveniles burrow into the muscle tissue and remain there in an encysted state. If pork that is so infected is consumed without being sufficiently cooked to kill the cysts, the latter mature in the human intestine. Some of the eggs may even hatch in the digestive system, and when the juveniles have attained a certain stage they burrow through the intestine to muscle tissue, where they encyst as they do in swine.

Ascarid worms, which are also parasitic nematodes, commonly occur in the digestive system of many kinds of animals as well as man. Since they do not attach themselves to the intestinal wall or live upon the tissues of their hosts, they are not as serious a danger as some of the other nematodes. They live primarily upon the predigested food mass that they inhabit. Sometimes, however, they occur in great numbers. On one occasion we dissected a harbor porpoise in the museum and found more than two quarts of nematode worms in the stomach of this small cetacean that measured only about five feet from snout to tail flukes. Out of curiosity we computed the actual number of worms present, and it exceeded fifteen thousand.

Endoparasites of the type we have been discussing have many problems that free-living organisms do not have to contend with. One of these is the securing of oxygen while living in an oxygen-free environment. They have solved this problem by producing enzymes that break down carbohydrates to simple substances, thereby releasing oxygen, which is utilized to yield energy.

8

THE MOSS ANIMALS AND LAMP SHELLS

There are several groups of animals that are each placed in separate phyla of their own but are known collectively as lophophorates. This name is derived from the fact that they all possess a special food-gathering device known as a lophophore. This lophophore appears externally as a circular or horseshoe-shaped ridge, which bears ciliated tentacles and surrounds the mouth. The tentacles are extensions of the body wall and are hollow internally. The cavity within the tentacles is actually continuous with the body cavity. The action of the cilia on these tentacles serves to set up a current through the lophophore so that small organisms may be captured for food.

The lophophorates, although represented in the world today by relatively small and obscure species of animals, are interesting from the standpoint of the evolution of higher organisms in the animal kingdom. On the basis of their method of embryonic development, the higher animals are divided into two great groups—the Protostomes and the Deuterostomes. The Protostomes include the segmented worms, the sipunculids, the echiuroids, the mollusks, and the arthropods. The Deuterostomes comprise the higher organisms, including the echinoderms and chordates.

The lophophorates are a very old group. It is believed that they evolved at a point in evolutionary history when these two great lines, the Protostomes and the Deuterostomes, were just diverging. The fact that they bear certain resemblances to each line gives considerable support to this theory.

The moss animals. These are so named because of their superficial resemblance to mosslike growth on submerged rocks. Of the nearly four thousand known species, about fifty occur in fresh water and the rest are marine. The moss animals are placed in the phylum Ectoprocta at present, but their true relationship was long misunderstood.

Superficially the ectoprocts bear a likeness to certain hydroid coelenterates. This is partly because of their colonial organization and also

67

because the presence of tentacles on the lophophore surrounding the mouth produces the appearance of a polyp-like organism.

Most species of moss animals are found close to shorelines on rocks, reefs, and pilings or attached to other organisms. However, there are deep-water forms that have been dredged from eighteen thousand feet in the ocean.

The lamp shells.   These animals are in the phylum Brachiopoda. Superficially they resemble bivalve mollusks, because of the presence of a pair of hinged shells. These shells, or valves, however, are very different from those of a mollusk. In a clam the shells are on either side of the body, but in

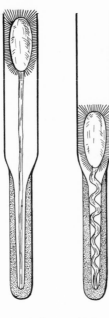

Diagram showing a lamp shell (*Lingula*) attached by a long stalk to the bottom of its vertical hole in the sand.

extended   withdrawn

the lamp shells the valves are above and below, or dorsal and ventral. Furthermore, in the lampshells the lower valve is generally larger than the upper one and is frequently attached to the substratum. The attachment may be direct or indirect by means of a stalk.

All the lamp shells are marine. Most of them occur in shallow water close to shore, where they are attached to rocks or live in burrows in sand or mud. The group is a very old one. Fossil brachiopods are known from

Cambrian deposits estimated to have been formed more than five hundred million years ago. It is interesting to note that only about 4 percent of the more than seven thousand species that have been recorded are alive today. The rest are all known from the fossil record, which indicates that they were once a dominant group of animals in the world.

9

THE HIGHER WORMLIKE ORGANISMS

The largest and best-known wormlike organisms belong to the phylum Annelida. These are the segmented worms that include such familiar kinds as the earthworms, pileworms, and leeches. In all these annelids the body parts are repeated, both externally and internally, so that the organism consists of a series of essentially similar segments arranged in a linear manner with a nervous system and digestive system extending the whole length of the body. We refer to this arrangement as metamerism. Many theories have been presented to account for it. It is generally believed that once bilateral symmetry was established in the more primitive Bilateria, the organs of the body tended more or less to distribute themselves evenly. Then, when undulatory or wavelike movement came into use, it was associated with the development of segmental muscles, which in turn divided the body into fairly equal segments. The segmented bodies of annelids have led most zoologists to believe that annelids are related to arthropods, which are the highest of the Protostomes. Possibly they arose from a common ancestor.

There are three major groups of annelids: the polychaete worms, which are marine; the oligochaete worms, which are freshwater or terrestrial; and the leeches, which may be marine, freshwater, or terrestrial.

Polychaete worms are widely distributed over the oceans of the world, but the kinds one is most likely to see are found along the shore, living in mud, sand, or tide pools, under rocks, in clumps of algae, or among masses of other organisms such as barnacles or bivalve mollusks. Residents of the seacoast are familiar with polychaetes, although they refer to them as pileworms or sandworms. It is a common custom, when going fishing, to search among mussels and barnacles on wharf pilings or reefs exposed at low tide for large green worms whose bodies are segmented and which possess a pair of bristled appendages on each side of the segments. These nereid worms (they belong to the family Nereidae) make excellent bait for

70

sea perch and other marine fishes. Some species have a bluish tinge or are iridescent.

In parts of the Pacific as well as the Atlantic Ocean there are marine worms that are luminous. This luminescence, however, is periodic and associated with the reproductive cycle. In the waters around Bermuda there is a polychaete that produces bioluminescence for about one hour each month in the late summer. The females rise to the surface of the sea shortly after sunset and swim in circles as they produce light and lay eggs. The males, probably attracted by the light, also rise and enter the circle, where they fertilize the eggs, which glow for a short time.

While many polychaetes crawl about in various shoreline habitats or on the ocean bottom and others are free-swimming, there are numerous species that spend most of their lives in tubes and therefore are sedentary. One has but to spend a few minutes looking into a tide pool to realize the abundance of tube worms. When the water is quiet, a living fan may emerge from a coiled or twisted calcareous tube that appeared to be uninhabited. These fans are the gills of the tube worm. They are often brightly colored and look like a flower. Some of the larger species are commonly referred to as feather dusters, which aptly describes their shape but fails to do justice to their beauty.

Many tube worms are very sensitive to light, although their eyes are quite simple, consisting of paired masses of pigment and photoreceptor cells. Even the shadow of one's hand momentarily passing over them produces an instantaneous reaction, and the gills are retracted into the tube so rapidly that one cannot follow the motion.

The tubes of these polychaetes generally are composed either of grains of sand or of calcareous matter. One group, known as the sabellids, cements sand together by means of a binding mucus to form a protective tube. The serpulid worms have special glands that secrete calcium carbonate to form their tubes.

The oligochaetes are better known to persons who do not live along the seacoast. There are few boys that have not dug up representatives of this group for bait. They are variously sold to fishermen as night crawlers, earthworms, and angleworms.

It is estimated that there are more than eighteen hundred species of earthworms. They occur principally in the temperate parts of the world, but many species have been inadvertently introduced by man into various regions. The organisms themselves or their eggs are easily transported in

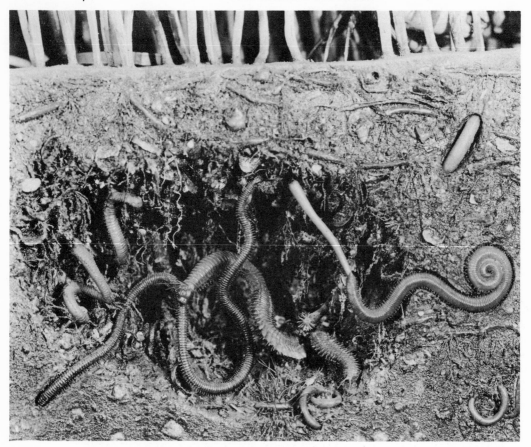

Annulate group showing polychaete worms burrowing in mud about the roots of eel grass.
AMERICAN MUSEUM OF NATURAL HISTORY

small quantities of soil. They range in length from a small fraction of an inch up to nearly ten feet although even the largest rarely exceed half an inch in diameter. The largest species are found in the tropics and on the Australian continent.

Earthworms play an important part in cultivating the soil. They occur in great numbers in favorable situations and may extend their burrows from the surface down to depths of six or eight feet. The burrows tend to loosen and aerate the soil, and the earth that actually passes through the worm's body is brought to the surface and deposited there in the form of castings. Furthermore, when the surface soil is moist and there is green vegetation, earthworms extend themselves out of their burrows at night and feed on growing plants, thereby taking organic material down into the ground. This role that the earthworm plays in nature was commented upon by Charles Darwin more than one hundred years ago.

Not all oligochaetes are earthworms. There are a number of species that live in lakes or streams and one family that has become parasitic on crayfish.

Some tube worms such as *Eudistylia polymorpha* are known as "feather dusters."
R. T. ORR

The leeches comprise the third group of segmented worms. They are medium-sized annelids, ranging mostly from one-half inch up to eight inches in length, with flattened bodies. At both ends of the body there are suckers, which serve to attach the parasitic species of leeches to their prey and also aid in locomotion. In moving along a surface, a leech advances somewhat like an inchworm.

With the exception of most oceanic islands, leeches are worldwide in distribution. There are a few marine forms and some that are terrestrial in moist tropical regions, but the majority of the more than three hundred known species inhabit freshwater lakes and rivers. Many kinds live on the blood of vertebrate animals. A few remain permanently attached to their host, but they usually drop off as soon as they have become engorged with blood.

For centuries leeches have been used for so-called medicinal purposes. In fact one species is named *Hirudo medicinalis*. The use of these animals was based on the theory that a reduction in the amount of blood in the body was a form of therapy for certain diseases. To most people this is a repulsive custom. I have seen the bodies of persons, in leech-infested waters, attacked by these blood-sucking organisms, and it is not a pleasant sight.

A number of other wormlike animals belong to small, obscure phyla that are mainly known by the specialist. Brief mention may be made of two of these, both of which are marine. One group consists of the peanut worms, or sipunculids, which live in the ocean substratum from depths of as much as fifteen thousand feet up to high-tide level. They may occur in sand or mud or occupy empty shells of mollusks or even tubes of tube worms. Their bodies are cylindrical and often have a circle of tentacle-like structures that surround the mouth. Most of them are six to twelve inches long and moderately thick.

Another group consists of the echiurids, which superficially look like the sipunculids and whose sausage-shaped bodies are frequently excavated from their mud burrows by clam diggers. Although most echiurids occur along the shoreline, recent deep-sea dredging by Russian oceanographers has revealed their presence at depths as great as twenty-seven thousand feet in the Pacific Ocean.

Both the sipunculids and echiurids are believed to have arisen long ago from primitive annelids, or the ancestors of both annelids and arthropods, which are the invertebrates with segmented bodies. However, as neither the peanut worms nor the echiurids show signs of segmentation, it is likely that they branched off before this advanced feature evolved.

IO

THE MOLLUSKS

The phylum Mollusca is one of the best known in the animal kingdom and contains many of the most recognizable kinds of organisms. We are all familiar with some of them: snails, slugs, clams, oysters, mussels, limpets, and chitons. The squids, octopuses, and nautiluses are also mollusks, but less readily identified as such.

Mollusks constitute the second largest division in the zoological world, being exceeded in numbers only by the arthropods. Close to one hundred thousand living species have been discovered, and an additional thirty-five thousand fossil forms are known. Because of their hard outer covering, which resists rapid deterioration, mollusks are particularly suited for fossil preservation. The majority of them live in water, where their shells often sink to the bottom after the living organisms die. Here they are gradually covered with sedimentation, which later may harden to form rock. The shells contained within are thereby preserved, and in time become petrified. Some of the oldest molluscan fossils go back more than half a billion years.

From the standpoint of human economy, mollusks are important organisms. Abalones, scallops, clams, and oysters are highly rated as items of food, and certain fisheries industries are dependent upon them. Land snails and slugs may be serious garden and agricultural pests. The giant African snail, which was introduced into some of the Pacific islands during World War II, has proved to be a menace to native vegetation. There are also mollusks that serve as intermediate hosts for parasitic worms that infest man and various other backboned animals.

Mollusks are Protostomes and therefore related to the segmented worms and arthropods. The resemblance to these two groups is not easily seen, because mollusks do not show any signs of segmentation and have become greatly modified in body form. In their early development, however, the more primitive kinds have a larval stage, known as a trochophore, which very much resembles that of marine annelid worms. It has been suggested that once the Protostome and Deuterostome lines separated from a common lophophorate-like ancestor, the Protostomes very soon branched again. One of these branches gave rise to the annelids and the arthropods, and the other to the mollusks.

Mollusks resemble other protostomes in having a complete digestive system, parts of which are encased in muscle tissue; a well-developed circulatory system with a heart; and a body cavity in which most of the visceral organs are situated. They differ in having the body divided into a head, a foot, and a visceral region, and also in possessing an outgrowth of the body wall called a mantle. The latter is responsible for secreting the

". . . silver bells and cockle shells . . ." R. T. ORR

calcareous shell, or exoskeleton, which is characteristic of so many members of this phylum.

There are five different molluscan classes: the Amphineura, or chitons; the Gastropoda, which are the snails and slugs; the Pelecypoda, or bivalves; the Scaphopoda, a group commonly referred to as the tooth shells; and the Cephalopoda, which include the octopuses, squids, and the nautilus-like mollusks.

The Amphineura. The principal amphineurans are the chitons, of which there are about six hundred known species living today. These animals will be found along any rocky coast in the intertidal region, but they are neither as abundant nor as conspicuous as their relatives the gastropods. A few species occur in the depths of the sea, one having been recorded at 13,800 feet.

The shell of a chiton is divided into eight separate plates. AMERICAN MUSEUM OF NATURAL HISTORY

Most mollusks have a shell consisting of one or two parts. In the chitons, however, the shell is separated into eight distinct elements or plates. These plates overlap one another like shingles in a line along the back. Each has a winglike process that extends out and forward on either side, where it is partly covered by a fold of the mantle.

Along the Pacific coast of North America there is a giant species that attains a length of up to twelve inches. The plates of this species are pure white; they are often washed up on beaches. Their winglike shape is responsible for their being called butterfly shells. Equally large chitons are found on the Great Barrier Reef. Most species are much smaller, averaging several inches in body length; the smallest known chiton when full grown measures about half an inch.

Chitons, like snails and limpets, can move about on rocks by muscular wave action on the part of the foot. They are not great travelers and often stay within an area of a few feet for months at a time. The shell and mantle are generally dull-colored and not too different in appearance from the rocks on which these animals live. This makes them rather inconspicuous. In some species the mantle on either side of the plates may be covered with hairlike spines or scales, which disguise them even more.

Chitons are vegetarians; their food consists of marine algae, on which they browse. Most of their feeding is done at night, although some species are active in the daytime. Few animals will attack them because of the

The plates of the giant Pacific coast, or gum boot, chiton (*Cryptochiton stelleri*) often wash up on the beach and are referred to as "butterfly shells." R. T. ORR

protection afforded by their calcareous plates and hard, often spiny, mantle. As a rule chitons adhere very tightly—by means of suction produced by the foot and margin of the mantle—to the rocky surface on which they live. If they are pried loose, they will roll up very much as sow bugs or armadillos do in times of danger.

The Gastropoda.   More than thirty-five thousand living species of gastropods are known—by far the largest group of mollusks. Furthermore, the members are more widely distributed over the world than those of other molluscan groups. There are marine, freshwater, and terrestrial gastropods. Their shells vary in size from less than one-sixteenth of an inch in length in some land snails to as much as eighteen inches in the case of the giant triton of the South Pacific and Indian oceans. Many of the marine species that we are familiar with live in the intertidal areas along shore, where they are found on rocks or moving about in tide pools, on mud flats, and even on sandy beaches. Some of the most beautifully colored marine gastropods

At low tide black turban shells (*Tegula funebralis*) are often found in large aggregations on exposed rocks along the Pacific coast. R. T. ORR

are lacking a shell and are known as nudibranchs. Those with shells are often exquisitely sculptured and marked.

An interesting and important structure possessed by gastropods is the radula. This is a flexible, ribbon-like band containing a number of transverse rows of teeth. The radula is situated within the retractile proboscis and is used as a rasping organ when feeding. In some species it cuts soft vegetation, but in others it may drill through hard shell and in this way serve to kill the prey.

The collecting of snail shells as a hobby has long been practiced by many people of various lands and is still a popular one. Some species are very rare—such as the famous *Conus gloria-maris* or "glory of the sea" of the East Indies, which has sold for over $1,000 per specimen.

Not all marine gastropods are shore-dwellers. Some occur in deep water, even at depths of more than two thousand fathoms, and a few swim freely in the open ocean. Although there are not nearly as many kinds of freshwater snails as marine species, there are few ponds, lakes, rivers, and streams in the world that are not inhabited by gastropods. Occasionally, under favorable conditions, freshwater gastropods occur in fairly large numbers.

Terrestrial gastropods, represented by various kinds of land snails and slugs, are of very widespread occurrence. Some species have adapted themselves to subalpine situations, while others inhabit boreal forests, woodlands, grasslands, jungle, and even the most arid deserts. Land snails are found not only on all the continents except Antarctica but also on many oceanic islands. Man, sometimes accidentally and at other times on purpose, has been responsible for transplanting many species into new areas, where they have become established, often to the regret of the agriculturist and gardener.

The gastropods are divided into two main groups on the basis of their respiratory organs—the gill-breathers and the air-breathers, or pulmonates. The distinction becomes a little confusing when we find that not all the gill-breathers live in water. Some tropical gill-breathers are terrestrial. Furthermore, not all the air-breathers live on land. Most of the freshwater snails are pulmonates, and so are a few marine species. However, in general, the vast majority of marine gastropods respire by means of gills, and most terrestrial snails and slugs have lost their gills and developed a lung-like respiratory chamber in the mantle cavity. In the case of the freshwater pulmonates we find that this chamber has secondarily become adapted for breathing in water.

Among the more primitive gastropods are the abalones, the keyhole limpets, and the limpets proper. Abalones, whose shells are really coiled, although the coiling is perhaps not apparent at first glance, are gastronomic delicacies in certain parts of the world. The largest species have shells that may attain a length of over nine inches. The shells of these animals are perforated by a row of holes near the edge. These apertures permit water to pass in and out of the respiratory chamber, which contains two gills.

Along the shores of the north Pacific Ocean, abalone shells frequently wash up on the beaches.
R. T. ORR

The foot of an abalone is a large, thick, muscular structure, which not only enables the animal to move about slowly but also functions as a powerful suction cup to hold it onto the rocky substratum of its environment. For those of us who live along the northern Pacific coast, abalone hunting or fishing, whichever term is more appropriate, has long been a popular sport. It is a rugged one, however, since the ocean is cold and the best low tides during the legal season are in the early morning or very late afternoon hours. A low tide is essential to the operation, unless one is a skin diver, since it is then that parts of the reefs and rock ledges where these animals live are exposed. The edible portion of the abalone is the foot, which should be sliced rather thin, pounded lightly, and fried quickly in a batter.

Keyhole limpets and volcano shells are related to abalones, but they have lost all trace of a spiral. Both these kinds of mollusks have an oval or

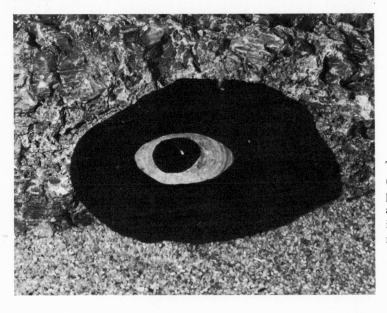

The giant keyhole limpet (*Megathura crenulata*) has a pupil-like aperture at the apex of the shell. The latter is partly covered by the black mantle. R. T. ORR

rounded aperture at the apex of the somewhat conical shell. The giant keyhole limpet has a black mantle that extends up over the shell and may cover it almost entirely at times.

The true limpets have rather simple conical shells that lack any apical aperture. There are many species of limpets. Most of them are considerably less than an inch in length, but a few fairly large species have shells nearly four inches long. Limpets are among our commonest rock inhabitants in the intertidal zone. Like abalones, their muscular foot serves for locomotion, which is rather limited, and as a suction cup to adhere tightly to the substratum. Their food consists of algae that grow on the rocks they inhabit.

A limpet and several black turban shells on a tidal reef. R. T. ORR

Another group of gastropods includes such diverse forms as the periwinkles, moonsnails, slipper shells, and cowries, to mention just a few. It is a very large molluscan order, whose members are all characterized by having but a single gill and kidney as well as certain other structural features in common.

Periwinkles are among the commonest snails found along rocky shore-lines. They are also among the first kinds of snails that one will encounter in such regions. This is because they occur high up on shore, where they can be found at almost all times except during the highest tides. Peri-winkles are worldwide in distribution. Their food consists of algae. In the tropics there are species that live on the aerial roots of mangroves.

Most kinds of periwinkles are rather small, but they make up for this by their abundance. In European coastal cities these mollusks are collected by the ton and used for food. Although small snails have never been popular as food in the United States, they were formerly important in the diet of certain Indians. Along the west coast of North America the kitchen mid-dens of tribes who lived close to the seashore contain abundant evidence— in the form of shells—that periwinkles, along with turban and other shells, were commonly eaten.

Moonsnails, in contrast to the small herbaceous periwinkles, are large carnivorous mollusks of temperate and tropical waters. Their smooth globular shells, which in some species may attain a diameter of four or five inches, house a remarkably large foot, several times as long as the width of the shell. With this enormous flat foot the moonsnail plows along just beneath the surface of the mud or sand in search of clams and various other mollusks. Its prey is usually killed by suffocation, after which the snail sucks out the flesh of the victim with its proboscis.

Slipper shells are common along both the Atlantic and Pacific coasts of North America. They are either limpet-shaped or flattened and usually have an internal shelflike plate that closes a part or even half of the aper-ture to the shell. They derive their name from the fact that, when turned upside down, they resemble little boats or slippers. There are other related kinds, such as members of the genus *Crucibulum,* that occur along the Atlantic and Pacific coasts of the Americas. They have a saucer-like shell with a cup-shaped shelf inside and are known as cup-and-saucer limpets.

The cowries are found principally in tropical seas. Their richly colored shells are known to most persons and have been used as a medium of exchange by primitive peoples of the South Pacific and Indian Ocean regions for generations. Marco Polo is said to have found cowry shells in use in China in the thirteenth century. The money cowry has been the most important species used in trade in times past. This species inhabits coral reefs and sandy mudflats about Australia, the Pacific Islands, and parts of the Indian Ocean. The early traders used to gather shiploads of these shells in regions where they were valueless and exchange them for ivory and palm oil along the west coast of Africa, where they were in great demand. The tiger cowry is one of the larger and more beautiful species.

The heteropods and several families of freshwater and tropical terrestrial snails are also members of this order. The heteropods are mollusks of the

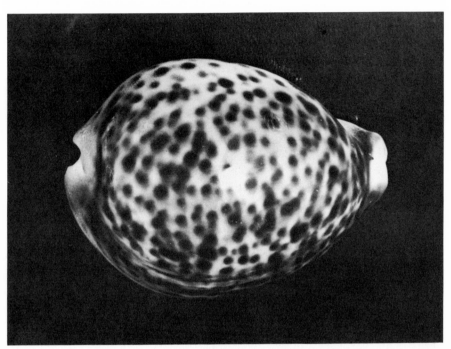

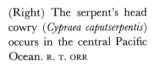

(Above) The tiger cowry (*Cypraea tigris*) is found in Hawaii and the Polynesian Islands. R. T. ORR

(Right) The serpent's head cowry (*Cypraea caputserpentis*) occurs in the central Pacific Ocean. R. T. ORR

ocean, where they either swim by means of a finlike foot or float freely. Some have shells while others do not. Certain kinds, such as the atlantids, rise to the surface of the warmer seas at night in vast numbers.

Another large and colorful order of gastropods—one that is entirely marine in occurrence—contains a number of boring species and some very poisonous snails. Among the former are the oyster drills, the murex shells, and the olive shells. The poisonous species are members of the beautiful cone shell group.

The oyster drill is a small, dull-colored snail that is one of the chief enemies of the oyster industry. These inconspicuous gastropods move into oyster beds, where they feed on the much larger bivalves. As with a drill, the animal bores a small hole by means of its powerful radula in one of the valves of the oyster close to the hinge of the shell, and then sucks out the soft parts. This results in the death of the oyster, which then opens up and makes the solid meat available to the enemy.

The large spiny murex shells, with their colorful pink interiors, are found primarily along the shores of tropical seas. In some places they may be fairly abundant. I have landed on small islands in the Gulf of California where murex shells were among the most conspicuous elements on the beaches.

The olive shells are, for the most part, inhabitants of the shores of the warmer seas, where they occur principally in sand, mud, or gravel into which they burrow. They extend their long syphons up to the surface and secure water for respiration.

There is one species, the purple olive, that ranges north along the Pacific coast of North America as far as southern Canada. Their white- and purple-banded shells are about an inch long. These shells were collected extensively by the coastal Indians and used both for ornamentation and as a medium of exchange. Purple olives can be found along almost any sandy beach from Baja California to Puget Sound in British Columbia.

The cone shells are among the most beautiful and most valuable to the collector, yet the most dangerous of the gastropod mollusks. They are carnivorous and adapted to capturing moving prey, which includes other mollusks as well as various marine invertebrates and fishes. The cone shell captures its prey by rapidly extruding the long proboscis from the head. The radula on the end of this organ has grooved teeth and glands from which poison flows. The harmful secretion is a neurotoxin. Fortunately, most species of cone shells are not injurious to man, but a few are reported to be capable of inflicting extremely painful stings, which may even result

Murex shells are common in tropical waters. One of the most beautiful is the royal murex
(*Murex regius*) of the eastern Pacific area. R. T. ORR

in death. The first time I collected live cone shells I was unaware of this.
Although I was not bitten, my initial enthusiasm soon waned when I
learned of the potential danger involved. However, cone shells as a rule
attack only the small animals that represent food to them. If disturbed,
they attempt to hide.

These shells, as their name implies, are cone-shaped and often very
beautifully marked with spots, lines, bars, triangles, or stripes. A few species
get into temperate waters, but most of the cone shells are inhabitants of
tropical seas. In life the brilliantly polished shell is usually covered with a
skinlike layer that makes it rather inconspicuous.

There is a group of marine gastropods that possesses but one auricle in
the heart and one kidney and has the shell and mantle cavity reduced.

A cone shell, *Conus principes.*
Cone shells are carnivores
and may inject a poisonous
toxin into their prey or their
enemies. R. T. ORR

Some of its better-known representatives are the bubble shells, the sea
hares, the pteropods, and the nudibranchs.

The bubble shells have thin globose shells, which are partly covered
with winglike extensions of the large body. These extended structures are
often very beautiful. There is one species in the Great Barrier Reef known
as the rosepetal bubble shell, whose delicately colored mantle encloses the
shell in a flower-like manner. These gastropods are carnivorous. Their
food consists of other small mollusks, which they swallow whole as they
forage through mud and sand. The shells of their prey are ground up in
their strong gizzards.

Sea hares are strange looking sluglike creatures whose shells are rudi-
mentary. They are widely distributed, although represented by relatively

few species. Sea hares live below the low-tide zones and are rarely seen on shore except after a storm. Some species attain a length of more than twelve inches. One of their peculiarities is their ability to emit a purplish fluid when attacked. This has the effect of coloring the water and making them difficult to see. This fluid was once considered to be poisonous but has since been shown to be completely harmless. In some of the Pacific islands sea hares have been used as food.

The pteropods are commonly known as the sea butterflies. Their resemblance to butterflies stems from the presence of two swimming disks (they appear to be outgrowths of the foot), which are flapped vigorously like wings as the animals swim through the sea. Pteropods are mollusks of the open ocean, where they often occur in great numbers, especially in the Arctic. There they may be so abundant that they serve as food for whales. Some species have thin, transparent shells, while the shell is entirely lacking in others. Like many other free-swimming oceanic organisms, pteropods tend to come to the surface of the sea at night and sink to depths during daylight hours.

The nudibranchs must be rated among the most beautiful of marine animals. They are soft-bodied gastropods that are lacking a shell in the adult form. Most of them are brilliantly colored and often have numerous plumelike adornments. These sea slugs are inhabitants of shallow water, but they are not restricted to intertidal areas. They may occur in beds of algae some distance from shore.

Despite their brilliant color, nudibranchs are often very difficult to see because they blend in so well with other colorful plant and animal organisms in their environment. It has always been a source of amazement to me to see some of these beautiful slugs glide out from rocks or algae in a tide pool and move along upside down beneath the surface film of the water as easily as though they were gliding on the underside of a piece of glass.

The remaining gastropods are classified as pulmonates. They, too, have only one auricle and one kidney but lack true gills. Respiration takes place in a special vascularized chamber in the mantle. There are two groups of pulmonates—those that are entirely terrestrial and possess two pairs of tentacles or feelers with eyes on the end of the back pair and those that live mostly in fresh water and have only one pair of tentacles with eyes located at the base of these structures.

We commonly refer to land mollusks with shells as snails and those without shells as slugs. This is a somewhat artificial distinction, since a

The redwood snail (*Helminthoglypta arrosa*) is a common pulmonate land snail in moist Pacific coast forests. R. T. ORR

small shell or even an internal shell may be present in some so-called slugs. Some land snails are carnivorous and predatory, living on other inverte- brate organisms such as worms, but the majority of land snails are her- bivorous.

Pulmonate land snails are very widespread. They occur on nearly every land mass and in most terrestrial habitats in the world. I have collected numerous tiny gastropods under rocks close to timberline in mountainous parts of western North America and have also found them on the driest desert areas. In the desert areas one usually see the faded and long un- occupied shells on the surface of the ground. The desert snails keep far below the surface of the earth, where they stay in a torpid state with the shell opening sealed except during brief periods of the year when weather conditions are favorable for them to emerge. Certain land snails are said to be able to survive in such a dormant condition for a number of years.

Some of the tropical land snails are as beautifully colored as their marine relatives. They exhibit considerable geographic variation over rather limited areas. This is especially true of some of the helices of the Philippines and the little agate shells that inhabit trees in the Hawaiian islands. Among the largest species of land snails are the agates of Africa, some of which attain a length of eight inches.

Slugs, like land snails, may be herbivorous or carnivorous. One of the largest of our native North American slugs is the great yellow, or banana, slug which may be as much as six inches long. This is an inhabitant of damp, forested areas along the Pacific coast. Its food consists entirely of

Banana slugs (*Ariolimax columbianus*) are the giants of this group of land mollusks. R. T. ORR

vegetable matter. The equally large gray slug, which was introduced into America from the Old World, will consume only animal matter and is often found around garbage in search of scraps.

Fungi provide food for many forest-dwelling gastropods. In the late 1940's, while my wife and I were on a museum collecting trip in the Rocky Mountains, we found two peculiar-looking slugs feeding on the cap of a fleshy fungus in a damp forest of cedar, fir, and larch. The larger of the two reminded us of an aircraft carrier because of its flattened back. Although we were not collecting mollusks, we saved one of these specimens (the other fell on the ground and was lost) and brought it back to an associate who was a specialist in this field. It later turned out that our find represented a new genus and species.

The majority of so-called "pond snails" are also pulmonates and usually come to the surface of the water to take air. They consume water plants and algal scum and, in turn, serve as important food for many other animal organisms, including some kinds of fishes and amphibians as well as ducks, rails, coots, and other water birds. They are also intermediate hosts for a number of parasitic worms, such as liver flukes, lung flukes, and blood flukes, that affect man and domestic animals.

Freshwater snails may occur at considerable depth in large lakes. One species is reported to have been dredged from a depth of six hundred feet in Lake Geneva, Switzerland. In regions where ponds and lakes freeze in winter, freshwater snails bury themselves in mud at the bottom in autumn and remain there in a dormant state until the following spring.

The Pelecypoda. This is the second largest group of mollusks. Pelecypods are commonly called bivalves, because their mantle secretes a shell that is divided into two parts. These parts are hinged dorsally so as to enclose the laterally compressed, headless body. The muscular foot is not used for gliding, as in gastropods, but is usually hatchet-shaped and may be used as a digging tool. Water containing food and oxygen is brought into the mantle cavity by means of one syphon and expelled with waste products through another. The two syphons are developed from a part of the mantle in most pelecypods, and are often fused together in burrowing species. In a clam we refer to these fused syphons as the neck. It is often capable of great elongation.

Pelecypods are worldwide in distribution. Although largely marine, there are some freshwater species. A few have been found at great depths in the ocean, but the majority occur along or close to the shore. Most of

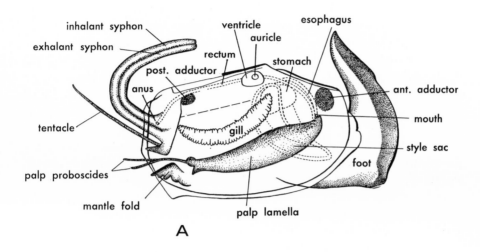

A

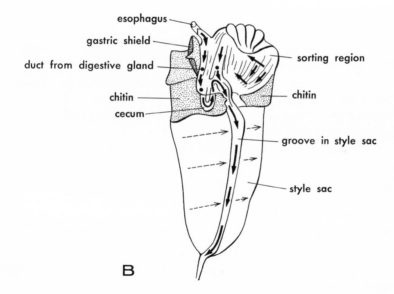

B

A. Diagram of a clam as seen in a lateral view showing some of the major parts of the body.
B. The digestive system of a bivalve mollusk.

them live in sand and mud or attach themselves to various objects. Others have become adapted to boring in rock and wood. There are even some free-swimming as well as parasitic kinds of bivalves.

The classification of pelecypods is based primarily upon the structure of the respiratory organs. Four orders are recognized, but most of the commonly known species fall within two of these groups. The first contains the mussels, the oysters, and the pectens, or scallop shells. The second includes the clams, the cockles, most of the rock-boring bivalves, the shipworms, and the freshwater pelecypods.

Mussels are found along all continental shores. They are easily recognized by their bluish-black shells as they adhere in masses to rocks and pilings in the intertidal zone by means of threadlike structures produced by the byssal gland on the foot. Because of their ability to attach themselves to ships and their rapid rate of growth, many species have been introduced into parts of the world where they were non-native. The European mussel, for example, is now common on both coasts of North America.

Mussels are excellent food (very tasty in my opinion), but few people in the United States eat them. This stems in part from the danger of mussel poisoning at certain times of the year. In the summer months poison produced by a protozoan known as *Gonyaulax* may accumulate in parts of the digestive system of mussels and make them deadly poisonous. Under favorable conditions as many as forty million of these organisms have been found in a single cubic centimeter of sea water. At such times they may cause the death of untold millions of fish and other marine organisms. Their presence in the water brings about a coloration known as "red tides." In Europe mussels are considered a delicacy and are sold in the markets. To provide for the demand they are cultured in certain areas.

Oysters are probably the best-known bivalves and certainly the most valuable economically. There are few persons in North America or Europe who have not enjoyed the succulent flesh of the edible oyster. The shell that houses these gastronomic delicacies is far from beautiful. It is irregular in shape and externally rough and gray.

Young oysters are free-swimming for a short time, but the "spat," as they are called, later settle on some kind of hard substratum, usually of rock or shell. They frequently grow in clusters attached to each other. In the tropics the mangrove oyster attaches itself to the air roots of the mangroves which extend down into the water. These small oysters are abundant along the Mexican coast and are peddled on the streets of most of the towns and villages. In the Pacific Northwest the tiny Olympia oyster, which is no larger than one's thumbnail, is the gourmet's delight. In Australia there are edible oysters as much as a foot in diameter.

Most kinds of oysters like brackish water, and their culture is carried on in bays, inlets, and lagoons. Here, suitable shell, to which the planted spat may become attached, is scattered over the bottom. Fences are constructed around oyster beds, not to keep these mollusks in but rather to protect them from their principal large enemies, the rays and skates. The harvesting of oysters in the Hood Canal off Puget Sound is a sight worth watching. Barges are towed in to the oyster beds and left there to await low tide. When the mudflats are exposed, masses of oysters are raked up and piled onto the barges, which are then towed away when the tide again comes in.

The pearl oyster is not a close relative of the edible oysters but belongs to a group of flat-shelled bivalves that occurs principally in tropical seas. There they are found on clean sandy bottoms down to depths of more than one hundred feet. The mantle of these mollusks secretes a thick coating of nacre, or mother of pearl, on the inside of the valves, and this in itself is of considerable commercial importance. If a foreign object, such as a grain of sand, gets into the mantle, it too will have nacre deposited on it, until it forms what we call a pearl. Man has learned to introduce foreign bodies into these pearl oysters and produce the so-called "seed pearls."

Some of the most attractive mollusks are the thorny oysters. These inhabitants of tropical waters have ribbed valves with spines or leaflike scales on them. They are often colored differently on each valve. Some

Accumulations of nacre or mother-of-pearl may sometimes become attached to the inner surface of a pearl oyster shell. R. T. ORR

species are variegated, but most of them are orange, crimson, or purple. They are highly sought by shell collectors.

The pectens are among the most beautiful of bivalves. Their vivid shells are unequal in size, are ribbed, and have earlike extensions on either end of the hinge. Most pectens are some shade of orange or reddish-orange. Pectens, or scallops as they are commonly called, are largely free-swimming during their entire lives. They accomplish this movement by rapidly clapping the two shells together. The mantle is edged with fringelike tentacles that bear brilliantly colored eyes, each of which contains a cornea, a lens, and a retina.

Deep ridges with "ears" on the side of the hinge are characteristic of the shells of pectens. Shown here is *Pecten vogdesi*. R. T. ORR

Pectens often occur in great numbers around offshore banks, where they are hunted commercially. The large muscle that closes the valves is cut off and sold in the market as a scallop.

The second major group of pelecypods contains some species that are valuable and others that are harmful from the human standpoint. The many kinds of edible clams are included here. The largest bivalve in the world is the giant clam, *Tridacna derasa*, of the South Pacific and Indian oceans. This huge clam, whose weight may run into the hundreds of pounds and whose shell with its fluted margin may exceed three feet in length, is regarded as a hazard to divers, who may inadvertently get a foot caught in this living vise. This clam and several other smaller members of

A brightly colored encrusted sponge on a rock. ROBERT AMES

A tide pool with giant green anemones (*Anthopleura xanthogrammica*) and ochre starfish (*Pisaster ochraceous*) in purple phase attached to rocks covered with coralline algae. R. T. ORR

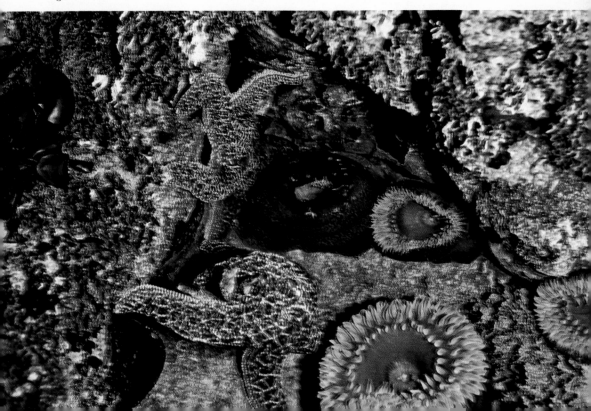

Polychaete on a sea star. ROBERT AMES

The jewel top snail (*Calliostoma ligatum*) occurs along the Pacific coast of North America.

ROBERT AMES

The so-called sea slugs are among the most beautiful of marine organisms. Shown here is the clown sea slug (*Triopha carpenteri*). ROBERT AMES

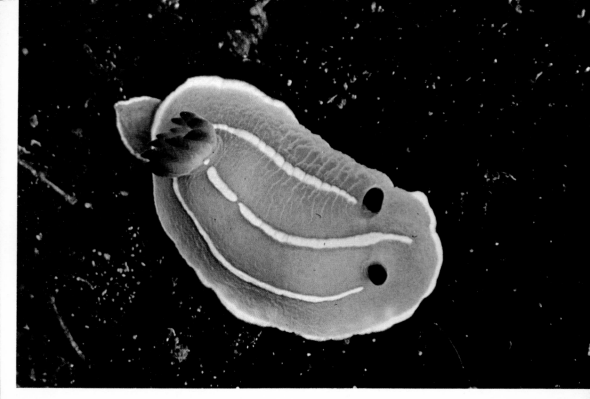

A nudibranch or sea slug (*Glossodoris macfarlandi*) named after the late Dr. Frank M. MacFarland, a noted authority on this group. ROBERT AMES

The California mantis shrimps (*Pseudosquilla bigelowi*) are among the most colorful of the crustaceans. R. T. ORR

A goliath beetle (*Goliathus*) of Africa on the hand of a native. EDWARD S. ROSS

(*Opposite*) A hermit crab (*Pagurus*) inhabiting a sea shell on which some barnacles are also living. ROBERT AMES

A swallowtail butterfly that has just emerged from its chrysalis. EDWARD S. ROSS

A scarab beetle. Some members of this group of beetles were regarded as sacred by the ancient Egyptians. EDWARD S. ROSS

A bee gathering pollen and nectar. EDWARD S. ROSS

The yellow crab spider which has just captured a beetle blends in beautifully with the yellow flower on which it waits for prey. EDWARD S. ROSS

The red, hourglass-shaped spot on the abdomen of the female black widow spider (*Lactrodectus mactans*) is diagnostic. EDWARD S. ROSS

The "plumes" of the turkey fish (*Pterois*) possess venom glands which can cause serious injury to one who touches them. R. T. ORR

Though not very large, the common piranha (*Serrasalmus nattereri*) which inhabits certain South American rivers is one of the most ferocious of fishes. R. T. ORR

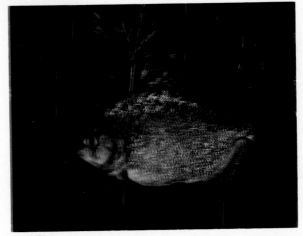

Puffers of the family Tetraodontidae have the ability to inflate their bodies with air or water when alarmed. ROBERT AMES

the genus are common residents of the Great Barrier Reef of Australia. Most of them have colorful mantles that extend beyond the wavy margins of the valves.

Less exciting but equally important are the many smaller species of clams that live in mudflats and sandy beaches in other parts of the world. Coastal inhabitants, both primitive and modern, have long regarded many of these pelecypods as articles of food. So popular is the sport of clam digging that most coastal states in the United States have found it necessary to restrict collecting to certain seasons and place a limit on the number taken.

The razor clams occur in many sandy beaches in the temperate parts of the Northern Hemisphere. These long, slender-bodied bivalves are gathered during extremely low tides by alert collectors. Once the telltale syphon hole has been located, the clam must be raked or dug out quickly, because it can move down through the sand with great rapidity by using its bladelike foot and within a very short time be several feet under the surface.

The largest of the burrowing clams is the famous geoduck, which occurs in mudflats along the west coast of North America. This giant species has been known to attain a weight of six and a half pounds. The enormous body and spyhon cannot be contained within the shell, which itself may be seven inches long.

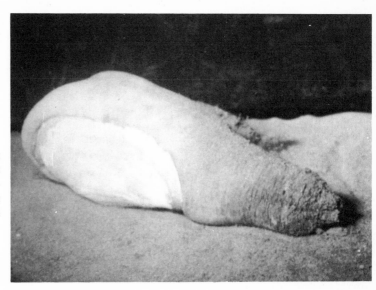

The body of the geoduck (*Panope generosa*) of the coast of northwestern North America is so large that it cannot be contained within the valves. JOHN TASHJIAN

Also members of this group are the cockles, or heart shells as they are often called. They have highly arched, globose valves that are strongly ribbed, with the ribs radiating from the hinge. On occasions when we have "Oysters Rockefeller" at home, they are always baked in the large cockle-shells that we gathered along the coast of Mexico.

Most clams burrow in mud or sand, but some are capable of boring through clay and rock. Among the better known are the piddocks. These clams have rasplike laminations over the front of each valve. The young free-swimming piddock attaches itself to a rock and makes an entrance by rubbing sand with its foot over the site of its future home. Once it has a cavity formed by this abrasive activity, it keeps burrowing with the rough anterior part of the shell. Naturally, the clam grows as it moves inward, so that it is permanently imprisoned. The syphons are extended out through the entrance hole into the water. Piddocks, in my opinion, are among the most delicious-tasting of mollusks, but to collect them one must work hard with a geologist's pick in rock that is not too hard to break. Piddocks are capable of boring through granite.

The most destructive of the bivalves are the shipworms, *Teredo navalis*. Their elongate, tubelike bodies, which may be as much as six inches long, have a tiny pair of shells that cap the anterior end of the body. These shells have cutting ridges on their surface and are used for drilling through wood. The free-swimming young will settle down on any wood in the sea and drill in to form a permanent home. Enormous damage has been done in the past to ships' hulls, wharves, pilings, bridge piers, and other wooden structures.

There are several families of freshwater clams. These mollusks are found in most of the major river systems and lakes of any size in the world. They live on the sandy or muddy bottoms and for the most part are of no economic importance.

The Scaphopoda.   This class comprises a very small group of marine mollusks commonly known as the tooth shells. The shell, which is responsible for the name of the group, is shaped like a miniature tusk. It is tubelike and generally about one or two inches long. Both ends of this slightly curved, tapering tube are open.

Scaphopods live in sandy or muddy situations, through which they are capable of burrowing with their foot. They are found in all the oceans of the world and occur from close to shore out to depths of as much as one thousand fathoms.

Along the Pacific coast of North America tooth shells were formerly used by the Indians as money. It is reported that a string of twenty-five was worth the price of either a canoe or a wife.

The Cephalopoda. Here we come to one of the most interesting groups of invertebrates. In long-past geological times, the cephalopods dominated the seas. Today they are represented by only a few hundred species, but these include such fascinating animals as the octopus, the giant devilfish (or giant squid, which is the largest animal without a backbone), the paper nautilus, and the pearly nautilus.

We like to associate shells with mollusks, but the only living cephalopods that possess shells are the nautiluses. In the squids there is an internal remnant of a shell called a pen, or cuttlebone, but none in the octopuses.

In all members of the class the anterior end of the body is surrounded by a circle of tentacles, or arms. These correspond to the foot in other mollusks. In the octopus there are eight arms, but the squids have an additional pair of somewhat longer tentacles. The nautilus has many times this number of arms.

Cephalopods have well-developed eyes, much like those of vertebrates, although they are formed in a different way. These eyes are capable of producing an image, rather than merely determining the presence or absence of light. All cephalopods except the nautilus possess an ink sac close to the posterior end of the intestine. This gland secretes a black concentrated fluid that can be ejected in time of danger and forms a screen for protection. Another fascinating feature of most cephalopods is their ability to change color very rapidly, so as to blend with their environment. An octopus or a squid can do this in a matter of seconds.

All members of the class are carnivorous, living on fish and various invertebrates. They possess not only a radula, or rasping organ, in the mouth, like gastropods, but also sharp beaklike jaws that can rapidly tear up flesh.

Octopuses live in caves and caverns or among rocks, mostly in shallow water close to shore or even in intertidal areas. There are a few deep-sea species. The entrances to their homes are usually strewn with the remains of their prey. The size of these animals is often greatly exaggerated, as is also their danger to man. Assertions of their danger to man may stem from stories of fights with these creatures by such famous novelists as Victor Hugo and Jules Verne. The largest individuals usually have a body no more than a foot long, although the tentacles may be up to sixteen feet in length. These tentacles, with their adhesive disks, are used in walking across the ocean bottom and in swimming.

The squids have more elongate bodies and relatively shorter arms. Their mode of locomotion is basically jet propulsion. Water is taken into the mantle cavity, then forcibly expelled through a funnel, thereby propelling the torpedo-shaped animal through the water with exterme rapidity. Most squids are small. They travel in very large schools in the open ocean, thus providing food for many other kinds of animals, including whales and various pinnipeds. The giant squid, *Architeuthis,* is the largest animal in the

The octopuses are inhabitants of sea caves and crevices in rocks. The one shown here is in a diorama at the AMERICAN MUSEUM OF NATURAL HISTORY.

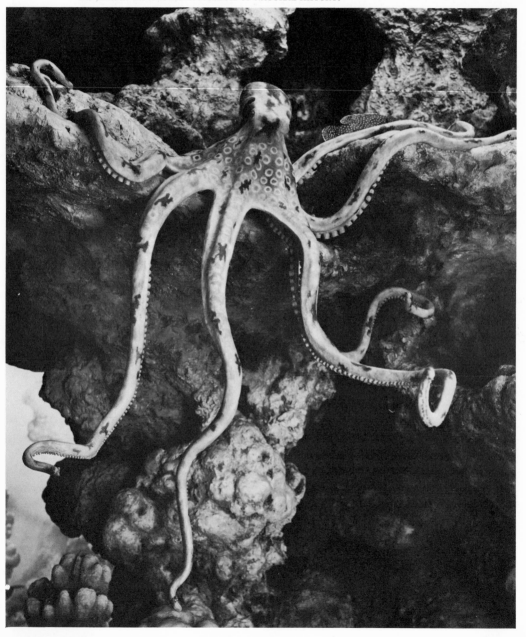

invertebrate world. One specimen taken in the North Atlantic measured fifty-five feet in length. The tentacles comprised thirty-five feet of this, and the body circumference was twelve feet.

Large squids, including *Architeuthis*, provide food for sperm whales, the largest toothed cetaceans. These giants of the sea are reported to engage in mortal combat with one another, as indicated by huge sucker scars sometimes seen on the big whales.

Related to the octopus but superficially resembling the nautilus is the paper nautilus, or argonaut. This animal sails the warmer seas. Its shell is white and as thin as paper. The occupant is not attached to the shell but holds onto it with two tentacles. The occupant is always a female.

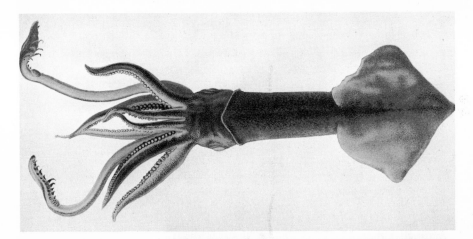

(Above) Squids live in the open ocean where they can swim with great rapidity by expelling water from the mantle cavity. AMERICAN MUSEUM OF NATURAL HISTORY

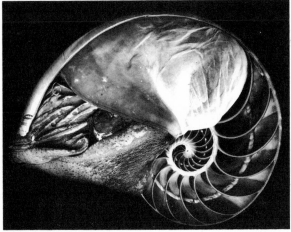

(Right) Members of the genus *Nautilus* are the only living cephalopods with shell. The animals inhabit the last chamber. AMERICAN MUSEUM OF NATURAL HISTORY

This was known to Aristotle, but the explanation was not found until almost the middle of the nineteenth century. It was then shown that this female octopod, when quite young, begins to secrete a shell in whose entrance she lives. The shell itself later serves for the protection of her eggs until they hatch.

The pearly nautilus is one of the beauties of the sea. It has been immortalized in Oliver Wendell Holmes's famous poem "The Chambered Nautilus." Of all living cephalopods, it is most closely related to the long extinct ammonites that once dominated the Paleozoic seas. The pearly nautilus has a beautifully coiled, bilaterally symmetrical shell, which is divided into compartments that become larger and larger, proceeding from the center of the spiral to the mouth of the shell. Only the outermost chamber is occupied by the living animal. The chambers, however, are all connected by a tube and are filled with a gas that is rich in nitrogen. This maintains the shell in an upright position. The several species that are known are found principally in tropical seas, where they range from shallow water to depths of several thousand feet.

II

THE ARTHROPODS

The phylum Arthropoda contains the most widely distributed and abundant forms of animal life so far as number of species is concerned. Its members, which include crustaceans, insects, millipedes, centipedes, spiders, ticks, and mites, are found just about everywhere in the world. Some occur on land, where many are capable of flight; others live in fresh water or inhabit the sea. It is conservatively estimated that more than seven hundred and fifty thousand species of arthropods are known today. This represents about 80 percent of the animal kingdom. And there are many new species still to be discovered and named.

Arthropods are believed to have originated from primitive segmented worms and are regarded as the most highly developed Protostomes, just as the chordates represent the culmination of the Deuterostome line. Our knowledge of these animals goes back more than half a billion years to the Cambrian period at the beginning of the Paleozoic era. At that time the dominant forms of animal life belonged to a group known as the trilobites. These were primitive crustacean-like creatures with segmented bodies divided lengthwise by two longitudinal rows. Trilobites were marine in occurrence. They became extinct about two hundred and fifty million years ago, but paleontologists have discovered fossil remains of more than two thousand species.

Although these early arthropods have long been extinct, the phylum to which they belonged is today a most successful one. This success may be attributed principally to two factors—the development of a tough outer skeleton composed of chitin, which covers the segmented body of arthropods, and the presence of jointed appendages attached to each side of the body segments.

The chitinous exoskeleton with which we are familiar on a beetle or a crab serves for protection and also provides a rather solid base for muscle attachment. This covering is noncellular and nonliving and is secreted by the outer cells of the body. Because it hardens soon after it forms, this covering must periodically be shed and replaced in order to permit growth. This is necessary at least until maximum size is attained. In some arthropods, especially many insects, the periodic molts, which are essential to allow for growth, are accomplished during the larval stage. Arthropods differ, therefore, in this respect from mollusks, whose outer skeleton grows as the body grows and needs not be shed.

The jointed limbs that characterize the arthropods have undergone great changes in different groups of these animals. Their ancestors are believed to have possessed a pair of biramous, or two-branched, appendages attached to each body segment. This primitive condition, however, has been subject to great modification since arthropods first evolved. Some of their appendages have developed into sensory antennae, others into mouth parts, legs, or swimmerets, while still others have disappeared completely.

The number of recognized classes of living arthropods has not been fully agreed upon by specialists. For practical purposes, only the following four groups are considered here: the crustaceans, the insects, the myriapodous arthropods (centipedes and millipedes), and the chelicerates (spiders and their relatives).

CRUSTACEANS

On land the vast majority of arthropods are insects, but in the sea almost all arthropods are crustaceans. The numbers of individuals found in favorable places in the ocean are almost beyond comprehension. This is true especially in Arctic and Antarctic waters. Some idea of the volume of crustaceans in these polar seas is gained when we consider that some of the smaller kinds, known as krill, provide the principal food for the largest forms of animal life, the whales.

With few exceptions crustaceans live in the water, and all breathe by means of gills. Their segmented bodies are generally covered with a heavy armor, which may be made entirely of chitin or of chitin impregnated with calcium salts. Most crustaceans have a body that is divided into three parts—a head, a thorax, and an abdomen. Each of these in turn is composed of a number of segments. Sometimes the head and thorax are combined into a cephalothorax, which may be covered by a shell-like structure called a carapace.

The trilobites possessed but one pair of antennae, but living crustaceans all possess two pairs. Their jointed, paired appendages are usually divided into two branches, although one of these may be reduced or even absent. The appendages of the head are usually either sensory (the antennae) or concerned with the capture and chewing of food. Those of the thorax are primarily for locomotion. The abdominal appendages, when present, sometimes form swimmerets, and the gills are often attached to their bases.

The living members of the class Crustacea are sometimes simply divided into two subclasses: the Entomostraca, comprising the water fleas, brine shrimps, barnacles, and an array of small crustaceans that lack abdominal appendages; and the Malacostraca, comprising the crabs, lobsters, shrimps, and their relatives. Other zoologists prefer to recognize five separate sub-classes: the Branchiopoda, the Ostracoda, the Copepoda, the Cirripedia, and the Malacostraca. This arrangement is used here.

Branchiopoda. The branchiopods are primitive crustaceans whose thoracic appendages are leaflike in appearance. The brine shrimps, the fairy shrimps, and the water fleas (cladocerans) are representative members of this group. Brine shrimps (*Artemia*) may occur in fresh water but are far more common in pools, lakes, or parts of bogs where the salinity is very high, and it is from this preference that they derive their name. It is in such highly concentrated saline situations in the warmer, arid parts of the world that they are most protected, since few other organisms can survive in such an environment. Brine shrimp eggs are able to stand heat and desiccation for long periods of time and may be blown far and wide by the wind. In recent years the eggs, because of their durability, have been sold by various supply houses for laboratory rearing or even home use as fish food. The brine shrimp is one of the very few forms of life found in some of the most alkaline lakes of the world such as the Great Salt Lake.

The fairy shrimp is a close relative of the brine shrimp and, like the latter, produces eggs that are distributed by the wind. I have seen small vernal ponds on the desert come alive with these tiny transparent crustaceans. Both these kinds of branchiopods keep the ventral part of the body directed toward the source of light. As a result they appear to be swimming on their backs most of the time.

The most common water fleas, or cladocerans, are members of the genus *Daphnia,* which are to be found in great numbers in almost any pond or lake. These small crustaceans are between one-eighth and one-sixteenth of an inch in length. Their carapaces are bivalved. They swim in a jerky manner by means of the actions of a pair of branched antennae.

Ostracoda. The ostracods are among the smallest and probably the

Brine shrimps (*Artemia salina*) magnified many times. EDWARD S. ROSS

least known of the crustaceans. Nearly two thousand species have been
described. Most of them are marine, but some live in fresh water. Ostracods, like the water fleas, have a bivalved carapace that superficially resembles a minute clam's shell. The carapace is often semitransparent, so
that one can see through it and observe the heart beating. Ostracods have

a pair of well-developed eyes situated on each side of the body. They swim by means of movement of the second pair of antennae. The first pair are sensory. Most species possess seven pairs of appendages, but the segmentation of the body is difficult to see.

The majority of ostracods are no more than one-twenty-fifth of an inch in length. They are usually bottom inhabitants. Some occur in mud and debris on the floor of lakes and ponds, others in tide pools or along the shore, and some on the bottom of the ocean at great depths. Relatively little is known about their behavior.

Copepoda.   Copepods are also tiny crustaceans, the largest of which may attain a length of one-sixteenth of an inch. They make up for their small size by their abundance, especially in marine waters. Of the several thousand known species belonging to this group, more than 90 percent are found in the sea. In the colder waters of the ocean these plankton organisms are sufficiently abundant that they serve, along with certain other crustaceans, as food for baleen whales.

Studies made on the distribution of various kinds of plankton, which includes all small floating or free-swimming organisms, have shown that some species of marine copepods undergo marked vertical migrations during a twenty-four-hour period. In the daytime they stay far below the surface, being most numerous at depths of from one thousand to fifteen hundred feet. At nightfall they move toward the surface and by midnight may be at depths of from thirty to fifty feet. By dawn they are again well on their way down to lower levels.

Copepods tend to have teardrop-shaped bodies and two pairs of antennae on their large heads. The first pair serves as the principal organ of locomotion. As the animal swims, these antennae are moved in unison, producing a jerky effect. There is usually a single, median eye. One of the most common genera of freshwater copepods is *Cyclops,* so named because of the single eye. It can be found in most ponds and lakes. In many species the female bears a pair of prominent egg sacs attached on each side of the first abdominal segment.

Not all copepods are free-swimming. A number of species have become parasitic on other animals, especially fishes and polychaete worms. In most of these parasitic forms the eyes have been transformed into hooks that serve to attach the animal to its host. The mouth has become specialized for sucking juices. The so-called "fish lice" are members of this group.

Cirripedia.   It is difficult to find any solid object that has been immersed for any length of time in the sea that is not encrusted with some of the more than eight hundred known species of barnacles. They are found on rocks, reefs, pilings, ships' hulls, and floating bits of wood, and on living organisms ranging from whales to small mollusks and crustaceans. Few marine organisms occur higher on the shoreline than some of the barnacles. Some individuals seem to rely largely on spray, because they are so situated that they are immersed only at the highest tides.

The barnacles that are seen on shore-side rocks are roughly placed in two categories—the acorn barnacles and the stalked barnacles. In neither type would the casual observer suspect that the organism encased within the hard carapace, or shell, is a crustacean. Actually the body is only indistinctly segmented. The appendages usually consist of six slender pairs, which are used to gather food.

The stalked barnacle attaches itself to objects by means of a long, flexible neck, which actually represents the anterior part of the head. The carapace, which would be equivalent to the shell on the back of a crab, develops into a mantle that secretes shell-like plates. In the acorn barnacles the plates are arranged in the form of a cone that is open at the top and crater-like in appearance.

Because of their habit of attaching themselves to drifting objects, to wide-ranging forms of living animals such as whales, and to ships, barnacles are among the best-traveled forms of animal life. Except for crabs, lobsters, and their relatives, barnacles are probably better known to most persons, at least by name, than any other crustaceans. A few species of cirripeds have become parasitic and attach themselves by rootlike structures to the hosts on which they feed.

All barnacle-like crustaceans, even those incapable of locomotion on their own part as adults, have a free-swimming larval stage through which they pass before settling down. The adults are generally hermaphroditic. Sexual maturity may be reached before they are three months old.

Malacostraca. Most of the crustaceans mentioned so far, with the exception of the barnacles, have been so small that they can be examined only under a low-power microscope. The Malacostraca, on the other hand, are mostly of medium or large size. The group contains the better-known types of crustaceans that we commonly encounter along the ocean shore, ranging from sand hoppers to crabs and lobsters. It also includes some forms that are adapted to life on land, such as the familiar pill bugs that live under rocks and logs, as well as a few parasitic crustaceans. The major groups of malacostracans are the amphipods, the euphausiaceans, the isopods, the stomatopods, and the decapods.

Anyone who has lived on a seacoast and walked along a beach is familiar with the sand fleas, or sand hoppers. The name "sand flea" has been applied to these amphipods, not because they are related to fleas but because of their ability to hop. Almost any mass of seaweed washed up on the beach will provide cover for literally hundreds of these tiny crustaceans. Their most obvious physical characters, apart from small size and leaping ability, are their laterally compressed bodies, the absence of a large shell, or carapace, on top of the head and thorax, and the presence

The rocks of the intertidal zone along the Pacific coast are often covered with mussels and barnacles. R. T. ORR

of separate body segments covered by shiny transparent plates of chitin. Most sand hoppers live in burrows in the sand, and the larger species are often dug up by fishermen as bait for surf perch. There are many other kinds of amphipods besides the sand hoppers, but the latter are the best-

Stalked barnacles (*Polliceps*) crowded against mussels (*Mytilus*) on which acorn barnacles (*Balanus*) are also growing. R. T. ORR

known members of the group. Some species live in tide pools, among masses of algae on reefs, or in the open sea. Others are commonly found in freshwater lakes and ponds, and a few occur within the bodies of various marine organisms.

Related to the amphipods are the euphausiaceans—a group of pelagic, shrimplike crustaceans. That they are abundant can be attested by the fact that they are the principal food of whales. The baleen whales, which are the largest living animals in the world, are most prevalent throughout much of the year in the polar seas. These giants lack teeth but have strainers made of plates of baleen in their mouths. After inflating their accordion-pleated throats with great mouthfuls of sea water, they expel the water and then swallow the small organisms that are sieved out. In these cold waters the most abundant free-swimming organisms are a type of euphausiacean known as "krill." Krill, along with certain copepods, not only constitute the principal food for baleen whales but also provide important food for penguins and, no doubt, for many kinds of fishes and other marine organisms. At certain seasons of the year in the Antarctic the sea literally becomes red because of the abundance of krill.

Isopods are dorsoventrally flattened instead of being laterally compressed. They occur in both salt and fresh water as well as on land. The pill bugs are good examples of terrestrial isopods. These flat, gray crustaceans that are found under boards and debris in gardens are capable of rolling up like an armadillo. Presumably this is for protection and is responsible for the name "pill bug."

Many marine isopods are to be found along shore, living in masses of algae and in crevices in reefs. Most of them live on debris, but some are predacious. There are also several kinds of isopods that have become parasitic, living on the bodies of other species of crustaceans and on marine vertebrates. Certain fishes become heavily parasitized with these isopods. One often notices them even on the surface of the bodies of rapid-moving oceanic fishes, such as sailfish or marlin.

There is a type of marine isopod that is a serious menace to docks and wooden pilings. This is the gribble (*Limnoria lignorum*). It is widespread along the Atlantic and Pacific coasts of North America as well as the coast of Europe. Like the wood-boring mollusks or so-called "ship worms," it causes a great deal of damage annually. The organism itself is small, being no more than an eighth of an inch in length, but it bores into pilings at the rate of about half an inch a year. The young do not have a free-swimming stage after hatching but start digging into the wood adjacent to the mother. Thus a colony continues to increase like a fungus growth, ultimately causing the deterioration of the timber in which it is located.

The stomatopods are usually known as the mantis shrimps. They are rarely seen except by skin divers. They are found along the seashore deep beneath the lowest intertidal rocks. Some even live below the tidal level in burrows. Mantis shrimps may attain a length of eight inches and are

The rock louse (*Ligyda pallasi*) is a common type of isopod just above the high tide level. R. T. ORR

often brilliantly colored. They have stalked eyes and possess three pairs of walking appendages in addition to their swimming limbs. The posterior appendages are flattened and serve for rapid backward propulsion, much like those of a crayfish.

The decapods are the most advanced and probably the best known of all the groups of crustaceans. They derive their name from the fact that they possess ten legs. The anteriormost pair of legs is often developed into clawlike structures called chelipeds. We are familiar with the delicious chelipeds of a Maine lobster, but we call them claws. The other legs are used for walking.

In the decapods we find that two of the three major parts of the body—the head and thorax—are combined together to form a cephalothorax. This cephalothorax is covered by a chitinous armor-like carapace. A crab may appear to have its body completely covered by this carapace, but if we turn it over we see that the abdomen is folded underneath.

There are few parts of the world where members of this crustacean order are not known and where some are not consumed for food. Many coastal communities have their entire economy dependent upon decapods, principally shrimps, prawns, crabs, and various kinds of so-called lobsters.

The shrimps are the little members of a group that contains the largest crustaceans. Lobsters, for example, are known to reach weights of more than forty pounds, which is very large for an invertebrate animal. The first two or three pairs of legs of a shrimp bear claws, or chelae, like the first pair of legs of a crab, but they are generally very small, so one is not in danger of being pinched while picking up one of these animals. In the snapping shrimps and pistol shrimps, however, one member of the first pair of claws is remarkably enlarged and capable of making a loud noise in the process of closing. Snapping shrimps are abundant in bays and coastal waters and were the cause of great annoyance to the United States Navy during the early phases of World War II. The hydrophone, which is a microphone used in picking up underwater sounds, had been developed and was being employed at strategic points along the Atlantic coast of the United States to provide a warning of the approach of enemy submarines. Snapping shrimps were a source of considerable interference; in some instances their sounds were reportedly responsible for false alerts. Pistol shrimps in tide pools often startle uninformed observers who do not realize the source of the unusual explosive sound.

Shrimps and prawns are extremely prevalent in most coastal waters and an important source of food. They are usually captured by nets. Most persons are familiar with the pinkish color of cooked shrimps, but their beauty in life is often quite striking. Some species are of a delicate green or blue color with red or orange mottling or borders on the legs and the tail fin or telson. Despite this brilliant coloration, their mottling makes them difficult to see. Shrimps are abundant in tide pools along any rocky coast, but one may look for a long time before finally locating one. They can move with great rapidity when alarmed and will dart out of sight into a rock crevice in an instant.

Not all shrimps are coastal in distribution. Many occur out in the open ocean, and deep-sea collecting has shown that some species may be found at depths of up to four miles.

The name "lobster" has been the source of much confusion. It is commonly used for two different kinds of decapods. The first are the true lobsters, well known to seacoast residents of eastern North America. These are large marine crustaceans whose first pair of legs possesses powerful claws for crushing. The crayfish is a relative of the true lobster and is much more widely distributed over the world. Crawdads—crawfish or crayfish of one type or another—are found on all the continents and on many of the major islands of the world. They live on the bottom of streams and lakes, where they hide in burrows or beneath stones. Some like fresh water; others prefer stagnant ponds or even marshy meadows. Irrespective of these differences, they must have water that is high in calcium carbonate. Like their larger relatives, the lobsters, their first pair of legs ends in large claws that are used both for defense and to pick up bits of food. They can walk forward, backward, or sideways, but they swim backward, like a shrimp, with a rapid movement of the fanlike tail segment or telson.

The second group of decapods commonly referred to as lobsters are the

Alternating light and dark bands on the appendages and bodies of shrimps and prawns make them difficult to see unless they are moving. R. T. ORR

spiny or rock lobsters. These crustaceans in many respects look like the true lobsters but lack their powerful claws. In fact, the first pair of legs is entirely lacking in claws and serves only for walking. Spiny lobsters are widely distributed along the shores of the various continents, especially in warmer waters. They may occur in tide pools or out to depths of as much as twenty to thirty fathoms.

As the name "rock lobster" implies, these animals live in rocky situations which provide them protection from numerous enemies, including large fishes and octopuses. Their hard shells contain many spines, which serve as additional defense. They feed principally at night, and their food consists of both plant and animal matter, either living or dead.

Two of the most interesting kinds of decapods are the ghost shrimps and the hermit crabs. The ghost shrimps have rather long, thin, whitish or semitransparent bodies that are very fragile. They live in burrows, which they construct in mud or sand. The burrow may be an inch in diameter and extend a foot or more below the surface. These burrow openings are often exposed at low tide and may be mistaken for clam burrows. Ghost shrimps, while seemingly delicate and defenseless outside their burrows, have great mobility within them. They can turn rapidly and thereby move in any direction. On the Pacific coast of North America a small fish known as the blind goby lives in the same burrow with a ghost shrimp of the genus *Callianassa.*

Hermit crabs have become adapted to living in the old shells left by various small marine snails. As a result, a part of the body has lost its hard outer covering and is kept within the cavity of the adopted shell. As the hermit crab literally grows out of its shell, it looks about for a larger one, into which it moves as soon as it has discarded the old one. Hermit crabs abound in pools and among rocks on coastal reefs, where they may be observed at low tide. Like most decapods, they are quite wary and will not reveal their presence if they suspect danger. However, if a person remains quiet for a few minutes, he will be rewarded by seeing something which had at first appeared to be a snail start to walk about rapidly on jointed legs. These little animals pull themselves tightly into their shells when disturbed and make a door with their armored claws. Related to the hermit crabs are the coconut crabs, which have adapted themselves to life on land.

Long stretches of sandy beach are generally rather barren as far as abundant crustacean life is concerned. Sand hoppers are present, to be sure, and in certain regions, such as along the warm Pacific coastal beaches of Mexico, the amazing little ghost crab is constantly moving in and out of his burrow with the greatest of caution. I have watched these ghost crabs by the hour on the beach at Mazatlán but have never been able to approach close enough to photograph one. There are also other kinds of ghost crabs that occur in other parts of the world.

There is a relative of the hermit crab known as the sand crab, which belongs to the genus *Emerita*. It is present in vast numbers in the intertidal sand of most beaches. These little animals have an oval carapace that seems almost to cover the body when viewed from above. They live in the sand which may be exposed at low tide. Sometimes they momentarily come out on the surface as the water washes over them. A handful of wet sand picked up by a person who is wading may contain a dozen or more of these crustaceans. When placed back on the beach, they can burrow out of sight within a matter of seconds. Interestingly enough, they burrow into the sand backwards just as they walk backwards on the surface. Sand crabs are an important source of food, not only to many kinds of surf fishes but also for shore birds. Various species are found along both the Atlantic and Pacific shores of North America and in South America.

The true crabs have a dorsoventrally compressed body covered above with a wide carapace. On turning a crab over, one will see the segmented abdomen, which is very small and reversed in position. It is rather markedly triangular in males and somewhat U-shaped in females. The name of the group to which crabs belong is the Brachyura, which means short-tailed. The first pair of legs possesses claws, which are generally very large and, in some species, can be a formidable weapon. The other four pairs of legs are used for walking, which is done sideways. Because their pincers are used for fighting and protection, crabs often lose one of their front legs. This, however, is no serious problem, since these limbs are soon regenerated.

Crabs show amazing diversity in size. Some have a body that is not as large as a ten-cent piece, but others attain gigantic proportions. The largest crustacean in the world is the spider crab, which lives at great depths in the Pacific Ocean. It is reported to exceed twelve feet across, from the tip of one extended leg to that of another on the opposite side.

Crabs, like all crustaceans from the smallest to the largest, must molt periodically if they are to grow. This means loss not only of the armor on the limbs but also of the shell on the back. The loss, however, is only temporary, because a new soft shell is beneath the old one and in a short time will harden up with calcium carbonate. Such newly molted crabs are called soft-shelled and are often cooked and eaten entire.

As a group crabs are widely distributed, but most species require salinity in the water they inhabit. Some live fairly far up coastal streams and rivers where the water is barely brackish. There are also a few freshwater species. Others occur in bays and estuaries, where they live in mud or sand, among

Sometimes called the Dungeness crab, *Cancer magister* is a gastronomic delicacy along the Pacific coast of North America. R. T. ORR

rocks, or in holes in banks. Many crabs occur along continental and island shores, where they are often among the most active inhabitants, being seen in tide pools, on reefs, and even along open sandy shores. Crabs of various species are abundant offshore below the tidal level. Some species even live at considerable depths in the ocean.

Many other organisms, such as barnacles, bryozoans, and various kinds of algae, are found growing on the backs of crabs. These animals and plants are able to move about with their hosts in this commensal arrangement. The crabs whose backs are so adorned are in turn provided with a natural camouflage, which makes them appear more or less like a rock. This may serve to protect them from some of their enemies.

One of the most interesting species of crabs is the fiddler crab, which is an inhabitant of the higher parts of sandy beaches. In the male one claw is very much enlarged, while in the female both claws are small. These little animals, like the ghost crabs, live in burrows that they dig in the sand. They, too, are very wary of intruders, but if one waits patiently for a few minutes after approaching an area inhabited by them they will cautiously come out of their burrows, with the males extending their single large claw. They dig their burrows by bringing out the sand in small balls, which they carry with their walking legs. The slightest movement on the part of an observer results in their darting rapidly into their holes.

Other crabs have developed unique methods of protecting themselves against their enemies. One rather unusual species common on the Great Barrier Reef of Australia is the red and white spotted crab, a species that lives among the deadly stinging tentacles of the giant anemone along with two other animals, a small fish and a shrimp. The anemone does not seem to harm them.

INSECTS

The fact that considerably more than half of the known species of animals are insects attests to the success of this group of arthropods. Although they are essentially absent from the sea, insects are present and usually abundant in nearly all other habitats. There are also many species that live in fresh or brackish water during a part or even all of their life cycle. As a group they range from the Arctic to the Antarctic and occur on practically all land masses, small and large.

Insects are of great importance to man. Beneficial types include those responsible for the pollination of many plants, those that prey upon other species that are injurious to crops or otherwise harmful to man, and those, like the honeybee and silkworm, that produce materials of value. Types regarded as bad are the various agricultural pests, vectors of disease, parasites, wood-eating and boring forms, and many biting species.

Basically, insects have segmented bodies, like other members of the phylum Arthropoda. The body is divided into three parts—a head, a thorax, and an abdomen. The walking legs, which consist of three pairs, are jointed and attached to the thorax. This is also the part of the body to which the one or two pairs of wings, if present, are attached. Insects have mouth parts that may be adapted to securing food by chewing, sucking, or lapping.

There are no really large insects, although many millions of years ago there were dragonflies with a wing expanse of as much as two feet. The largest known modern insects are some of the moths of tropical regions, whose wingspread may reach twelve inches. A rhinoceros beetle in the West Indies and a wood-boring beetle in South America measure six inches in length. Some of the termite queens in Africa are almost as large. Measured by body weight, it is likely that the heaviest insects are the Goliath beetles. The majority of insects are small, some being barely visible to the naked eye.

Insects may be grouped into three categories, based on their method of growth. The most primitive kind, often placed in the subclass Ametabola, hatch from the egg as miniatures of the adult. Growth consists principally in an enlargement of the basic parts, which are all present. The second group, the Hemimetabola, contains those insects that hatch from the egg into a form that bears only a partial resemblance to the adult. In this form the insect is frequently referred to as a nymph. These larval forms usually have heads that are very large in proportion to thorax and abdomen size. The third and most advanced group of insects, the Holometabola, undergoes a complete metamorphosis in the process of growth. The egg hatches into a larval form often called a maggot, grub, or caterpillar. The larva grows and then goes into the pupal stage, in which further development occurs and from which a fully formed adult emerges.

The more than three quarters of a million kinds of living insects are grouped by entomologists into about thirty different orders. To describe adequately the distribution, appearance, and behavior of such a vast assemblage of organisms would require many volumes. All we can do here is to mention a few of the better-known types of insects belonging to the major orders and tell something about their habits and certain principles that they illustrate.

The springtails and silverfish. The springtails are small wingless insects that are considered to be very primitive. The oldest known fossil insects are members of the order Collembola, to which this group belongs. Springtails undergo no metamorphosis, but during their growth the young add new segments onto the posterior part of the body in a wormlike manner. Furthermore, unlike higher insects, they have remnants of appendages on the anterior abdominal segments. They live in decaying organic matter and humus, and are often exceedingly abundant on wild mushrooms that are beyond maturity. I have seen thousands of minute springtails literally covering a single fungus.

Silverfish are well-known household pests, because of their liking for sugar, starch, and glue. Their fondness for glue makes them a serious menace to books and, of course, libraries. They derive their name from the presence of silver scales that cover the body. Like the springtails, they too have vestigial appendages on the abdomen. Silverfish prefer darkness and are therefore most active at night. There are some species that inhabit ant nests.

The dragonflies and damselflies. Most children learn about dragonflies at a rather early age—partly because these insects are always conspicuous during the warmer months of the year and partly because of the superstitions concerning them. Dragonflies are frequently called "devil's darning needles" because of the cylindrical body and the superstitious belief that they will sew up one's ears.

Actually, dragonflies are the hawks of the insect world. Their streamlined bodies are equipped with two pairs of transparent wings. These wings are often beautifully tinted in shades of red, orange, and blue. Dragonflies are rapid and skillful fliers. They possess very large eyes, which no doubt assist them greatly in the capture of various smaller insects pursued on the wing. In many ways dragonflies are very beneficial in controlling populations of gnats, small flies, and mosquitoes. Damselflies are somewhat similar in appearance but smaller and less predacious.

Both these kinds of insects are associated with water, rarely being found very far away from the ponds or streams in which their early stages of development take place. The eggs of the dragonfly are usually dropped into the water while the female is in flight. Those of the damselfly are inserted into plant tissue in the water. The nymphs, or naiads as the young are referred to, live under rocks in the water for some months or even years and feed upon various animals that they can catch. When about fully grown, they climb out onto a rock and the aerial adult emerges.

The mayflies. These delicate little insects are perhaps best known to trout fishermen, who often try to imitate them with artificial flies in the hope that the fish will not recognize the difference. Mayflies are commonly seen fluttering over or on the surface of freshwater ponds and streams. They have two pairs of wings but are most easily recognized by the two or three long filaments that extend posteriorly from the end of the abdomen.

Damselflies are smaller members of the order to which the dragonflies belong.

Adult mayflies are very short-lived. Most of them last from only a few hours to several days after emerging from the nymph stage. They do not eat but, instead, devote their limited adult life to perpetuating the species. The nymphs, which are aquatic, require from about one to three years to mature. Like the adults, they too have abdominal filaments but not such long ones.

The cockroaches. These are medium- to large-sized insects with two pairs of wings, a flattened oval-shaped body, and legs adapted for running rapidly. The very word "cockroach" is repulsive to most persons, because a few of the many species have, in a sense, become domesticated and live in association with man against his wishes.

Under natural conditions cockroaches are primarily inhabitants of the tropics, where they live on decaying organic debris and are therefore useful scavengers. The domesticated species, unfortunately, have become widely distributed over the world by means of ships, trains, and trucks.

In human communities cockroaches are associated with food. For this reason they are common in restaurants, dairies, food processing and manufacturing plants, and household kitchens. They are active at night and avoid light whenever possible. Their greatest damage to food in homes, apartment houses, and eating establishments is not so much from food consumption as from contamination. They can travel rapidly over a considerable distance and thereby move from one apartment to another along drains, conduits, and pipes, or through cracks. Germs from the ill can be transported by these insects to the food of those who are well.

The termites.   These interesting social insects are sometimes called white

Adult mayflies, unlike the nymphs, are very short-lived.
EDWARD S. ROSS

ants, which is a poor name for them since they are not closely related to true ants. Termites have soft bodies and chewing mouthparts. Except for the sexual forms, they are mostly wingless. They live in total darkness in wood, in the ground, or in surface or arboreal nests that they construct themselves. If they have to move, this is accomplished by the construction of a tunnel, so that they are not exposed to their enemies at such times.

The food of termites consists principally of wood pulp or other kinds of cellulose, which they are unable to digest by themselves because they lack the proper enzymes. Digestion is accomplished, however, by flagellate protozoans that live in the intestinal tract. The flagellates are capable of breaking down cellulose into digestible sugar and, although they consume some themselves, there is plenty left for the host. This mutual association is beneficial and essential to the lives of both organisms. Newly hatched termites immediately begin licking older termites to obtain a necessary culture of the protozoans. Furthermore, older termites may lose their intestinal flagellates when they molt and most reinoculate their systems from other termites. These insects could not survive a solitary life for long.

The fact that termites live largely on wood has made them one of man's major insect enemies. There are few parts of the tropical or temperate regions of the world where wooden buildings, bridge timbers, or telephone poles are safe from these wood-chewing creatures. They are especially bothersome in the tropics, where they attain their peak of development. In Africa some kinds of termites build enormous postlike nests that are many feet in height. In the tropics of the New World, large termite nests are often constructed on the branches of trees. The orange-fronted parakeet of Mexico and Central America has taken advantage of this by tunneling into these arboreal homes of the termites to construct its own nest. The parrots do not bother the termites, and the latter are afforded some protection by the birds.

Termites are of great interest to scientists because of their well-developed social system, which parallels in a way that of some of the hymenopterous insects like ants and bees. Colonies are started at certain times of the year, such as after the first fall rains or in the spring, depending upon the species. When this occurs, the sexually active males and females, both of which possess wings, engage in a nuptial flight. Many are consumed by other animals at this one vulnerable time in their lives when they expose themselves to the light of day. Those that survive break off their wings and try to establish a new colony. This is formed around a queen, whose body grows to many times the size of the others. Her function is to produce eggs, and this she may do at the rate of many thousands a day. The bodies of some of the African queen termites are the size of a potato and are highly relished by Africans as a choice delicacy.

The nests of termites in the tropics look like large posts. JOHN TASHJIAN

Young termites need very little attention, but they are cared for by the workers, who gather food and do the nest-building. The colony is guarded against enemy attack by soldier termites, whose jaws are greatly enlarged as defense weapons. In fact, the soldiers cannot chew wood or pulp and have to feed on the soft bodies of other members of the colony, whether living or dead. The queen herself is cared for by the workers, just like the young.

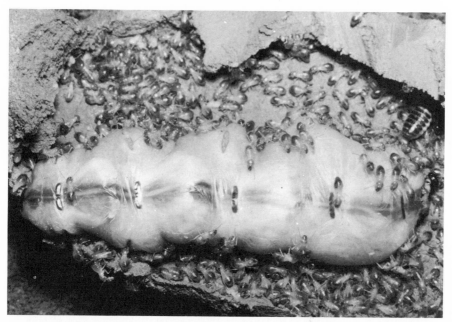

The huge body of a queen termite serves only for the production of eggs. EDWARD S. ROSS

The stoneflies. These are members of a small group of insects whose life cycle somewhat resembles that of the mayflies except that the aquatic nymphs or larvae are carnivorous rather than herbivorous. The adults are of rather large size and possess two pairs of membranous wings, the largest of which is the hind pair. They lay their eggs in the water, and the nymphs, whose bodies are quite flat, live under rocks. These larvae are important food for certain freshwater fishes and are also used by fishermen as bait.

The grasshoppers, katydids, and crickets. This is an important group of medium- to fairly large-sized insects that is well known to most persons. Its members generally possess two pairs of straight wings, the first of which is thick and tough, forming a covering for the second pair. These wings are very well developed in most grasshoppers and locusts but are much reduced or even absent in some of the crickets.

Adult stoneflies possess two pairs of wings which they fold over the back when resting. EDWARD S. ROSS

The most notable feature of many members of this group is their greatly enlarged hind legs. These legs and the wings may both play a part in the sound production for which these insects are famous. The sounds, therefore, are instrumental rather than vocal; they are produced only by the male. In the crickets, sound is effected by rubbing the forewings over the hindwings' veins, which produces a chirping noise. The speed of the chirps is dependent on temperature; the higher the temperature, the more rapid the rate of utterance.

Many of these insects are subject to great fluctuations in population numbers. Plagues of locusts are recorded in the Bible and still occur today in parts of the world. I have seen periodic outbreaks of grasshopper invasions in western North America when all low vegetation was eliminated and the insects were at times piled up in windrows. Modern chemical sprays have greatly reduced such infestations.

Grasshoppers and crickets form valuable food for many other kinds of animals. We have all read the story of the gulls of Great Salt Lake that saved the Mormons from an invasion of crickets in the early days of the settlement of Utah. There are many other birds, such as herons, quail, turkeys, hawks, and owls, that prey exclusively on such insects if they are present in sufficient numbers. Foxes, coyotes, skunks, and many other mammals do likewise. The pallid bat, which ranges from southern British Columbia south to central Mexico, shows great preference for Jerusalem crickets. This happens to be a species of bat which I studied for a number of years. When searching cliffs and caves for colonies of these bats, I soon learned that piles of the discarded tough hind legs of these big banded crickets were a clue to the presence of the bats.

The embiids. These long, slender-bodied insects, sometimes called silk spinners, are known to few persons. They occur in limited numbers in tropical or subtropical parts of the world. Superficially they bear some resemblance to earwigs and may be either winged or wingless.

Grasshoppers have powerful hind legs which enable them to jump many times their own length. EDWARD S. ROSS

Katydids are related to grasshoppers and crickets. Most of them are green and all possess long antennae. EDWARD S. ROSS

A female dectid katydid showing the long ovipositor on the posterior end of the body. EDWARD S. ROSS

(Right) The Jerusalem cricket (*Stenopelmatus longispina*) is a ground dweller. Its powerful legs are used for digging in the soil where it feeds on tubers as well as various kinds of insects.
EDWARD S. ROSS

(Below) A walking stick (*Phasmida*) from Peru which, like other members of this group of orthopterous insects, so resembles a twig that it is difficult to recognize. EDWARD S. ROSS

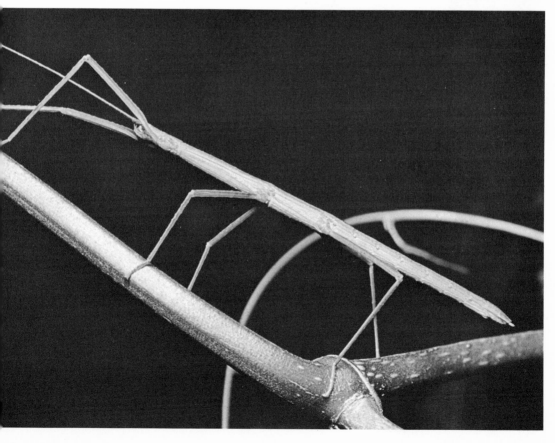

Embiids are notable for the presence of spinning organs on their forelegs. By means of these they construct silken tunnels on rocks, logs, or tree trunks. In their tunnels they are capable of running backward as readily as forward. The tunnels lead into crevices in the substratum and also out to the feeding areas, thus providing protection at all times. The food of embiids consists principally of decayed organic matter.

The earwigs. These are also insects with elongated, flattened bodies and chewing mouthparts. The posterior section of the body is peculiar in possessing a pair of forceps-like structures, which present a formidable appearance but are not a defense mechanism.

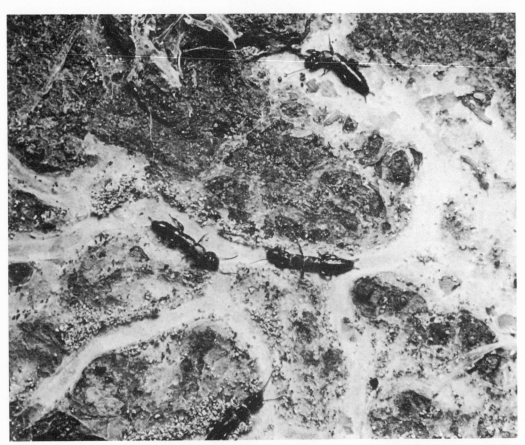

Embiids or silk spinners move forward or backward with equal ease in their silken tunnels.
EDWARD S. ROSS

Imprisoned many millions of years ago in Baltic amber, this silk spinner (*Electroembia antiqua*) closely resembles modern species. EDWARD S. ROSS

The name "earwig" was long ago applied to these insects in the belief that they crawled into the ear at night and punctured the eardrum. This is a widespread superstition unsupported by fact. Their nocturnal character and their propensity for cracks and crevices may account for their reputation in this regard. They are somewhat omnivorous. A European species that has inadvertently been introduced into North America is very harmful to cultivated plants and is now a garden pest.

The lice. Of the three major groups of lice, each belongs to a separate order. The groups are the book lice, the sucking lice, and the biting lice. They are all small and lack wings.

Book lice are common in old dusty books and are frequently encountered on library shelves. Their food in such places consists of glue and paste used in bookbinding. Not all members of this group, however, are confined to

The European earwig (*Forficula auricularia*) has become established in parts of North America where it is a serious garden pest. EDWARD S. ROSS

such a literary habitat. Some live under bark and lichens; they are called bark lice. If one pulls off a piece of loose bark harboring a colony of these insects, they will usually huddle together immediately. Some species can spin silk, which they use for the protection of both the eggs and the adults.

The sucking lice are unpleasant ectoparasites on man and various other warm-blooded animals. Human lice are common in areas where cleanliness is not a virtue. They live in the hair and attack the skin. Fortunately, advancing civilization is gradually resulting in their elimination in most parts of the world.

One of the interesting things about this group of parasites is that some species have adapted themselves to life on marine mammals. Their abundance on these animals is sometimes amazing. Not long ago I was holding a young sea lion so that it could be photographed. When I put the animal down after several minutes, my sweater contained thousands of lice.

The biting lice are commonly called bird lice, although they are not restricted to birds. Unlike the sucking lice, they do not feed on body juices but rather on external parts such as feathers and hair. As an adaptation to moving between such structures, their bodies are quite flattened. One of the most unusual situations in which lice of this group occur is inside the pouch of pelicans. Since feathers are lacking here, it is believed that the lice subsist on epidermal scales.

Feather lice rarely leave the body of a bird on which they live unless the host is in close contact with another individual of the same species, such as

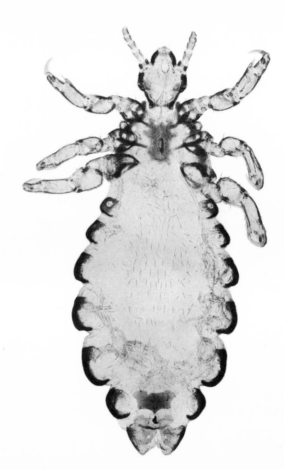

A human body louse (*Pediculus humanus*) greatly magnified. EDWARD S. ROSS

may occur in the wild during the nesting season when adults are brooding young. As a consequence certain species of bird lice are often restricted to a single species of bird.

The cicadas, scale insects, and plant lice. These and their relatives are insects whose mouthparts are adapted to sucking the juices of vegetation. Like other members of the Hemimetabola that have been discussed here, they have only a partial transformation, or metamorphosis, during their growth, which, in some species, may take many years.

This group not only is a fairly large one, as well as one of considerable economic importance, but contains some kinds of insects that seem to bear little resemblance to one another superficially.

The largest are the cicadas. These insects are most abundant in warm or tropical climates, where the loud buzzing of the males sometimes produces

Bird lice do not suck blood but live on the feathers and skin debris of their hosts. EDWARD S. ROSS

a steady din throughout the day. In North America there is a well-known cicada commonly called the "seventeen-year locust." Although it is not a locust, it does have a larval period that may last for seventeen years. The adult females lay their eggs in holes which they drill in living trees. The larvae hatch in a few weeks, drop to the ground, and quickly burrow into the soil, where they slowly grow for many years. Finally, when an individual has attained its full growth, it changes into a pupal form and tunnels to the surface, where it climbs up a tree trunk and the adult emerges from the pupal skin.

The leaf hoppers, white flies, spittlebugs, scale insects, and plant lice, or aphids, are all members of the same order to which the cicadas belong, but most of them are of much greater economic significance because of the damage they do to crops and cultivated plants. Among the best known are the aphids, whose delicate green or gray bodies when seen in clusters on our rose bushes in the spring will cause us to dash for the spray can.

However, we know from their feeding habits that a poison applied to the leaves or stem on which they are located will cause them but little harm, since they have sucking, rather than chewing, mouthparts and obtain their nourishment from juices beneath the surface. Contact poisons are therefore essential in their control.

One of the most interesting things about these insects is their peculiar mode of reproduction, which is termed "parthenogenesis" or virgin birth. During most of the active part of the year females alone are produced, and they are capable of producing other females at a very early age. The young are born alive during this asexual period of reproduction. Occasionally, however, both sexes are produced, and the fertilized females lay eggs. Parthenogenesis permits very rapid increase in an aphid population. Aphids are generally wingless but sometimes winged generations are produced, which permits population movement.

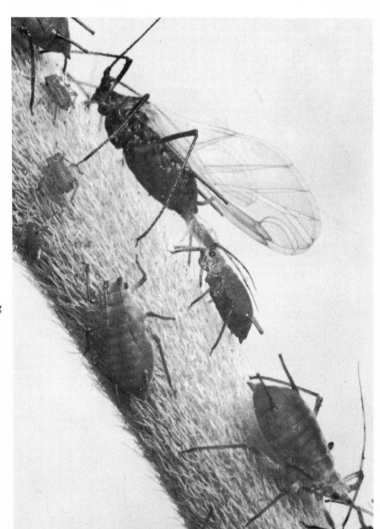

Winged, wingless and young aphids. EDWARD S. ROSS

The relationship between aphids and ants is a fascinating one. The aphids secrete a sweet substance called "honeydew" from the anal aperture and from two tubes located on each side of the abdomen. Certain species of ants use the exudate for food, and they care for the aphids just as we might care for a herd of milk cows. The aphids are guarded, moved to favorable locations for feeding, and milked of their honeydew periodically.

The true bugs. The term "bug" is often applied loosely to any insect, but properly speaking it refers to a special order of insects whose mouthparts have developed into a sucking beak for feeding on plant and animal juices. The wings of these bugs overlap across the back, and the anteriormost pair have membranous tips and thick bases.

Some of the better-known members of this group, which contains more than fifty thousand species, are the squash bugs, the assassin bugs, the water boatmen, the water striders, and the bedbugs. The various kinds of squash bugs are well known to most farmers because of the harm they do to cucumbers, gourds, squash, pumpkins, and various melons. One of their characteristic features in their unpleasant odor.

Some of the true bugs that are bloodsuckers are capable of transmitting disease to man and other warm-blooded animals. This is true of the assassin or conenose bugs, which transmit Chagas' disease. The causative organism is a protozoan closely related to the protozoan that causes African sleeping sickness.

Bedbugs are also unpleasant bloodsucking insects, feeding on warm-blooded animals, including man. These ectoparasites were once common and widespread, but the use of insecticides and greater cleanliness have resulted in their elimination in much of the civilized world.

There are related species of bugs that live on other animals. Close relatives of the bedbug are found on bats. These insects usually live in crevices in caves or rocks where the bats roost; they attack while their hosts are at rest.

One interesting and rare group of sucking bugs is associated with a single family of bats, the so-called "free-tailed bats," which occur about the warmer tropical and semitropical parts of the world. I searched for ten years before I found my first bat bug, which was living in the fur of a mastiff bat, the largest species of bat in the United States. At that time fewer than one hundred specimens of the entire family to which these insects belong were known.

The water striders, which have a remarkable ability to skate over the smooth surface of ponds and streams, and the water boatmen, which live

A stinkbug of the family Pentatomidae with eggs. EDWARD S. ROSS

A bedbug (*Cimex lectularis*) feeding on human blood after piercing the skin with its sucking mouthparts. EDWARD S. ROSS

beneath the surface, are also true bugs. There are few insects that are adapted to marine life. Among those that are oceanic are some of the striders.

Water boatmen and the rather closely related back swimmers are common inhabitants of most freshwater ponds and streams. They may be seen rising to the surface to secure a bubble of air, which they take down with

Water striders of the genus *Halobates* are the only true sea-going insects. EDWARD S. ROSS

them for respiratory purposes. All these aquatic bugs are predacious, feeding on other insects and even small fish. They are capable of hibernating in the mud at the bottom during the winter and can also fly if necessary. Water boatmen are harvested and dried for bird food in certain regions.

The ant lions, lacewings, and Dobson flies.   These are among the first of the holometabolous insects—that is, those insects that have a complete metamorphosis.

Adult ant lions, which are flylike insects with two pairs of wings, are little known except to entomologists. However, the crater-like pits or cone-shaped depressions constructed by the larvae in fine dry sand or earth are a familiar sight to many. Buried in the bottom of these pits are the predatory larvae of ant lions waiting for some other insect to wander along and fall into the trap. When this happens, the victim is taken apart by

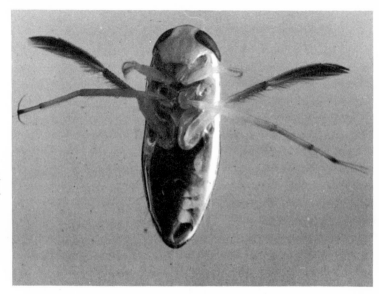

Water boatmen prey on other kinds of insects in ponds. EDWARD S. ROSS

their powerful jaws and consumed. They throw refuse, like sand or dirt, out of the pit by placing it on the top of their flat head and then making rapid jerking motions.

Lacewings are small, soft-bodied insects with large green or golden lacelike wings, which are usually folded together over the back so as to be held in a vertical plane. The Dobson flies are much larger and possess four strong wings, which are folded flat on the back. The head is characterized by two enormous jaws. The larvae of Dobson flies are aquatic; they are commonly called "hellgrammites." They live under rocks in streams and

An adult ant lion (*Brachynemus*). From *Insects Close Up*.

The larval forms of ant lions are sometimes referred to as doodle bugs. They bury themselves at the bottom of conical pits and prey upon other insects that fall into their traps. R. T. ORR

are active principally at night, when they prey upon the larvae of other aquatic insects. They attain a length of several inches and are often sought after by fishermen for bait.

The caddis flies. Like many other kinds of aquatic insects, the larval stage of the caddis fly is better known to most of us than the adult. These are the strange little creatures that construct a tube of bits of bark, leaves, grains of sand, shells, and other objects. In the spring, if you watch the bottom of a stream, you are apt to see many of these animated larval cases moving slowly along the bottom. Within each of the elongated tubes is a cylindrical caddis larva that is capable of spinning the silk that holds all

(Above) Lacewings, like ladybird beetles, are very beneficial to man because their principal food consists of aphids and scale insects. EDWARD S. ROSS

(Right) Caddis flies resemble moths to which they are thought to be related. Their larval stage, however, is spent in water. EDWARD S. ROSS

the various and sundry objects it has collected to form the protective covering. When the larva has completed its growth, it seals each end of the tube
with silk and enters the pupal stage. When the pupa is ready to emerge as
an adult caddis fly, it opens one end of the case and crawls out of the water.

The butterflies and moths. These constitute the second largest order of
insects and number well over one hundred thousand species. Its members
all undergo a complete metamorphosis, starting out as an egg, which
hatches into a caterpillar with chewing mouthparts. When fully grown this
larval form develops into a pupa called a chrysalis. The pupa of a butterfly
is usually attached to some object by a strand of silk. The pupa of many
moths is encased in a covering made of silk, called a cocoon. The adult
butterfly or moth that ultimately emerges bears no resemblance to either
the larva or pupa that preceded it. In this stage the mouthparts are suctorial if they are functional at all.

Butterflies and moths possess two pairs of wings. The wings of butterflies
are usually held vertically over the back when at rest; those of moths are
held horizontally, either folded or unfolded. The beautiful colors and

A tiger swallowtail butterfly. EDWARD S. ROSS

patterns of this group of insects are the result of minute scales that cover both surfaces of the wings. Many species exhibit amazing protective coloration, and some mimic the color of poisonous or obnoxious-tasting species for security.

Butterflies in general are considered to be diurnal, while moths are nocturnal. There are, however, many kinds of moths that are active during

Adult tomato hawk moth (*Protoparce sexta*). EDWARD S. ROSS

the daytime. Another commonly accepted distinction concerns coloration. Most butterflies are more brightly colored than the majority of moths, but again there are dull butterflies and brilliantly colored moths. The true butterflies have clubbed antennae with the tips enlarged.

Butterflies and moths are very widely distributed over the world, occurring from the Arctic to the tropics. They are found not only on all the

(Above) The tomato hornworm which is the larval form of the tomato hawk moth. EDWARD S. ROSS

(Left) Pupa of the tomato hawk moth. EDWARD S. ROSS

continents but also on most islands. Some species, like the well-known monarch, have very extensive ranges. The monarch is found throughout the Americas, Australia, many of the Pacific islands, and Europe. It is a species that is capable of lasting over the winter. In order to continue their existence through the winter months, populations living in the north engage in extensive migrations south to areas of more favorable climate. There they gather on special trees that are used year after year. These "butterfly trees" are often covered with tens of thousands of monarchs during the entire winter. At my home in central California I can watch the leisurely monarch migration each spring and autumn because one of the

A skipper (*Atelopedes campestris*). These insects resemble both butterflies and moths, but they really represent a separate group belonging to the same order. EDWARD S. ROSS

major wintering areas on the Pacific coast of North America is on the Monterey Peninsula about one hundred miles south of San Francisco.

Butterflies and moths, from a purely human point of view, may be regarded as both beneficial and harmful. Since most of them are nectar feeders in the adult stage, they play an important part in the pollination of many plants. Sometimes a single species is solely responsible for the successful pollination of a particular kind of plant. A good example of this is shown by the pronuba moth of southwestern United States, which pollinates the yucca.

Naturally, many of these insects are injurious, but this is in the larval stage. Caterpillars live primarily on vegetation, and many kinds show a preference for crops and garden plants. A few live on other substances, such as the larvae of the clothes moth, which feed on wool.

The true flies. These insects are known as Diptera, because they have no more than two functional wings. The posterior wings, which appear as small projections on the body, are known as halteres.

Most flies are small and soft-bodied, the largest being some of the gad-flies, or horseflies, and the crane flies, which are sometimes referred to as "daddy longlegs." Their mouths are designed basically for sucking, but in some flies they are adapted to lapping and even piercing.

With the exception of the mosquitoes and a few others, most dipterans are active only in the daytime. Many species are scavengers, living on decaying plant and animal matter. Some are harmful to man and other animals. Malaria is transmitted by the bite of mosquitoes of the genus

Cecropia moths of the genus *Hyalophora* are among the largest of flying insects. EDWARD S. ROSS

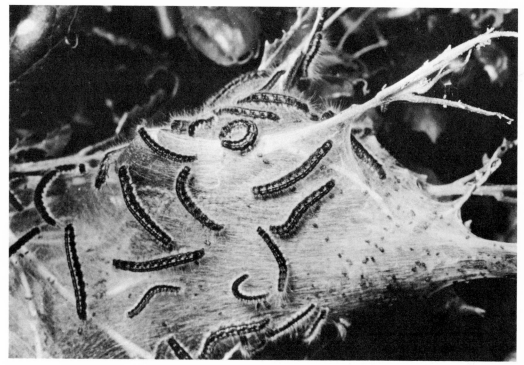

Tent caterpillars belong to the same family as the inch worms, the Geometridae. The family name which means "earth measurers" is based upon the common trait of its members to progress in a looplike gait. EDWARD S. ROSS

The buckeye (*Precis*) is an extremely variable and very widely distributed butterfly. EDWARD S. ROSS

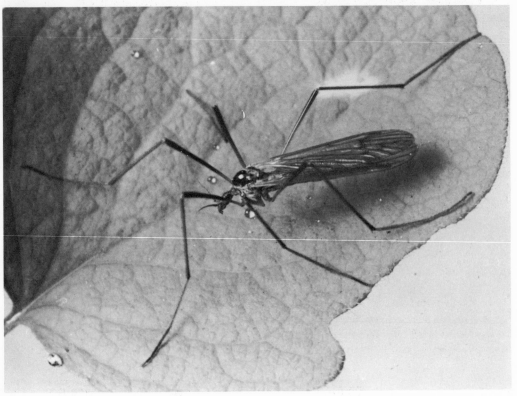

Craneflies bear a superficial resemblance to giant mosquitoes with very long, delicate legs.
EDWARD S. ROSS

Anopheles, while mosquitoes of the genus *Aedes* are responsible for the transmission of yellow fever. In Africa the dreaded sleeping sickness, caused by a protozoan, is carried by the tsetse fly, which inoculates both man and herd animals. Houseflies, which breed in excrement and decaying material, are believed to be responsible for spreading many human diseases, including typhoid and cholera as well as lesser maladies.

Many flies suck the blood of various animals, including man. This is true of female mosquitoes, deerflies, gadflies, black gnats, and midges. A few deerflies, or horseflies, may be a considerable source of annoyance, but the smaller midges, or "no-see-ums" as they are commonly called, occur literally by the millions in the spring and early summer in some localities. Their presence can make life extremely miserable for the few hours that they are active in the late afternoon. Their larval stage is spent in water.

The bloodworms, which often occur in enormous numbers in lakes, are the larvae of midges.

There are a few families of parasitic flies. The most serious are the botflies, or warbles. These insects lay their eggs on the hair of various kinds of mammals. The eggs may be licked by the host and thus get into the digestive tract. The larvae, upon hatching, move out into connective tissue beneath the skin. Here they move about the body of the host until they finally settle down, usually on the back or underside of the neck, where they live on serum and obtain their air by drilling a hole to the surface. When full-grown each larva eats its way out and drops to the ground, where it pupates for some weeks before hatching as an adult.

There are other flies that are ectoparasites. These belong to species that live in the feathers of certain kinds of birds and in the hair of mammals. Owls, hawks, and grouse have flies that live among their feathers and feed on their blood. Bats are parasitized by a family of flies that have largely lost their wings. Their bodies are flattened and louselike. The egg hatches and the larva develops within the body of the female until it reaches the

A female tree hole mosquito (*Aedes varipalpus*) sucking blood from a human hand. From *Insects Close Up*.

The larvae of many mosquitoes, such as these of *Aedes varipalpus*, hang head down from the surface film of the water. Air for respiration is obtained through the posterior end of the body. EDWARD S. ROSS

pupal stage. The adults can move very rapidly through the hair of their host and are often difficult to catch.

Although the scavenger flies and blowflies live on flesh in their larval stage, there are many flies that are vegetarians. Notable among these are the small fruit flies. Some do great damage to ripening fruit and are therefore regarded as serious agricultural pests. On the beneficial side, much of

A robber fly (*Erax barbatus*) holding a leafhopper that it has just captured. EDWARD S. ROSS

our knowledge of genetics has been acquired from studies made on fruit flies of the genus *Drosophila*.

There are special groups of flies that live on fungi. Some of these spend their larval stage in the fleshy parts of mushrooms and toadstools. One family, known as the flat-footed flies because the males have very broad hind feet, spends its larval stage in the gills of fungi. The life cycle of such species is closely synchronized with that of the host plants.

The dance flies, which may sometimes be seen in swarms in patches of sunlight in the woods, have developed very interesting habits connected with courtship and mating. In one group, known as the balloon flies, the male carries a small balloon or bubble of froth, which is offered to the female. Females are reported to select the males with the largest balloons.

Another group of dipterans is known as the bee flies. These flies are very rapid moving and simulate certain bees in appearance, although they have only one pair of wings. This mimicry may have some protective value.

The fleas. These are members of a small order of wingless ectoparasites. They all have flat, laterally compressed bodies. As adults, they suck the blood of most kinds of warm-blooded animals. There are few birds and mammals that are not afflicted with these small but annoying parasites. We are most familiar with those that live on human beings, dogs, and cats.

Head of a robber fly showing the compound eyes.
EDWARD S. ROSS

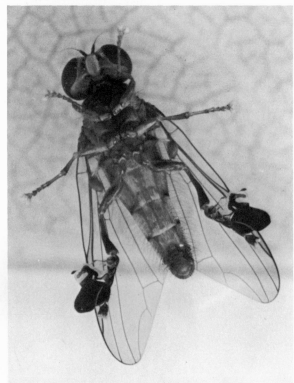

(Above) A fleshfly of the genus *Sarcophaga*. EDWARD S. ROSS

(Left) Members of the family Platypezidae are commonly called flat-footed flies because of the shape of the hind feet in the males. EDWARD S. ROSS

The eggs of dog and cat fleas are laid on the hair; since they are not attached, these tiny white spheres fall to the ground. The larvae, upon hatching, live in cracks or in bedding, where they feed on small particles of organic matter such as flakes of skin, hair, adult flea excrement, and other materials found in dust. When they are full-grown, they pupate in a tiny cocoon, which they spin; finally they emerge as adults, ready to jump onto the first suitable host that passes.

If you keep pets in the house and then board them in a kennel during a summer vacation, you will usually find a houseful of fleas on your return. Numerous adults will have developed and be eagerly awaiting the first meal. When your dogs or cats are at home, they normally accommodate the needs of these bloodsucking pests. Modern sprays have proved very effective in controlling these insects.

Fleas not only produce itching welts on the body but may serve to transfer certain diseases from animals to man. The most serious of these is bubonic plague, which is carried by rat fleas that can transmit the causative bacteria from infected rats to human beings. This dreaded disease, variously named in the past as the Black Death and the Black Plague, was

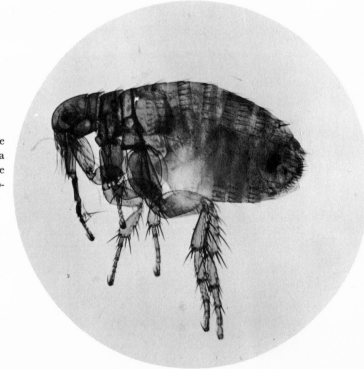

A photomicrograph of the dreaded Indian rat flea (*Xenopsylla cheopis*), one of the main carriers of plague. EDWARD S. ROSS

known in the pre-Christian era in Asia and Africa but did not appear in Europe until the sixth century. It has been estimated that in the fourteenth century it caused the death of forty million people in a period of twenty years. Bubonic plague is a disease associated with poor living conditions, lack of sanitation, and starvation. There is little chance today for any major outbreak in the world.

The beetles.   This is the largest living group of animals. The order Coleoptera, to which the beetles belong, is estimated to contain three hundred and fifty thousand species—or about one-third of the species known in the animal kingdom.

Beetles are usually recognized by the character of their first pair of wings. These structures are hard and shell-like, forming a covering for the posterior wings, which are used for flying. The anterior wings, called "elytra," are often beautifully polished and brilliantly colored. The mouthparts of these insects are built primarily for chewing, but in a few kinds, such as the weevils, the mouth may be a piercing organ.

A click beetle (*Chalcolepidius striatus*) from the upper Amazon basin of Peru. This insect, if turned on its back, can snap itself into the air because of its hinged body. EDWARD S. ROSS

Like other holometabolous insects, beetles have a complete metamorphosis. The larvae are often referred to as grubs. The group shows great diversity in size for insects. Some, like the great goliath beetles, are among the world's largest insects, while certain weevils and wood borers are not much bigger than the head of a pin.

A wide variety of food is consumed by different kinds of beetles in both the larval and adult stages. They may feed on leaves, flowers, pollen, stems, roots, tubers, bark, dung, or living and dead animal matter. Because of the many kinds of food eaten, some species are beneficial and others are harmful to man's interests.

The ladybird beetle is a good example of a beneficial type of insect because of its preference for aphids and scale insects. This predilection has caused ladybirds to be in great demand in many parts of the world. The potato beetle represents a harmful species, whose larval form lives on the leaves and stems of the potato plant.

Some of the bark-boring beetles are highly injurious to forest trees. Pine

Ladybird beetles sometimes gather in large aggregations.
EDWARD S. ROSS

beetles come into this category. These insects destroy the living cambium layer beneath the bark of pines, and before long this results in the death of the trees. A serious infestation can destroy large areas of forest in a few years. Under natural conditions certain insect-eating birds such as woodpeckers play an important part in control of these pests.

Darkling ground beetles or pinacate beetles of the genus *Eleodes* are common in desert areas. They have the protective habit of raising the posterior end of the body and exuding a foul-smelling fluid when disturbed. EDWARD S. ROSS

Weevils and various flour beetles are a serious menace to grain and flour in storage. However, one kind of flour beetle (*Tenebrio molitor*) is raised commercially and sold in the larval form, known as a mealworm. These mealworms are used as food for many kinds of birds, small mammals, and reptiles, as well as for fishing bait. The boll weevil is the greatest enemy of the cotton grower.

Museums are constantly on the watch for carpet beetles and other species that consume fur, feathers, and the skins of animals. In this connection it might be of interest to note that most natural history museums make use of cultures of carrion beetles in cleaning skeletal material for exhibit and study. I have used dermested beetles for this purpose for years. When these beetles are kept in warm, dark containers, the adults will lay their eggs on dried carcasses placed in with them. The young, on hatching, consume the dried flesh, leaving only the bone.

Certain beetles provide food for their young. The dung-rolling scarabs have developed this habit. They may be seen rolling balls of dung along the surface of the ground. They place these balls in holes in which the eggs are laid and thus provide food for the larvae when they hatch.

The long beak of the female acorn weevil (*Curculis uniformis*) is used to drill holes in acorns. The eggs are then deposited in these holes and the young feed on the seed. EDWARD S. ROSS

Some species of scarab beetles make balls from the manure of large herbivores. These balls are rolled away and buried and may provide food for the adult dung beetles or their young.
EDWARD S. ROSS

The beetles represent such a large group of insects that it is not surprising to find that many have adapted themselves to life in water. There are few ponds or lakes that do not contain a number of species of water beetles. Many of them are predacious in both the larval and adult stages.

The ants, bees, wasps, and their relatives.   These are insects belonging to the order Hymenoptera (meaning membrane wings), which is considered by some to represent the most advanced group of arthropods. Many of these insects have a highly developed social organization. Some have acquired interesting parasitic habits.

Most hymenopterous insects have two pairs of transparent, membranous wings and are capable of flight. Their mouthparts are adapted mainly to chewing, although some are used for lapping. They undergo a complete metamorphosis.

Since about eighty-five thousand species are known in this order, we can use only a few examples of the major groups—the ants, the bees, the wasps, and the ichneumon flies.

Ants are distinctive-looking insects that can always be recognized quite readily although there are a great many kinds. They are social insects, living in colonies with different castes to perform different activities. In most colonies there are five castes: the winged males and winged females, which participate in the nuptial flight leading to colony formation; the large workers; the small workers; and the soldiers.

After a queen has completed her nuptial flight, she loses her wings and begins to produce eggs. The eggs hatch into larvae, which she cares for. These larvae in time turn into workers, which are females that will never reproduce. Soon the workers are able to take care of the larvae produced by the queen and by the new queens that develop. The workers build tunnels, usually in the ground or in wood, and gather food for the queens and the young. Some are vegetarians, while others are carnivores. Many ants are fond of sugar. They will search for nectar and keep aphid colonies going in order to be provided with honeydew. Some colonies have a caste whose bodies serve only as storage chambers for nectar. Their stored honey is used in time of need.

Among the most interesting ants are those that raise fungus gardens. The queen, or potential queen, before she starts a new colony, takes a culture of the fungus with her. This is cultivated at first with salivary and anal secretions. Once the new colony is established, the workers feed the underground fungus garden with pieces of vegetation, which they cut. From the southern United States south to the tropics the sight of lines of

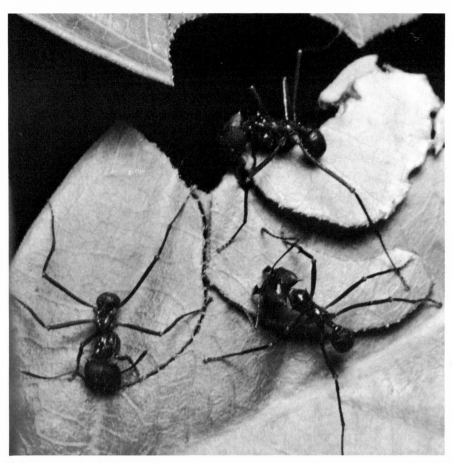

The vegetation harvested by leaf-cutter ants (*Atta*) is used by these insects to culture fungi in subterranean tunnels. EDWARD S. ROSS

ants carrying pieces of leaves to their nests is a common one. Because of this habit they are called leaf-cutting ants.

Many colonies of ants have soldiers that serve as guards to ward off attacks by other colonies. Sometimes slaves are captured and made to work for the captors.

Certain kinds of bees are solitary, but others have developed the most complex social system to be found in the invertebrate world. The honeybee is a well-known example. This species lives in hives or holes in trees, where the colony is ruled by a queen. The queen is capable of producing both workers, which are sterile females, and potential queens. She may also produce drones, which are the males. The latter develop from unfertilized eggs. Both workers and queens come from fertilized eggs, but to produce a queen the colony queen must be fed a substance known as royal jelly.

The workers are responsible for the care of the hive, the gathering of nectar and pollen, the production of honey, which is stored in the combs, and the care of the young and of the queen.

For many years it has been known that bees are able to communicate with one another and inform other members of the colony of the location of new sources of food. The exact method by which this is accomplished was discovered a few years ago by an Austrian scientist named Karl von Frisch. The communication is effected by means of a dance performed by the scout that has made the discovery. If the source of food is less than fifty yards away, the worker turns in short circles. If it is farther away, the scout takes a series of short steps between turns and at the same time wags the abdomen. The direction is indicated by the direction of the straight steps. If the food is in the direction of the sun, the worker takes the steps vertically up the side of the hive. If it is away from the sun, the run is vertically downward. If the food is 20 degrees to the right of the sun, the straight run is 20 degrees to the right of the vertical. In this way the exact location can be disclosed to the others. Furthermore, the bees can detect the position of the sun on overcast days since their eyes are sensitive to ultraviolet rays.

Worker ants of the genus *Campanotus* caring for their larvae. EDWARD S. ROSS

Many hymenopterous insects are parasitic on other species. Best known are the ichneumon wasps, which lay their eggs on or in the bodies of various kinds of insects, usually when the host is in a larval stage. When the wasp larvae are fully grown, they emerge and go into the pupal form, while the host generally dies. These parasitic wasps play a very important part in controlling certain insect populations.

The digger wasp paralyzes caterpillars as food for the larvae. EDWARD S. ROSS

There are many kinds of solitary wasps that construct a cell, often in the ground, in which the young will develop. After the cell is made, the female goes off in search of one or more hosts on which the larva may live. Some wasps parasitize spiders; others use insects such as caterpillars and grass-hoppers. The intended victims are first paralyzed by the sting of the female. Then they are dragged or carried to the cell, in which she deposits an egg before closing the opening. The young, upon hatching, have living food to sustain them through the pupal stage.

There are also colonial wasps, like many of the hornets, that have a social organization consisting of a queen, workers, and drones. These hornets build paper-like combs made of chewed plant fiber and wood

(Left) A sand wasp (*Bembix occidentalis*) digging.
EDWARD S. ROSS

(Below) A tarantula hawk (*Pepsis*) with a tarantula that it has paralyzed. EDWARD S. ROSS

A paper-like cover encases the combs of the yellowjacket (*Vespula*). R. T. ORR

pulp. Some tree-nesting species enclose their combs in a delicate paper shell. Hornets often secure the pulp for their homes from man-made structures such as fences and buildings that have old paint adhering to them. This is chewed off with the wood, so that the resulting wasp nest is occasionally rather colorful.

The Myriapodous Arthropods

The two classes of myriapods are the centipedes and millipedes. For many years these two groups of arthropods were placed together in the same class, but zoologists today believe that they are not closely related. Both, however, have numerous body segments equipped with legs. This was responsible for the name Myriapoda, which was formerly used to include both groups as well as two other small groups of arthropods.

Centipedes occur in most temperate and tropical parts of the world. They are secretive in their habits and are rarely seen unless one turns over rocks and logs or searches under bark, rotting wood, or humus. They are active mainly at night. Their food consists entirely of animal matter that they capture. They prey largely upon other small arthropods in their environment, which they capture by stinging with their poison claws. There are large species in the tropics that are known to kill and feed on small vertebrates.

The poison of many kinds may be quite painful to human beings. For the most part, centipedes are not considered dangerous, but there are a few species whose poison is reported to have caused human deaths.

Centipedes are predacious and feed principally at night. Their poison claws are used to sting the prey. EDWARD S. ROSS

Millipedes can be distinguished from centipedes by the presence of two pairs of legs to each body segment instead of one pair. Their large number of legs has given rise to their name, which means "thousand legs," although none has anywhere near that number of appendages.

Some millipedes have flattened bodies, but most of them are cylindrical and capable of rolling up in the manner of a pill bug for protection. Unlike centipedes, they cannot inject poison into other animals. Their food consists entirely of vegetable material. Some species, however, do have

Millipedes belong to a group named the Diplopoda because they possess two pairs of legs on each body segment. EDWARD S. ROSS

poison glands on the sides of the body, which either exude or actually squirt an obnoxious liquid on any animal that bothers them. This exudate is said to contain hydrocyanic acid as well as iodine and may be quite toxic to their enemies. It may cause irritation if it contacts human skin.

THE CHELICERATES

The arthropods are sometimes divided into three great groups or subphyla. The first of these comprises the trilobites, which, though once dominant in the world, are long extinct. In the second group are the crustaceans, the insects, and the myriapodous arthropods. They are often called the mandibulates, because they possess mandibles. Other features by which they may usually be distinguished include antennae and a body that is generally divided into a head, thorax, and abdomen. The third group consists of those arthropods known as chelicerates. They lack antennae and have a body that is divided into two parts. The anterior portion, which is somewhat comparable to the cephalothorax of some of the crustaceans, is called the prosoma, while the posterior part, or abdominal region, is referred to as the opisthosoma. The prosoma has six pairs of appendages, the last four of which are used for walking. The presence of four pairs of legs alone readily distinguishes all chelicerates from insects. The first pair of appendages, called chelicerae, are modified as pincers and are used in feeding. The second pair, called pedipalps, are used for walking, capturing prey, mating, and other purposes.

There are three classes of chelicerates. One of these includes the living horseshoe, or king crab, and the fossil water scorpions. The horseshoe crabs are members of an ancient group that is represented by about five species in the world today. They are found along the eastern Asiatic coast from Korea to the East Indies, along the Atlantic coast of North America, and in the Gulf of Mexico. Their bodies are covered above by a horseshoe-shaped carapace, from which a long spinelike tail or telson projects posteriorly. These arthropods may attain a length of two feet. The giant water scorpions, or eurypterids, have been extinct for many millions of years but were once abundant predators in marine, brackish, and freshwater habitats. Some of these ancient carnivorous arthropods attained a length of more than nine feet.

The second group of chelicerates comprises a small number of species known as sea spiders, or pycnogonids. They are little known to most people but occur fairly commonly from the intertidal areas to the depths of the ocean. Most of them are small, but some of the deep-sea forms are known to have bodies several inches in length and legs extending as much as two feet from tip to tip. They are carnivorous, living mainly on coelenterates and bryozoans.

The remainder of the chelicerates are all members of the class Arachnida. Included here are the scorpions, the spiders, the real daddy longlegs (not to be confused with crane flies, which are also called daddy longlegs), and the mites and ticks. Although the ancestors of arachnids are believed to have been the water scorpions, the present-day arachnids are primarily terrestrial. A few have secondarily reverted to life in water. Most members of the class are predacious, and therefore important in controlling other small animals, especially insects. Some species have developed poison glands, whose venom may be harmful to human beings. For this reason arachnids, as a group, are looked upon with disfavor. It is unfortunate that the faults of a few should result in the condemnation of a great many, most of whom are beneficial.

Scorpions are found primarily in the warmer parts of the world. They prefer tropical or semitropical regions, although a number of species are found in deserts. They are readily recognized by the great enlargement of their second pair of appendages, the pedipalps, which form large pincers resembling those of lobsters and crayfish. The pincers are used to capture prey, which consists mostly of insects. The victim, upon being caught, is stung and either dies or becomes paralyzed.

The stinging apparatus is at the very posterior tip of the long body and consists of a sharp curved barb that is hollow like a hypodermic needle. Two venom glands inside of the last body segment are connected by a duct to the base of the stinger. They contract when the scorpion raises the posterior part of the body up and forward over the head and inserts the barb into the victim.

Most scorpion stings are no more harmful than those of hornets, and just about as painful. A few species, some of which are found in North Africa, the southwestern United States, and Mexico, produce a powerful neurotoxin. When injected into man, it may cause convulsions with death resulting from cardiac and respiratory failure. I have always made it a

A scorpion in defense attitude. The venom is injected into the victim through the hollow barb on the raised tip of the body. EDWARD S. ROSS

habit to shake out my shoes and clothing carefully every morning in scorpion country. I recall that a week after we had returned from a scientific collecting trip into Mexico one of my associates shook a large and venomous scorpion out of the sleeve of his jacket. Fortunately it had been very warm, and he had had no need to wear the garment.

Scorpions are nocturnal, and therefore seldom seen in the daytime unless one turns over rocks and logs. During the reproductive season the male and female engage in a rather elaborate courtship, which involves a dance. The young, upon hatching, move onto the back of the female, where they remain for the first week or so.

There are a number of other small groups of chelicerates, such as the solpugids, or sun spiders, the pseudoscorpions, and the whip scorpions. These groups are related to the true scorpions and spiders, but few persons are aware of their existence. The true spiders represent the second largest group of chelicerates and unquestionably are the best known. About thirty-five thousand species have so far been described.

Spiders as a group are very widely distributed over the world. They have four pairs of walking legs on the prosoma. The chelicerae have developed into hollow fangs connected with poison glands, and assist in the capture of prey. The poison of most spiders is harmless to man, but that of a few species is quite dangerous. In North America the black widow, a shiny black species with a red hourglass-shaped spot on the underside of the large globular abdomen, is to be avoided. The bite of a female may cause serious illness in adults and even death to small children. However, black widow females do not attack people but inflict bites only in self-defense or, as is more often the situation, in defense of their eggs.

Another very interesting specialization in spiders concerns the pedipalps. In the male these appendages are strangely modified into organs that serve to transfer sperm to the body of the female.

Most spiders have eight eyes arranged on the head in two rows. Their vision is fair but generally functions only at close range. Some species of jumping spiders have remarkable visual acuity.

An outstanding feature of spiders is their ability to spin silk. This is produced by six or eight spinnerets located on the underside of the abdomen. The silk itself is formed in glands and is a protein product that emerges from the body in liquid form. It hardens, not as a result of contact with air, but from tension and stretching. In some species it may be produced in very strong strands.

Silk plays a very important part in the lives of most spiders and no doubt

A jumping spider showing one of its rows of eyes. EDWARD S. ROSS

has influenced their evolutionary development. Many species build elaborate webs in beautiful geometrical designs, such as those constructed by
the orb weavers. The webs serve as traps to capture flying insects. There
are fast-running ground spiders that construct silken tunnels in which
they live and from which they may spring with great speed to secure passing prey.

One of the most important functions of silk is for the protection of the
eggs. These may be kept in a hollow ball of silk that resembles a cocoon.
As already mentioned, some females, like those of the black widow spider,
guard these egg nests until the young hatch.

Spiders use their silk also for locomotion and location. They can readily
lower themselves from the ceiling to the floor on a silken thread and again

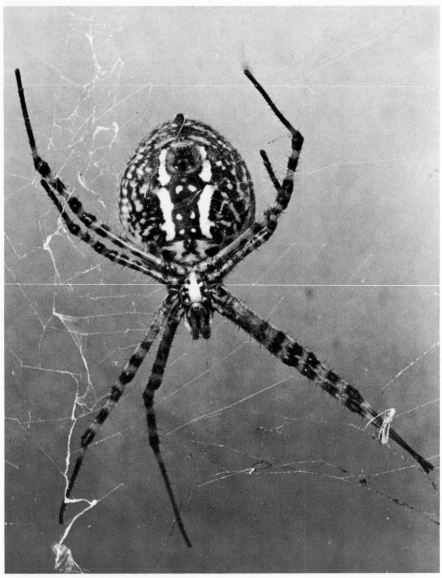

An orb weaver spider in its web. The spinnerets which produce the silk can be seen on the posterior part of the abdominal surface. EDWARD S. ROSS

return by climbing this same strand. Spiders always attach themselves to the substratum by means of silk, and this enables them to return to their starting point. If you blow a spider from a table or wall, you will see that it falls only a certain distance and then is suspended by its thread. If undisturbed, it will gradually climb back up to the site from which it was dislodged.

In certain localities, especially in the summertime, you may see strands of spider web floating through the air. If you examine the strands carefully, you will discover that most of them have tiny spiders attached to them. This is a means of distribution. In this way the young may be blown for many miles into new territories, which they can colonize. Floating spiders have been recorded as high as five thousand feet above the ground.

Related to the spiders are the daddy longlegs, or harvestmen. In spiders there is a marked constriction between the prosoma and the opisthosoma, but this is lacking in the daddy longlegs group, so that the body appears to be almost oval. The legs are extremely long and slender. These harmless arthropods are most common in the tropics, where some may have a leg spread of four or five inches. They also occur in temperate regions.

Mites and ticks belong to an order known as the Acarina. They are extremely abundant in the world and have a grave economic impact. Many kinds are ectoparasites on man and other animals, some are injurious to crops, and others serve as vectors of disease.

There is little indication of a separation of the body into a prosoma and an abdomen in the Acarina. The chelicerae and pedipalps are variously modified in different groups. Some of these appendages form pincers for

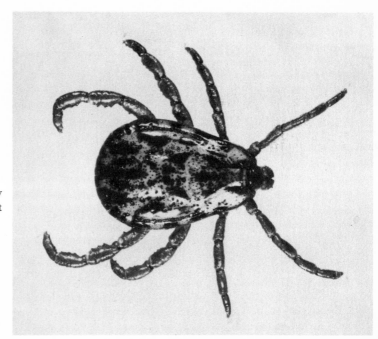

Ticks may be recognized by their flat bodies and eight legs. EDWARD S. ROSS

holding; others have teeth on them to anchor the body onto that of the host. Some have developed into piercing organs, while others function for crushing.

Most species of birds and mammals are parasitized by mites. I have often found two different kinds on a single bat. There are also ticks and mites that live on cold-blooded animals. In western North America, Rocky Mountain spotted fever is transmitted by the bite of a tick known as *Dermacentor andersoni.*

Not all members of this order feed on living matter. A handful of humus from a forest floor will contain many kinds of mites that live on decaying organic material. There is also a group known as the water mites, which is aquatic. Most water mites are tiny but colorful. Some feed on algae, while others are predacious or even parasitize mollusks and fishes.

12

THE ECHINODERMS

The phylum Echinodermata, which means spiny skin, contains the sea stars, sea urchins, sand dollars, brittle stars, sea cucumbers, and their relatives. It is not a large phylum as contrasted with the mollusks, but some of its approximately five thousand species are very well known in parts of the world. Starfish are truly symbols of the sea to most people.

One of the most striking features of the echinoderms is their pentamerous, radial symmetry; the body is usually divided into five essentially equal and similar-appearing parts. However, the echinoderms are not related to the much more primitive radiate animals—the coelenterates and ctenophores. It is generally believed that the radial arrangement of the body in the echinoderms is a secondary development and that these animals evolved from an advanced bilaterally symmetrical group of animals around the time that the lophophorates arose. In their embryonic development they show relationship to the chordates, which include the backboned animals.

All members of this phylum have a skeleton consisting of calcareous plates that may or may not be joined together. Projecting from these plates are spines, which are sometimes very prominent. Echinoderms also possess a unique set of body canals, through which water may flow and be forced, under pressure, into numerous rows of soft tubelike feet, or podia. The podia have sucking disks terminally and can move about as well as be extended under water pressure. This hydraulic apparatus, which is known as the water-vascular system, serves as a means of locomotion.

If you place a starfish on the side of a small aquarium, you will see that the underside of the body is not spiny like the top surface. In the center there is an opening into the digestive system, and radiating from this are five grooves, each of which extends out to the tip of an arm. In the grooves are rows of slowly moving tube feet that will adhere to the glass and soon begin to move the starfish along.

There are no microscopic echinoderms and none that attain any great size. The smallest sea stars and brittle stars are about half an inch in diameter, and the largest of the many-rayed stars rarely exceeds three feet.

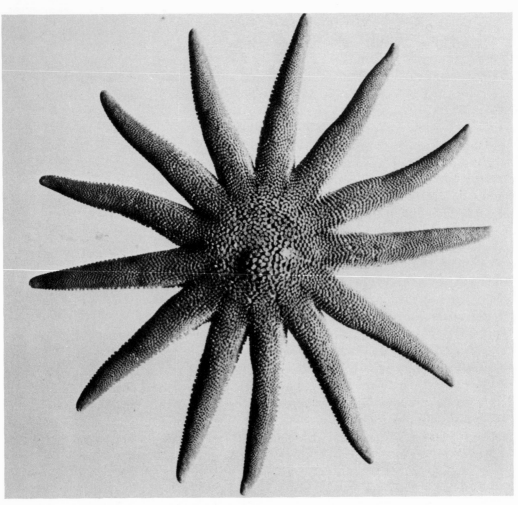

One of the many-rayed stars. AMERICAN MUSEUM OF NATURAL HISTORY

Echinoderms are divided into five classes: the Asteroidea, or sea stars; the Echinoidea, represented by the sea urchins and sand dollars; the Ophiuroidea, or brittle stars; the Holothuroidea, or sea cucumbers; and the Crinoidea, which are the sea lilies.

The Asteroidea. The starfish, or sea stars, unquestionably are the best-known members of the phylum. They range from the shoreline, where they are among the most conspicuous invertebrates at low tide, to the depths of the sea. During the course of their lives they move about slowly on rocks or on a sandy or muddy bottom. There are others that are free-swimming as adults; they are found in all the oceans of the world.

The majority of sea stars have five armlike structures extending out from a central disk, but the number may be four or five times this in some species such as the twenty-rayed sunflower star. The arms may be long or short, but they are relatively thick and incapable of rapid movements, as compared with those of the brittle stars. In some species, such as the bat stars, the arms are very short; in the pincushion stars they are barely indicated and give the body a pentagonal appearance.

One of the peculiarities of the sea stars is their ability to regenerate a new arm to replace one that has been broken off. There are even some species that may use this as a means of asexual reproduction. In these species, individuals are capable of breaking off rays of their own accord. Not only do they regenerate new rays to replace those lost, but the cast-off rays themselves develop a disk as well as additional arms, thus becoming new individuals.

Starfish are often very brightly colored in shades of red, maroon, orange,

The underside of a many-rayed star (*Pycnopodia helianthoides*) adhering to a glass aquarium with its tube feet. R. T. ORR

This Galapagos sea star possesses a beautiful pentagonal design. R. T. ORR

yellow, or blue. These colors are on the top of the body, where the short, protective spines are located. Also found here are numerous tiny stalklike processes that terminate in pincers. These are called pedicellaria. These minute jawlike structures, which may number as many as twenty thousand on a single sea star, function both for protection and for securing food. They open and close by means of individual muscles and, despite their small size, are quite efficient. The body is kept clean by means of their activity. Small animals that are unfortunate enough to crawl over a starfish may find themselves caught by hundreds of tiny jaws. These jaws are too small to hold onto the legs of a small crab, but they can grasp such things as bristles on the legs of a crab and by sheer numbers capture and hold such an animal until it is dead, or it can be slowly transferred to the mouth.

Starfish are carnivores, and they have several different methods of feeding. They may secure food by means of the pedicellaria, but the commonest method they employ is to move along slowly on the substratum until they find the proper prey—largely bivalves such as mussels, oysters, and clams. The starfish then engulfs its victim. If the captured animal is small, it is taken into the stomach and digested, and then the shell is expelled. If it is large, the stomach may be turned inside out and expelled through the mouth of the starfish. Then it envelops the clam or mussel, which is held tightly by the arms and suctorial tube feet. In this way a meal is literally digested outside the body. Later the stomach is withdrawn, and the empty shell of the victim is discarded.

Because of their liking for bivalves, starfish are looked upon with disfavor. They can do a great deal of damage to clams and mussels, especially the latter, and in areas where oysters are raised commercially they may be a source of serious economic loss.

The Echinoidea. These are the hedgehogs of the sea, or the sea porcupines as they are sometimes called. Members of the class are better known as sea urchins, heart urchins, and sand dollars. Although there are not many species, large numbers of individuals may be found in favorable localities. Sea urchins are more often found in rocky situations, while sand dollars prefer a sandy substratum. Representations of both groups may be found in the low intertidal area, but the heart urchins are animals almost entirely of deeper water.

All the echinoids are free-moving like the sea stars, but there are certain urchins that bore into rock when they are small and finally become imprisoned there. This burrowing is accomplished by slow rotation of the spines, which has a grinding effect, and also by means of a chewing apparatus known as "Aristotle's lantern," which consists of five pyramidal calcareous plates that are capable of being projected a short distance through the mouth.

The outer surface of the sea urchin contains long movable spines. Between these spines are rows of podia, which are operated by the water-vascular system as in a sea star. Both the spines and the podia assist in locomotion. In some species, especially in the tropical Pacific and Indian oceans, there are poison sacs at the tip of each spine containing a highly toxic and painful fluid. If one steps on one of these urchins, serious injury may result. Even along the Pacific coast of North America I have suffered from punctures by spines of the purple sea urchin. There are some tropical species, however, that have very thick, blunt spines that are incapable of causing injury.

Beneath the outer spiny covering of sea urchins, the calcareous plates of the skeleton are fused together to form a globular shell, or "test" as it is usually called. These shells are found along beaches and are often used

Purple sea urchins are protected by an outer covering of numerous spines. R. T. ORR

for decorative purposes. They can be made into attractive shades for miniature lamps.

The heart urchins and sand dollars lack the long spines of the oval sea
urchins, but they make up for this by being covered with a great number
of short spines. Since these animals live in sand, elongate spines would
probably prove a hindrance in moving about. The heart urchins derive
their name from their heart-shaped appearance, while the sand dollars
are disk-shaped. In both types the oral or under side of the body is flat and
the upper surface convex, although the degree of curvature is much less
in the flattened sand dollars, Shells, or tests, of the sand dollars are commonly found along sandy beaches, although the living animals themselves
are only to be seen at low tide in favorable situations.

The food of all members of the class consists of small or minute animal
or plant organisms, which may be living or dead. It is gathered by means
of the pedicellaria, the spines, and the podia and is transferred to the
mouth. The digestive system of the echinoids, unlike that of the sea stars,
has an anal opening on the aboral surface of the body. Furthermore, the
stomach is not capable of being everted.

The Ophiuroidea. The brittle stars, or basket or serpent stars as they are
sometimes called, are little known in comparison with the sea stars. Most
of them occur at the bottom of the sea, but there are a number of shoreline
species, and in some localities they may be very abundant. To see them,
however, it is usually necessary to turn over rocks under which they are
hiding, or else to hunt for them at night when the tide is low. Like many
other invertebrates, they are most active after dark.

Brittle stars have small disklike bodies with relatively long, slender arms
that are capable of moving and lashing around with considerable rapidity
in contrast to those of sea stars. These arms lack any groove on the underside and have the podia greatly reduced. When handled or even touched,
the arms come off very easily. A wiggling brittle star is actually capable of
shedding its own arms. These can be regenerated in a short time. The arms
are relatively thicker in the serpent stars. Although ophiuroids basically
have five arms, these may be branched in the basket stars.

As in the asteroids, the digestive system has a single opening. But the
stomach, unlike that of members of the asteroid group, cannot be everted
to feed. There is no intestinal tract. The food of brittle stars and their
relatives consists largely of organic debris that sinks to the bottom.

The Holothuroidea. This is another small group of echinoderms, consist-

A brittle star (*Ophiocoma alexandri*), one of the Ophiuroidea. Courtesy CALIFORNIA ACADEMY OF SCIENCES

ing of about five hundred species commonly called sea cucumbers or bêches-de-mer. They have elongate, cylindrical bodies that are soft and lacking true spines. The skeletal elements, which are so conspicuous in the sea urchins, are microscopic in size. They do resemble the echinoids in the absence of any arms and in having a digestive system that has an intestine and both an oral and aboral opening. The mouth, which is at one end of the long body, has a circle of tentacle-like structures about it, which assists in the gathering of food. These are really modified podia. Sea cucumbers feed primarily on plankton.

Most members of the class are rather dull-colored and slow-moving. They burrow in sand and mud and are found in all oceans of the world. Some species occur in the intertidal areas along shore, while others live at great depths. They are highly sought after in parts of Malaya and the South Pacific, where they are collected, dried, and sold as trepang. Trepang is used especially by the Chinese for soup. When soaked in water, the meat of the animal enlarges greatly and becomes gelatinous.

Not all sea cucumbers are edible. Some species produce a poison, which they discharge if disturbed so as to kill their enemies. One of the poisonous species of sea cucumbers that occurs off the Florida keys serves as a home for the pearlfish, which finds protection within the hind part of the gut of the echinoderm. Aërated water that is taken into this part of the sea cucumber's body for its own respiration is also utilized for the same purpose by these small fishes. In other regions there are fishes that live within various parts of the bodies of different species of holothuroideans.

A sea cucumber. R.T. ORR

The Crinoidea.   The fifth class of echinoderms consists of the sea lilies and feather stars. Although this is not a large group, it is a very old one that is well represented in the fossil record. Back in Paleozoic times sea lilies were very abundant. These ancient echinoderms were all stalked just like the modern sea lilies. The stalk is on the aboral side, which is attached to the substratum. It may be two feet long in some of the largest living forms. The uppermost side has the mouth. In this respect these crinoids differ very much from the sea stars, the urchins, and the brittle stars.

Crinoids are basically pentamerous, but the arms have numerous side branches that produce a flower- or feather-like effect responsible for their name. The feather stars are much more numerous, as regards species, than the older sea lilies. Unlike the latter, they are not stalked but swim freely or else crawl along the ocean floor. Almost all members of the crinoids are deep-water inhabitants. A few of the feather stars are found in shallow water in such places as the Great Barrier Reef.

13

THE CHORDATES

The phylum Chordata contains a vast assemblage of diversified animals ranging from microscopic colonial organisms to man. It is exceeded in numbers of species only by the arthropods and the mollusks.

In spite of the great differences that obviously exist between simple chordates like the tunicates or sea squirts and the most advanced backboned animals, they all possess three features in common. The first of these is a structure called a notochord, which is an internal strengthening rod that represents the beginning of an endoskeleton. In the lower chordates the skeleton never advances beyond this stage, but in the vertebrates it is supplemented and finally replaced in adult life by a vertebral column.

The second character common to all chordates is the presence of a dorsal tubular nerve cord, which is hollow, unlike the solid ventral nerve cord of lower organisms. The third character is the presence at some stage during life of pharyngeal gill slits permitting the passage of water from the pharynx to the outside in those forms that respire by gills. Even the highest chordates—like reptiles, birds, and mammals—develop these slits during embryonic life, but they are modified later into other structures, such as the Eustachian tube, the tonsils, the thymus gland, and the parathyroid glands.

The chordates represent the peak of development of the deuterostome line from which the echinoderms branched off farther down the phylogenetic tree. They are generally divided into four subphyla known as the Hemichordata, the Urochordata, the Cephalochordata, and the Vertebrata.

The hemichordates. These are marine organisms known as the tongue worms or acorn worms. They live in burrows, which they make in sandy or muddy tidal flats. Their only claim to be members of the phylum Chordata lies in the presence of pharyngeal gill slits and a structure that looks like a notochord. It has recently been shown that this is not a true notochord, and most students of classification now place the acorn worms in a separate phylum by themselves. Their larval stage in many respects is similar to that of echinoderms.

The urochordates.   These are the tunicates or sea squirts, which are restricted to marine waters. Most of them are sessile, being attached to rocks and piling, principally along shores, but there are some free-floating planktonic types. Tunicates may be solitary or colonial. In the adult form they possess two syphons, which bring water and food into the pharynx. It is in the larval stage that their chordate relationship is really shown. The larva has a tadpole-like appearance and possesses a well-developed notochord in the tail. This is lost as the tail is absorbed in the transformation to the adult form.

The cephalochordates.   To biologists these little chordates are very important because they represent a type of organism that is thought to resemble, in certain respects, the ancestors of vertebrates. They are sometimes called lancelets, but are more commonly known in laboratories by their former generic name, which was *Amphioxus*. It is thought that they may have evolved from a primitive tunicate stock. Their bodies are elongate, with a notochord extending their full length. They possess pharyngeal gill slits and a hollow dorsal nerve cord. Lancelets live in shallow ocean water, where they may be found buried in sand or swimming freely. Along the Asiatic coast they are often dried and used as food.

The vertebrates.   Vertebrates are commonly called backboned animals, although the lower forms actually do not possess bone. They might better be described as a group of chordates in which the notochord is replaced either in part or *in toto* or else supplemented by cartilaginous or bony elements called vertebrae. As a group the vertebrates undoubtedly must be regarded as dominant in the world today. They have availed themselves of essentially every habitat, from ocean floor to mountain top and from forest to desert. Included in the subphylum are the various classes of fishlike animals, the amphibians, the reptiles, the birds, and the mammals.

FISHES

There are three different classes of fishlike vertebrates. The lowest are the jawless fishes consisting of the lamprey eels and hagfishes. Next we have the cartilaginous fishes, best known by the sharks and rays. Finally we have the bony fishes, of great importance to man both for food and for sport.

The jawless fishes.   These are the most primitive of existing vertebrates.

The few living species are, in a sense, remnants of a group that flourished in the early part of the Paleozoic period, about half a billion years ago. Their skeletons are composed of cartilage. Their mouths, which lack any jaws, are round and responsible for the name cyclostome, by which they are commonly known. Cyclostomes lack fins and scales.

There are only two families of jawless fishes. One of these contains the hags and the other the lampreys. Hagfishes are strictly marine in occurrence. Their food consists largely of dead fish. Although they are largely scavengers, they will attack living species that are slow-moving. A row of tentacles around the mouth enables them to cling to their food, which they tear off by means of a rasping tongue. Their long slender bodies, which may attain a length of two and a half feet, are covered with numerous

The Pacific hagfish (*Eptatretus stouti*) with its jawless, suctorial mouth not only preys on slow-moving fishes but is a scavenger as well. R. T. ORR

mucous glands. This is responsible for the name "slime eel," by which they are sometimes known.

Lampreys somewhat resemble hagfishes but have a more highly developed cartilaginous skull and a suctorial mouth that enables them to attach themselves to various fishes, whose flesh they remove with their tongue. Most lampreys spend their adult life in the sea, although there are some that have become landlocked in the Great Lakes of North America as well as some that are strictly freshwater in occurrence.

Sea lampreys, unlike hagfishes, come to freshwater streams and rivers to spawn. Their movements in this regard are somewhat like those of salmon. After spawning, the adults die. Young lampreys spend several years in a larval stage, during which they remain buried in the sandy or muddy bottoms of streams. When they are ready to mature, they migrate down to larger tributaries or lakes and, if possible, move from there to the sea, where they remain until sexually mature. After the lampreys start moving toward the sea, they become parasitic and prey on other fishes.

In the Great Lakes the sea lamprey of the Atlantic has become a source of considerable economic loss by depleting the lake trout. Lampreys always had access to Lake Ontario by way of the St. Lawrence River, but once the Welland Canal was built in 1829 they were able to move into the other Great Lakes. By the early 1950's they were so widely distributed and abundant in these lakes that they preyed heavily on the trout, and commercial fishing was almost eliminated. In recent years control methods have been established with some success.

The cartilaginous fishes.   These are jawed fishes with a well-developed skeleton composed of cartilage, paired fins, four to seven pairs of separate gill openings, and external toothlike denticles on the skin known as placoid scales. Such scales do not contact one another, nor do they overlap like those of higher fishes. The intestine of cartilaginous fishes possesses a spiral valve that serves to increase its absorptive surface. These fishes, technically referred to as the Chondrichthyes, are commonly known as sharks, rays, and chimaeras.

The sharks.   All members of this group are medium- to very large-sized predacious fishes that are almost entirely marine in occurrence. There is one species that has become adapted to life in fresh water. This is a man-eater that lives in Lake Nicaragua. A few kinds occasionally enter fresh water for short periods of time, and a number live in the brackish water of bays. About two hundred and fifty species of sharks are known. The group is worldwide in distribution but more abundantly represented in warmer oceanic waters.

Sharks are the wolves of the sea. While many species are harmless to man, there are also many that will attack human beings with little or no provocation. The most deadly and most feared are the mackerel sharks, the requiem sharks, and the hammerheads. One of the most famous of the mackerel sharks is the man-eater, or great white shark. This is a large species of the open sea, but it occasionally comes into coastal waters, where it seems to attack anything that looks like food, including man. The largest individual ever captured measured more than thirty-six feet in length.

The California hornshark (*Heterodontus francisci*) has a prominent spine in front of each dorsal fin. R. T. ORR

Man-eater sharks can be recognized by their teeth if one cares to get that close to them. The teeth are triangular, with finely serrated or sawlike edges that are as sharp as razors. Several years ago three sea otters that had been found dead along the central California coast were brought to me to be preserved as museum specimens. The authorities who had found them were of the belief that they had been killed by skin divers. While skinning the first animal, we came across evidence to the contrary which deeply incriminated another animal. Not only were there semicircular rows of tooth marks on the body, but embedded in the flesh was a flat triangular tooth with serrate edges that had, without question, come from the mouth of a man-eater. I later cut my thumb on this tooth—it was so sharp. One of the other otters also had semicircular rows of tooth marks on the body.

Members of the largest family of cartilaginous fishes are called requiem sharks. Despite their name they are not all to be feared. Several species, however, are very dangerous—the tiger sharks of tropical waters and the man-eaters of Lake Nicaragua. Both have been responsible for many human deaths. Belonging to this same family is the famous soup-fin shark that was so greatly sought during World War II for its liver. Shark liver, for a while, was the principal source of vitamin A in America when cod-liver oil shipments from Norway were blocked.

One of the most dangerous sharks in both tropical and temperate waters is the hammerhead. The sides of the head of this type of shark are extended out laterally as lobes, on which the eyes are located. The body may attain a length of as much as fifteen feet. There are records of attacks

The leopard shark (*Triakis semifasciata*) is a common but colorful Pacific coast species. R. T. ORR

by hammerheads on human beings as far north as New York along the Atlantic coast and off southern California along the Pacific coast.

Strange as it may seem, the largest species of sharks are quite harmless. These are the whale sharks, the largest fish in the world, and the basking sharks, which are second in size. The former may reach a length of more than forty-five feet, and the basking shark may be almost as long. Both species feed on small fish and marine invertebrates and are reported to be quite gentle.

The so-called dogfishes are among the commonest of small sharks and also the best known. They are used for dissection in biology classes in many parts of the world.

The skates and rays. While sharks, with their torpedo-shaped bodies, are constantly on the move in open water, skates and rays dwell mostly on the bottom and have changed their shape to blend with this sort of environment. The body of a typical skate is flat with great winglike extensions on each side. These so-called wings are really front or pectoral fins that have become greatly enlarged.

Most skates and rays feed on clams, oysters, or other mollusks that they find on sandy or muddy bottoms, usually in moderately shallow water. There are species, however, that swim near the surface for their food and may occur far out in the open ocean. The mantas, or devil rays, have this habit.

Some of the mantas are the largest known skatelike fishes. One species is famous for a breadth of as much as twenty-two feet from the tip of one pectoral fin to the tip of the other. These giants of the sea live on small planktonic organisms. Food is directed into their mouth by means of finlike structures that protrude forward on each side of the head. The giant mantas are quite harmless, although one would be severely injured if hit by one of their enormous fins.

Skates and rays have teeth that are flat and adapted to crushing the bivalves on which most of them are dependent for food. Their teeth are not much good for defense. Some species, however, have developed special protective devices. One of these is seen in the stingrays. These fishes have a venom spine located on the top of the tail, but this spine is not hollow like the fang of a rattlesnake. Instead, the poison comes from glands that may be situated in a sheath surrounding the spine or in grooves toward its base. A number of human deaths have been caused by accidental contact with these venomous fishes. Death has usually occurred when the spine was injected into the abdomen.

Another noteworthy device developed in one family of rays is an electric organ capable of producing a powerful shock. There is one electric ray that is able to discharge more than two hundred volts of electricity. Electric organs occur in some other groups of bony fishes. While they may function for defense, this is probably not their primary purpose. In some species the electric charge is used to capture prey, but more often it is used somewhat like radar. An impulse is sent out and is then reflected back from objects in the water, making the fish aware of their presence. Most electric fishes live either in turbid water or at considerable depths in the sea, where vision plays no part in their lives and other senses must be used.

The sawfishes comprise another interesting group of rays, in which the front of the head is elongated into a flat blade with teeth on each side. This saw is a formidable-looking structure. It is used mainly to dig food out of the bottom or to club smaller fish.

The chimaeras. Another name for members of this aberrant group of fishes, distantly related to sharks and rays, is ratfish. Chimaeras are relatively rare and occur in north and south temperate ocean waters but not in equatorial regions. They feed on mollusks, much like skates, and have flat tooth plates which assist with this sort of diet. We know little of their ancestry, but they are believed to have been derived from primitive sharks.

The bony fishes. These are fishes whose internal skeleton consists partly or entirely of true bone. For this reason some ichthyologists place them in a class known as the Osteichthyes. This is the largest group of chordates. It is variously estimated that there are somewhere between twenty-five thousand and forty thousand species of bony fishes.

There are several schools of thought on the classification of this group. One of these recognizes approximately fifty different living orders. It would be impossible to cover such a large assemblage here; therefore a simpler and still widely accepted arrangement is used. This involves a basic division of the bony fishes into two major groups, the ray-finned fishes and the fishes with fleshy or partly fleshy fins. The ray-finned fishes include the cartilaginous ganoids, the bony ganoids, and the higher bony fishes. The fishes with fleshy or partly fleshy fins consist of the lungfishes and the coelacanths.

The cartilaginous ganoids. The most primitive living ray-finned fishes are members of a small group known as the Chondrostei that were very abundant in the sea as well as in lakes and rivers during the late Paleozoic. The cartilaginous ganoids, as may be judged from their name, have a skeleton that contains a great deal of cartilage. They also have a spiral valve inside the intestine like sharks. The name ganoid results from the presence, in some species, of scales covered with a shining material called ganoin.

There are three living types of this once very abundant group: the sturgeons, the paddlefishes, and the bichirs, or fringe-finned ganoids.

Sturgeons are large fishes found in temperate parts of the Northern Hemisphere. Some species occur only in fresh water while others are marine, coming into rivers only to spawn. The largest freshwater fish in the world is a species of sturgeon found in the Volga River in Soviet Russia. Individuals have been caught there that weighed over one ton.

Another name by which some sturgeons are known is beluga. This is somewhat confusing, because the white whale of the Arctic Ocean is also called a beluga.

Sturgeons are most famous for their eggs, or roe, known as caviar when properly prepared and salted. Russian caviar has long been considered the finest. Sturgeon eggs are also processed in Europe and America. Sturgeon flesh itself is excellent, especially when smoked.

The paddlefishes superficially have a sharklike appearance, but extending from the end of the nose is an elongate paddle whose function is not known. There are only two living species of these primitive bony fishes: One occurs in the Mississippi River of North America and the other in the Yangtse River in China.

The bony ganoids. The cartilaginous ganoids that were so dominant in the late Paleozoic were succeeded in the Mesozoic by the bony ganoids, or Holostei. These fishes were contemporary with the great reptiles that ruled the land. The only representatives left in the world today are the bowfin or dogfish of the eastern part of the United States and the several species of gars that are found from eastern Canada south to Panama. All are inhabitants of fresh water.

Bony ganoids have a skeleton that is largely ossified, and there is only a remnant of the spiral valve to be found in the intestine. Rhomboidal-shaped ganoid scales that contact one another and are arranged in diagonal rows are found on the bodies of gars.

Neither the bowfins nor the gars are considered valuable as food or sport fishes, but they are of great interest to biologists because of their dominance in former times and their intermediate character between the lower and higher bony fishes. A few years ago my wife and I were fishing in north-central Michigan where the daily catch consisted principally of walleye, great northern pike, and black bass. On one occasion, however, our young guide hooked onto another kind of fish, which he pulled up close to the boat. Just as I was about to express my delight at seeing a live bowfin for the first time, the guide gave a hard jerk on his line, freed the fish, and said disgustedly, "Just a dogfish." There was little use in my telling him that I had been lecturing on the anatomy of this species of fish for years without having the opportunity of seeing a living specimen.

Both the bowfin and the gars are predacious, living on other kinds of

The alligator gar (*Lepisosteus spatula*) is one of the largest of freshwater fishes. They may attain a length of about ten feet. R. T. ORR

fishes, some of which are of economic value. This becomes significant when we realize that the largest gars attain a length of more than ten feet.

The higher bony fishes. The majority of the fishes of the world belong to this group, known as the Teleostei. True bony fishes probably arose from the higher ganoids and supplanted them in the late Mesozoic as the domi-

The brown trout (*Salmo trutta*) has been introduced from Europe to many streams and lakes in North America. Courtesy STEIN-HART AQUARIUM

nant vertebrates in the sea. They still retain this position and are found from the polar areas to the equator. They are also abundant in most fresh-water streams, ponds, and lakes, and even in some springs. Probably more than four-fifths of the living fishes of the world belong to this group.

The teleosts have lost all trace of cartilage in their skeleton as well as any indication of a spiral valve in the intestine. Furthermore, their bodies are clothed with thin, flexible scales that lack any ganoin. These scales are attached to the skin anteriorly and overlap one another somewhat like shingles on a roof.

Since we cannot hope to discuss all the common groups of teleosts, a few have been selected to illustrate their numerical abundance as well as diversity in both structure and behavior.

Some bony fishes are worldwide in distribution. This appears to be true of various tunas, such as the bluefin and the albacore. Marked individuals of bluefins have been known to cross the Atlantic, and an albacore tagged along the California coast was recovered three years later off the coast of Japan. By way of contrast there are certain small minnow-like fishes belonging to a group known as the cyprinodonts that occur only in isolated springs in desert parts of western North America. It is believed that the springs in which these populations now exist were once connected as part of a great lake that dried up in recent geological times, leaving a few remnants of its former fish fauna in some smaller bodies of water.

The abundance of certain kinds of common fishes is difficult to com-

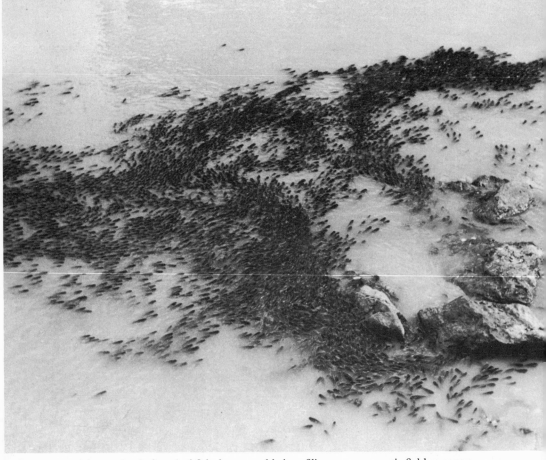

A large school of tropical fish that resemble iron filings on a magnetic field. R. T. ORR

prehend. One author recently estimated the population of the common herring at one billion billion. Herrings, anchovies, pilchards, and their numerous relatives are rich in body oil and fat and provide food for a vast number of other kinds of fishes as well as many marine animals. Some species of fish are extremely rare and known from only one or two specimens; others have been seen only in the depths of the ocean from the window of a bathysphere.

This great group of bony fishes shows considerable diversity in body form. The majority that we are familiar with, such as goldfish, trout, perch, bass, and the like, have elongate, somewhat laterally compressed bodies with two sets of paired fins, a tail fin, one or two fins along the back, and one on the ventral posterior part of the body between the vent and the tail. One of the most interesting and important groups that have changed from this typical form contains the soles, the flounders, and the halibut. These are called flatfishes.

When first hatched, flatfishes do not show any unusual features. As they grow, however, one eye begins to migrate to the opposite side of the head. The blind side of the body fails to develop pigment and soon serves as the underside of the fish. Furthermore, the unpaired fins on what was originally the back and the lower surface of the body grow both forward and backward and assist greatly in locomotion, somewhat like the pectoral fins of the rays. In this instance, the fish swims on its side.

The ocean sunfish is a strange creature to observe in the water. It has a huge disk-shaped body that is compressed laterally. There is only a fringe of a tail fin along the posterior part of the disk, and the posterior paired fins are gone. The unpaired back, or dorsal, fin and the lower, or ventral, fin are somewhat elongated in a vertical plane. The front pair of fins is present but small. Some of these sunfishes attain very large size and may weigh a ton. One gains the impression that they lack adequate stabilizing equip-

Many flatfishes, like the speckled sanddab (*Citharichthys stigmaeus*), are capable of changing their color pattern to blend with the background. R. T. ORR

(Left) The California monkey-faced blenny (*Cebidichthys violaceus*.) R. T. ORR

(Below) The male lingcod (*Ophiodon elongatus*) guards the eggs until the young hatch. R. T. ORR

ment to maintain an upright position in the water. On several occasions I have seen them slowly swimming by on their sides along the surface.

The various types of eel-like fishes, including the freshwater eels, the morays, and their relatives, have elongate, snakelike bodies. Posterior paired fins are lacking, and the upper and lower unpaired fins are continuous with the tail fin. This sort of body form has been developed in other, unrelated, fishes such as some of the blennies. It is particularly well adapted to life among and under rocks.

Unique in the fish world are the various sea horses and the related pipefishes with their well known tubelike noses and armor-like plates that cover the body. The sea horses have a tail that is prehensile, or grasping, like the tail of an opossum.

Most fishes move about by lateral movements of the hind part of the body and the tail. This is just as true of yellowtail, tunas, tarpon, marlin, and other rapid-moving species of the sea as it is of goldfish in a bowl. The paired fins play little part in such progression, serving primarily as stabilizers. There are, however, numerous exceptions to this general type of locomotion. Some fishes hop, some walk, and some fly, and there are a few that even hitchhike.

The mudskippers of tropical Africa and Asia use their large pectoral fins to hop about on tidal mudflats and especially in mangrove swamps. They can readily jump up on the roots of mangroves and are capable of surviving a considerable time out of water. In southeastern Asia walking perch have been known to make overland trips of several hundred yards at night during periods of drought. They are said to accomplish this movement by using their expanded gill plates as feet.

The flying fishes of tropical seas are species that have learned to glide in the air. This is done by building up great speed in the water as a result of lateral movement. During this time the very large winglike pectoral fins are held tightly against the body. Then the fish breaks the surface and takes to the air, expanding its fins as it does so. Sometimes extremely rapid tail movement in the water after the rest of the body has emerged aids in building up speed. Under exceptional circumstances a flying fish may glide as far as twelve hundred feet, but usually the distance is much less.

One of the most interesting methods of travel has been developed by a group of fishes known as the remoras, or suckerfishes. Remoras have a suction pad on the top of the head, which enables them to attach themselves to larger fish such as sharks, tuna, marlin, swordfish, and other expert swimmers. Some kinds even hold on to whales. These hitchhikers

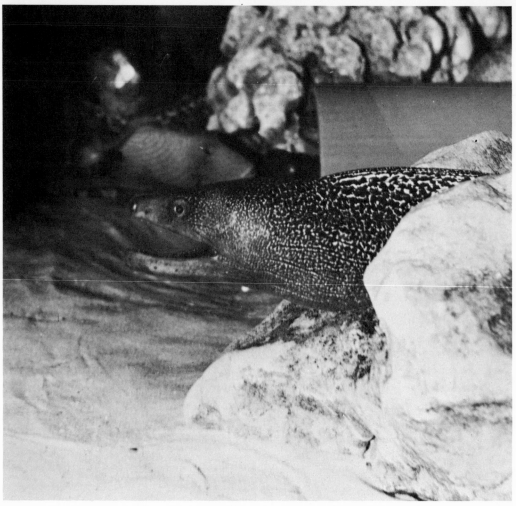

Moray eels of the family Muraenidae are inhabitants of rocks and reefs in which they hide.
R. T. ORR

actually pay their way in service, because their food consists principally of parasitic crustaceans attached to the bodies of the hosts.

Some bony fishes have special methods for catching their food. One of the most fascinating is that used by the archerfishes. They derive their name from the fact that they can shoot a stream of water accurately from the mouth into the air and knock a flying insect into the water.

Another interesting device for enticing prey within striking distance is employed by the anglerfishes. In these species the first ray on the dorsal fin is modified into a sort of fishing pole with a movable lever on the end. When this is extended forward and moved, it attracts small fish to their doom. There are also deep-sea anglerfishes that have luminous lures to attract prey in essentially total darkness.

Bioluminescence is not uncommon in many fishes living at abyssal depths. Such luminescent organs may serve not only to attract food but also for species or sex recognition. Biological light of this sort may be pro-

The tropical anglers (*Antennarius*) can literally walk about on the ocean floor by means of their fins. R. T. ORR

duced by light organs called photophores or else may result from aggregations of luminescent bacteria that are cultured in special parts of the body. The light in either type is a cold light like that of a firefly.

Some bony fishes have developed electric organs very similar to those of certain of the rays. Such structures appear in a number of different species, like the electric eel and electric catfish, both of which are capable of devel-

oping an extremely strong electrical charge, sufficient under certain circumstances to kill a human being. Many fishes have been found to have
weak electric organs that serve principally to assist in orientation. One
group, known as the mormyrids, has been the subject of considerable study.
It was found that these fishes are able to detect the presence of a magnet on
the outside of the tank in which they are kept. In one experiment some of
them were even conditioned to eat when a magnet was placed near the
tank.

Certain fishes are poisonous and others are definitely venomous. Some
of the most deadly to eat are the puffers. They have been known to cause
death in as short a time as twenty minutes. It is notable that the Japanese
have a special way of preparing puffers and making them quite edible.
There are many other fishes of the tropical Pacific that are poisonous only
at certain times of the year, and there are other species whose flesh is
perfectly good but which may have various organs that are poisonous to
man.

Venomous fishes are those that have poisonous spines or barbs of one
sort or another. Some fishes of the Pacific and Indian oceans are capable
of causing agonizing death. One group contains the scorpion fishes, so
named because of their poisonous spines. The most beautiful of the scorpion
fishes are the turkey fishes, whose elaborate plumelike fins resemble the
spread feathers of a displaying bird. However, the tips of the "plumes"
have venom glands that can produce serious injury. The most deadly of
the scorpion fishes is the stonefish, whose venom may cause death within
several hours. Stonefishes look like rocks and are therefore easily stepped
on by mistake. The result of such an error is an injection of neurotoxin into
the foot from one of the spines on the back.

There are other fishes that have slightly less formidable defense mech-
anisms on the body. The surgeonfishes, for example, have knifelike blades
located in pockets on each side of the body just in front of the tail. When in
danger, these herbivorous fishes can evert these blades for defense. They
can produce a serious cut on an unsuspecting fisherman.

Another protective mechanism is possessed by the triggerfishes of the
tropical Pacific. The first and second spines on the back have an inter-
locking device, so that when the first spine, which is large, is raised, it is
held firmly in place until the second spine is released. These fishes are often
chased into corals by predatory species. Here they elevate this large spine
to anchor themselves and avoid being dislodged.

The reproductive habits of bony fishes are extremely varied and a source of great interest to biologists. We are familiar with the Pacific salmon that spend their adult lives in the sea and then return to the same freshwater stream in which they were hatched to spawn and die. Freshwater eels make even more extensive migrations. The European eels inhabit the rivers and their tributaries of western Europe, where they take from five to twenty years to mature. When this occurs, they migrate down to the sea and cross the Atlantic to the Sargasso region. There they spawn at considerable depths and then die. The young, upon hatching, begin to drift with the Gulf Stream current and by their third summer arrive along the coast of Europe, where they remain until the following spring. At this time they move up into the freshwater streams, though not necessarily the same ones from which their parents came, and stay until maturity.

The grunion of the Pacific coast of North America is a species whose reproductive behavior is synchronized with the tides and the moon. Spawning takes place only on the first three or four nights following either the full moon or the new moon between late February and early September. At such times males and females are washed up on sandy beaches with each wave, and, in the few seconds that elapse before the next wave comes in, each female digs a hole with her tail, lays her eggs, and the males fertilize them. This activity is limited to one to three hours on the spawning nights and is taken advantage of by many local fishermen, who line up with buckets and catch the grunions by hand.

A number of fishes have developed methods of protecting their eggs until they hatch. The guarding is usually the duty of the male. The male sea horse, for example, has an abdominal pouch in which he incubates the eggs. The male of the blue gourami builds a nest of bubbles into which he blows the eggs that are laid by the female. Sticklebacks also build nests to hold the eggs until they hatch. There are several groups of fishes in which the male or female incubates the eggs within the mouth. These are known as mouthbreeders.

A very strange type of reproductive behavior is seen in the European bitterling, which lays its eggs inside a freshwater clam, where they are incubated. To accomplish this the female bitterling has developed a very long tubelike ovipositor.

There are many other interesting reproductive specializations in certain species of fishes, but the great majority show no concern either for their eggs or their young. Those that lay their eggs in the sea so that they float freely usually produce them in great quantities, often numbering in the hundreds of thousands. This helps to offset the terrific loss that must occur.

The seahorse (*Hippocampus*) has a prehensile tail. R. T. ORR

In San Francisco Bay I can tell when the herrings are spawning along shore by the great aggregations of gulls that gorge themselves with the eggs of these fish.

The fleshy-finned fishes. These differ from the various ray-finned fishes that have been considered here by the presence of a fleshy lobe to the paired fins. Furthermore, they possess internal and external nostrils which may serve to pass air back to the functional lungs.

The two groups of fleshy-finned fishes are really not closely related, but both go a long way back in the history of life on earth. Today one group is represented by a single known living species, and the other by three genera comprising about six species.

The coelacanths. About four hundred million years ago, in the middle of the Paleozoic era, a large group of fishes known as crossopterygians became the dominant backboned animals in fresh water. The abundance of fossil remains indicates that they were numerous. Most of them became extinct before the beginning of the Mesozoic. There was one exception, however, in a side branch called the coelacanths. The coelacanths took to the sea and survived up to the close of the Age of Reptiles. It was believed that they all became extinct before the beginning of the Cenozoic era, since no fossil remains of them had been found in any geological deposits of a more recent age than the Mesozoic.

The South American arawana (*Osteoglossum bicirrhosum*) is believed to incubate its eggs in its mouth. R. T. ORR

In 1939 the world learned of a great discovery. A living coelacanth had been taken by a trawler that was netting fish off the east coast of South Africa in the Indian Ocean on December 22, 1938. This strange fish, which was five feet long, was fortunately saved and later named *Latimeria chalumnae*. It is probably the most famous fish in the world today. Its picture has been in practically all newspapers and is to be found in nearly every textbook pertaining to zoology that has been published since 1940.

A model of the famous coelacanth (*Latimeria chalumnae*). Courtesy STEINHART AQUARIUM

Since the first living coelacanth was made known to science in 1939, a number of other specimens of *Latimeria* have been preserved. Their existence, however, had long been known to the natives of the Comoro Islands. Recently I had the pleasure of meeting a resident of one of those small Indian Ocean islands, and he informed me that coelacanths have long been sold there in the native markets. Imagine eating a "living fossil"!

Interest in crossopterygian fishes stems not so much from their former abundance and present-day rarity as from the belief that they were the ancestors of amphibians. It required relatively little change for air-breathing fishes to modify their fleshy, lobed fins into appendages suitable for walking on land. The earliest known fossil amphibians resemble these lobe-finned fishes in many respects.

The lungfishes. Branching off from the same ancient fishes that gave rise to crossopterygians was another group of air breathers known as the lung-fishes or dipnoans. These fishes also were numerous in the middle Paleozoic in fresh water and for many years were believed to be ancestors of the amphibians. They differ, however, from the ancient amphibians in so many respects that it appears obvious that they represent a side branch of the lobe-finned fishes—a branch that has barely managed to keep a few survivors in the world today.

There is a single species of lungfish living in Australia, one in South America, and four closely related species belonging to one genus in Africa. Modern lungfishes, like their ancestors from the Mesozoic, live in regions where periodic droughts result in the drying up of ponds and watercourses.

An Australian lungfish (*Neoceratodus fosteri*) showing the lobelike front fin. R. T. ORR

Both the South American and African species are capable of surviving a dry period in a mud cell or tunnel until rain comes. During this entombment they remain in a sort of torpid condition and breathe air. There is a record of an African lungfish that lived out of water this way for four years.

The Australian species does not build mud tunnels and go into dormancy, but it is capable of surviving in water that may become very stagnant. Furthermore, if the water is rich in oxygen, it does not need to come to the surface for air like the South American and African species.

AMPHIBIANS

The smallest living group of vertebrates, the amphibians, is represented in the world today by about three thousand species, most of which are frogs and toads. The other members of the class are the salamanders, of which there are about two hundred species, and a group of about seventy-five kinds of limbless amphibians known as caecilians.

In spite of their limited numbers the amphibians played a very important part in vertebrate history. They were the first backboned animals to venture out of the water and up onto land to live. They are believed to have arisen from a crossopterygian fish ancestor as a result of the development of certain structures necessary for terrestrial life, including limbs with five fingers and five toes. They make their appearance in the fossil record in the mid-Paleozoic, which was the Age of Fishes dominated by the lobe-finned types.

Despite the big step that amphibians made in getting out of the water, they could not go far from it. Even today most of our living amphibians must go back to the water to reproduce. Their young, which we know as tadpoles, breathe by means of gills until they reach the age at which they are ready to metamorphose and come out onto land as adults.

The ancient amphibians had one big advantage. Their enemies were probably all water inhabitants. Once a Paleozoic amphibian safely passed its larval stage and climbed out onto dry land, it had little to fear but other amphibians. There were no hungry herons, gulls, hawks, raccoons, otters, mink, or foxes. Neither were there any snakes. Reptiles, birds, and mammals had not yet appeared, so what we now consider the lowly amphibian was then the ruler of the land.

Today we find amphibians on every continent except Antarctica. Some spend most of their lives beneath the ground, while others live on the surface. There are arboreal species that never come down from the treetops. Their eggs are laid in rainwater caught in plant-made cups, and in these lofty ponds the young tadpoles grow. Amphibians are most abundant in the tropics, but there are desert species concentrated around waterholes and springs as well as high-mountain forms that live close to glaciers. Only the sea is devoid of members of this group. As far as we know, no amphibian has ever become adapted to a marine environment.

The caecilians. The relatively few known species of caecilians are found principally in tropical parts of the Americas, Asia, and Africa. Their bodies are adapted to a subterranean life. The eyes are mostly degenerate, the skin is smooth with scales embedded in it, and all trace of limbs has disappeared. These amphibians are wormlike in appearance and range from about seven to twenty inches in length.

Unlike most other members of the class, caecilians do not go to water to reproduce. The eggs of some species actually hatch within the body of the female. The young during the prehatching stage possess gills like other larval amphibians. Very little is known about the life history of the various members of this group. The adults appear to live on animal matter such as insects and worms.

The salamanders. This, too, is a small group, but one that is much more widely distributed than the caecilians. Salamander-like amphibians are found in most parts of the world except Australia, much of Africa, and southern South America. Strange to say, they are also absent from most of Malaysia.

Salamanders have moist skin, four legs, and a tail. The first two of these characteristics distinguish them from the caecilians, and the last one readily separates them from the frogs and toads. While most salamanders are small, the largest amphibians in the world today belong to this group. These are the giant salamanders. One species in Japan attains a length of more than five feet, and another in China has been found to measure nearly three and a half feet. A member of this family occurring in eastern North America is known as the hellbender. It may grow to nearly two and a half feet.

Salamanders are secretive animals that either inhabit dark, moist situations or else live in water. They are, for the most part, nocturnal and therefore seldom seen unless one hunts specially for them. Some of the aquatic species breathe by means of lungs. This requires them to come to the surface for air periodically. Others retain their external larval gills throughout life and even reproduce in this immature form. They are referred to as "neotenic."

Much has been learned in recent years regarding these neotenic species.

Today we know that it is largely a result of lack of iodine in the water in which they live. This lack inhibits the proper functioning of the thyroid gland. The administration of either iodine or thyroxin will induce metamorphosis in the adult. The first intimation of this was noted many years ago when a salamander known as the axolotl, which only occurs in the gilled form in Mexico, was transported to another country. There it changed into a very different-looking adult.

The members of the largest family of salamanders are called plethodonts. They are entirely lungless, respiring through the moist skin and the lining of the mouth. Some plethodonts are found in the water, but many live on land, where they hide beneath fallen logs, humus, or rocks, in the burrows of other animals, and even in holes in trees. Most of them are seen only during the late winter and spring in the North, or during the rainy season in the tropics. The family is largely New World in distribution.

There is at least one plethodont species that climbs trees. This is the arboreal salamander of western North America. Aggregations of several dozen individuals have been found in holes in oaks, and there is a record of one that was found sixty feet above the ground.

Some of the terrestrial species have internal fertilization, and the mothers may guard the eggs, which are laid in a moist, dark situation. There are

The arboreal salamander (*Aneides lugubris*) of western North America is one of the few tailed amphibians that climb trees. R. T. ORR

certain plethodonts that have fairly elaborate courtship dances during which the male stimulates the female by rubbing her with his chin gland.

Most salamanders are essentially defenseless against larger animals. They lack poison glands, body armor, speed in locomotion, and strong teeth. Several species, however, can bite and are capable of breaking the skin of the hand if one is careless in holding them. These include the arboreal salamander and the Pacific giant salamander. I have kept both of these species in captivity. The Pacific giant salamander is most attractive in appearance. Its body, which is about twelve inches in length, is beautifully marbled. Every week or so I fed my captive a large snail, which it grabbed viciously and swallowed with rapidity. This species, incidentally, is peculiar in that it can produce some vocal sounds.

Because of their inability to defend themselves and their propensity for dark places, it is not surprising to find that some species of salamanders have completely adapted themselves to subterranean caves that contain water. Such cave inhabitants lack pigment in the skin and look white or faintly pinkish. Their eyes are usually degenerate, which is only to be expected of an animal living in total darkness.

Unlike most tailed amphibians, the marbled salamander (*Dicamptodon ensatus*) can produce weak "vocal" utterances. R. T. ORR

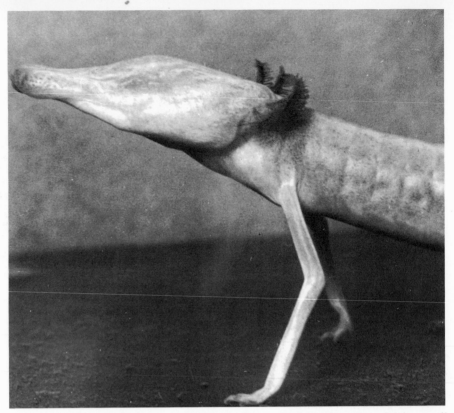

Some salamanders adapted to the total darkness of caves have lost the power of sight as well as their body pigment. The Texas blind salamander (*Typhlomolge rathbuni*) is one of these.
EDWARD S. ROSS

There is an interesting family of salamanders known as the Amphiumidae, in which the limbs have undergone partial degeneration and the body has become eel-like in shape. There are only two species of amphiumas, and they occur in swampy areas in the southern United States. One has two toes on each of its tiny feet and is sometimes called the Congo eel. It is principally eastern in distribution. From Alabama west to Texas it is largely replaced by the three-toed amphiuma. These salamanders are rather long and may reach a length of more than three feet.

The frogs and toads. These are the tailless amphibians; they are more widespread over the world than any other members of the class. They are known as the Salientia or Anura. Representatives range from the Arctic to southern South America and South Africa. They are found in Australia, New Zealand, and on a number of islands in the Pacific. They cannot survive in regions of permanent ice and snow.

Frogs and toads are the most abundant amphibians as regards species,

The skin of the female California newt (*Taricha torosa*) is very rough and dark in the breeding season. R. T. ORR

and populations are often numerous locally. They are well known to most persons, and on spring evenings choruses of these small hoppers frequently create quite a din. The young in the majority of species go through a larval stage in the water. These young, which we commonly call tadpoles, have a tail and external gills but lack legs. Later, during the process of meta-morphosis, they absorb the tail and develop legs, and the gills are replaced by lungs for respiration. When this occurs they are able to come out onto land. However, there are many strange and fascinating variations in the reproductive habits of some of these animals.

There is one group of frogs, known as the leiopelmids, that has very unusual breeding habits. The family is represented by three species in the high mountains of New Zealand and one in the northwestern part of North America. The New Zealand leiopelmids, instead of going to water to deposit their eggs, lay them in moist situations under rocks or logs or in wet tunnels along rivulets. Here the tadpoles emerge from the eggs and grow rapidly without really being emersed in water.

The leiopelmid of the Pacific Northwest is often called the tailed frog. The tail is not a real one, however, but an extension of the cloaca in the

male, which is capable of inserting sperm into the female. The males of
most frogs and toads fertilize the eggs after they are laid by the female.
This usually takes place in quiet water while the two sexes are close together. The tailed frog is a species that breeds in cold, fast-moving mountain streams. The rapid flow of water itself would make external fertilization almost impossible, hence this unique specialization. Tailed frogs are
not particularly common nor easy to find. I looked for this species for years
before finally achieving success on the Olympic Peninsula of Washington.

Another frog that has unusual reproductive habits is the so-called
"Surinam toad." It is not a true toad but belongs to a family of frogs that
lack any tongue and feed largely on refuse found in the water. Although
the family has representatives in Africa, the Surinam toad is a South
American species. Its flat body is shaped and colored like a dry leaf, which
serves as a disguise to fool its enemies. When the breeding season comes
around, the male finds a female whose body he encircles with his front
legs. This appears to assist the female in laying her eggs. The eggs are then
moved by the male to the back of the female. The skin on the female's
back begins to swell and ultimately encases each of the approximately five
dozen eggs in a separate chamber. The young develop and pass their larval
stage in these cradles on their mother's back and then emerge by pushing
up the lid and hopping out into the world.

In North America, Europe, southern Asia, and North Africa there are
members of a family of amphibians known as the spadefoot toads. Their
name is derived from the presence of a hard, bladelike projection on the
side of each hind foot. This blade is used in digging. In western North
America spadefoots occur in desert and prairie regions. They spend considerable time during the year several feet below the surface of the ground
in holes they dig for themselves. It is a rather peculiar sight to watch a
spadefoot that may be facing you slowly sink out of sight as it digs backwards into the ground.

In the arid parts of the West, spadefoots emerge to breed when sufficient
rain has fallen to create small pools or when spring thaws cause floods in
desert valleys. At such times the calls of these little amphibians fill the
night. I was camping in a valley in central Nevada one May when a sudden thaw caused the snow to melt on the adjacent mountains and flood
much of the lowlands. Spadefoots were out in no time, and the males could
be seen floating everywhere in the water as they kept calling to attract
mates. The females are noncroakers.

In desert regions the early stages of development of these spadefoots is exceedingly rapid. The tadpoles are said to hatch about thirty-six hours after the eggs are laid, and they metamorphose into small toads about twelve days later. This is an adaptation to an environment where small pools do not last too long. In winter they go deep underground and hibernate.

There is one family of frogs that has a distribution essentially the same as the pouched mammals—namely, the Leptodactylidae. Leptodactylids are found only in Australia and South America. Some of the New World species are both very large for frogs and also very belligerent. Some of them may weigh several pounds. The most vicious frogs are the South American horned frogs. Their mouths are enormous. This, plus the horns above the eyes, gives them a diabolical look despite their beautiful coloration. We have kept them in the Steinhart Aquarium in San Francisco, where they have been a considerable attraction to visitors, but care has to be exercised in feeding them because of their pugnacious character. In the wild they are said to capture and eat small birds and mammals.

The true toads are among the best-known amphibians and occur in most of the warmer and temperate parts of the world. They are absent, however, from the Australian continent. Toads have rather plump wart-covered bodies and proportionately short legs in contrast with those of most frogs. The warts are really glands that exude a secretion that is obnoxious to most animals. Dogs and cats rarely touch a toad more than once. The largest of these glands are the big, swollen parotoid glands situated just behind the ears. It is said that the poison from the glands of the marine toad that inhabits Central America is sufficiently toxic to kill a dog. This species, however, is considered so beneficial in controlling insects in sugar cane plantations that it has been introduced into other tropical parts of the world where cane is grown.

Toads, in general, are interesting and beneficial animals and should be encouraged about one's garden. We used to have two toads that inhabited drain tile in the patio. Each evening from about May to late September they would come cautiously to the opening in the drain at dusk. If we remained perfectly quiet for some minutes, one would give a faint call and then emerge and hop up a sloping bank toward the garden. Soon the other would follow. They disappeared each year by early October and, we presumed, went into hibernation deep in some hole or burrow.

Toads, like frogs, gather in the spring of the year at ponds and along roadside ditches, where the females lay their eggs and the young tadpoles develop. It frequently happens that the young toads all leave their watery homes at about the same time and appear in hordes upon the land. Such a "plague" should be welcomed, because there are few animals that are more beneficial. But hordes of toads are rarely welcomed. Last summer I read in a local paper of control measures that were being started to eliminate an "outbreak" of toads.

The males and females of most amphibians look very much alike. The Yosemite toad of the Sierra Nevada of California is an exception. The female of this species is very much larger and more brightly colored than the male.

There is one family of frogs that contains a single species, which is found only in southern South America. This species is often called the Chilean frog. The rather amazing thing about it is that the eggs are picked up by the male after the female lays them and are incubated in his vocal pouch. They remain there until the young have metamorphosed into fully formed small frogs.

Equally strange are the nurse frogs of South America, in which the male incubates the eggs and carries the tadpoles on his back. Belonging to the same family is probably the smallest amphibian in the world, the Cuban frog, whose total length is about half an inch. The female of this species lays but a single egg.

The tree frogs, or hylids, are among the best-known amphibians. Most of them are small and possess adhesive disks on the ends of their toes which enable them to cling to the leaves and stems of plants as well as to various vertical surfaces. They also exhibit a remarkable ability to change their color under different environmental conditions. It may surprise anyone who has caught a small green frog and placed it in a covered can to find that upon opening the container the captive is pale tan. This faculty of color change is a protective device that allows the animal to assume a color that blends with its background. It is brought about as a result of the migration of pigment granules in cells called chromatophores.

In North America most hylids, such as the spring peeper, the cricket frog, the Pacific tree frog, and its relatives, lay their eggs in jelly-like masses or strings in ponds, where they adhere to the stems of water plants. In South America certain members of this same family have quite different habits. In one species the female carries her eggs and later the young on her back. In several other species, including the marsupial frog, the female has a pouch on her back in which she carries her eggs until they are incubated. A tree frog in Paraguay glues leaves together in a tree overhanging water and deposits her eggs in this nest. The young, upon hatching, drop into the water below. The smith frog builds a small corral with walls of mud at the water's edge and lays her eggs inside so that they are protected from various enemies in the water outside.

The true frogs, belonging to the family Ranidae, are nearly worldwide in distribution. Included in this group are such well-known species as the bullfrog, the leopard frog, the pickerel frog, the wood frog, and the red-legged frog. Some representative is found in nearly every region where there is permanent fresh water. The true frogs are generally recognized by the slender, moist body, long hind legs, webbed toes, and prominent eardrums.

Frogs have long been regarded with humor, perhaps because of their bulging eyes and method of progression by great leaps. The Greek comedy writer Aristophanes, back in the fourth century B.C., titled one of his plays, a satire against Euripides, "The Frogs." "The Celebrated Jumping Frog

The large adhesive disklike toes enable this South American tree frog to adhere to leaves. Note the ant biting one of its toes. EDWARD S. ROSS

The Pacific tree frog (*Hyla regilla*). R. T. ORR

A female South American marsupial frog (*Gastrotheca*) with eggs in the dermal pouch on her back.
EDWARD S. ROSS

of Calaveras County" is Mark Twain's humorous story about the Gold Rush country of the West in the nineteenth century. In his honor a Jumping Frog Contest is held each year in Calaveras County, California.

The dissection of a frog is a *must* in every elementary biology class the world over. Frogs are used in laboratory experimentation for many different purposes because of their abundance and ready availability. Their legs are eaten and regarded as a delicacy by many. In North America the most important commercial species is the bullfrog, which is native to many areas east of the Rocky Mountains and has been introduced in places in

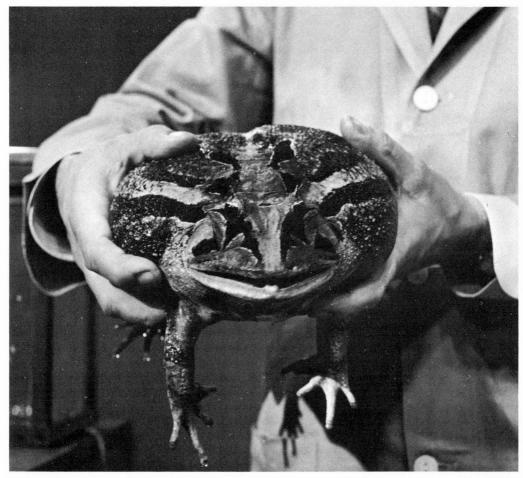

The Brazilian horned frog (*Ceratophrys varia*) is an extremely aggressive amphibian that is capable of feeding on other small vertebrates. Courtesy CALIFORNIA ACADEMY OF SCIENCES

the West. Its legs are nearly as large as those of a chicken. In Europe and Asia there are other large species, which have been relished by gourmets for centuries.

In parts of Asia, Africa, and Madagascar there are members of a family of brightly colored frogs known as the Rhacophoridae. Superficially they closely resemble the tree frogs, and many, like the latter, have large adhesive disks on their toes. However, they are really much more closely related to the true frogs. One member of this family deserves special mention because of the unusual sort of protection it provides for its eggs. This species is sometimes known as the Asiatic tree frog. When the eggs are laid, either in shallow pools or on land during rain, both the male and female beat the mass until it becomes very foamy. This is done with the hind legs. As the foam dries, a hard protective outer crust is formed. The crust keeps enemies from reaching the eggs and maintains air within for the developing young.

THE REPTILES

Reptiles arose from ancient amphibians back in the later Paleozoic era and became the second group of backboned animals to appear on land. Even before the Mesozoic era, which is known as "The Age of Reptiles," they had succeeded their amphibious progenitors in dominance. They ruled the earth, the seas, and the sky for nearly two hundred million years. While this was occurring, birds and mammals branched off, but they did not come into their own until the beginning of the Cenozoic era, by which time the giant reptiles were extinct.

Today but a relatively small number of reptilian forms inhabit the earth. Some, like the turtles, are very ancient. The largest are the alligators and the crocodiles, while the most numerous are the snakes and lizards. Some representatives are found in nearly every part of the world except the polar regions. They occur in the sea, in freshwater lakes and rivers, and on land from desert to mountain top. Many live in trees and some can glide, but no living reptile possesses the power of flight as did the pterosaurs, or flying reptiles, of the Mesozoic era.

Reptiles attained a great advantage over amphibians many millions of years ago by freeing themselves of the need for water in which to deposit their eggs. This was accomplished by developing structures that prevented the desiccation of both the eggs and the young. The reptilian egg, unlike that of amphibians, possesses a hard, relatively impregnable shell much like that of a bird. This offers protection against enemies and dry air.

The South African short-head (*Breviceps adspersus*) is able to inflate its body with air and to secrete a milky poison from glands in the skin for protection against enemies. EDWARD S. ROSS

Within the shell the reptile egg contains a large amount of yolk that serves as food for the future embryo. The embryo itself, which develops from the egg, has a special membrane that surrounds it and encloses a liquid that keeps it from drying. This is known as the amnion. It is also present in birds and mammals. Once these developmental features were acquired, reptiles no longer needed to come to water during the breeding season and could move into many habitats unavailable to their ancestors.

Living reptiles of the world are placed in either four or five orders. They include the turtles, the tuatara, the crocodilians, the lizards, and the snakes. Lizards and snakes are much more closely related to one another than any of the other groups and are sometimes placed in the same order.

The turtles. These are members of the order Chelonia, which is a very old one. It is believed to have branched off from the early stem reptiles back in the late Paleozoic and has changed very little since Mesozoic times.

The words "turtle" and "tortoise" are sources of considerable confusion. Their meaning has changed with time and still varies in different countries. In general, however, "turtle" refers to chelonians that live in or close to water, either fresh or salt. "Tortoises" are terrestrial chelonians, whose habitat is neither aquatic nor marine.

Chelonians are easily recognized as such. They all lack teeth and as a substitute have developed a horny bill not unlike that of a bird. Their bodies are generally somewhat flattened and contained within an upper and a lower shell known, respectively, as a carapace and a plastron. These are joined together on the side of the body. In most species the legs and neck can be drawn in tightly under the shell for protection. Some kinds draw the neck in backward, so that it is folded into an S-shape; others swing the neck sideways and tuck it under the side of the shell.

The shell of a turtle or tortoise is composed of two parts. Externally it usually consists of horny plates that are really scales. These scales are not shed like those of snakes or lizards, but they are subject to wear and must be replaced from beneath. Each new scale is larger than its predecessor. These external scales are often beautifully colored in some kinds of turtles. Underlying the horny scales are plates of bone that are really responsible for the shape of the shell. Parts of the body skeleton, including some of the vertebrae, the ribs, and even bones of the shoulder and pelvis, may be fused to this shell skeleton. Certain chelonians have lost the external horny plates and have only remnants of the bony plates embedded in the skin. This is true of the leatherback sea turtle.

There are freshwater turtles, sea turtles, and those chelonians known as tortoises that are truly terrestrial. A number of families of turtles are restricted to fresh water and several of these are represented by but a single species. One such family, containing only the Central American river turtle, ranges from southern Mexico to Guatemala. Another is restricted to southeastern Asia.

Best known, perhaps, of all freshwater turtles are the various common pond turtles, which are members of a widespread family with representatives on all the continents except Australia and Antarctica. They are most numerous in the Northern Hemisphere.

Most boys in the country catch pond turtles at one time or another and keep them as pets. I used to drill a small hole in the margin of the shell of each of my turtles so I could tie a wire leash on them. Even in cities, turtles are common pets. I have one neighbor who keeps three pond turtles in her garden and another who has had one for twenty-three years.

Members of this group like quiet water where they are not disturbed. During the day they often come out onto partly submerged logs or banks to sun themselves. In late autumn they go to the bottom of ponds and hibernate until spring. Pond turtles, like all chelonians, lay eggs. These are buried in the ground in a sunny situation. The hole in which they are deposited is dug by the female with her hind legs.

Some well-known members of the pond turtle family, in addition to the common pond turtles, are the box turtle and the diamondback terrapin. The latter is regarded as a gastronomic delicacy in some places.

Most freshwater pond turtles are rather omnivorous. They will eat various kinds of vegetation as well as snails and other small aquatic animals. The snapping turtles, members of a strictly New World family, are aggressive carnivores, living on fish, amphibians, other reptiles, and even small birds and mammals.

There are about forty kinds of land tortoises found in widely separated parts of the world. Some are continental, while others are found only on islands. In North America there are three species that are variously found in the southern and southwestern United States and in Mexico. One of these is the desert tortoise, which inhabits burrows and lives on the leaves and flowers of desert plants. It is a strange sight to see a turtle-like creature crossing a highway on a barren desert. Somehow it seems out of place.

The most interesting of the land tortoises are those occurring on various oceanic islands. They are found on the Galapagos Islands in the Pacific, and on the Seychelles Islands and other islands near Madagascar in the Indian Ocean. In the Galapagos, these giant tortoises have evolved into different forms on each of the major islands and were, in part, responsible for influencing Charles Darwin's ideas on evolution during his visit there on the voyage of the *Beagle* in 1835.

Some land tortoises grow to a very large size. There is one record of a captive animal from the Galapagos Islands that attained a weight of about four hundred pounds. The ages of many of these animals have been grossly exaggerated, but it is known that they can live for more than one hundred and fifty years, which is something that few, if any other, vertebrates can boast. Because they are slow-moving and good eating, giant tortoises on islands have suffered greatly by contact with man. Many forms have had their populations reduced almost or actually to the point of extinction.

Man, however, is not always to blame for this reduction. During the Galapagos International Scientific Project in 1964, several members of our expedition were taken by a United States Navy helicopter to the volcanic slopes of Fernandina Island. They hoped to find living examples of a form of giant tortoise known from a single specimen that had been taken by members of the California Academy of Sciences expedition of 1905–1906. After spending many difficult days on the hot, dry, lava-covered island, a few signs were found showing that a giant tortoise had bitten into cactus pads that were four feet above the ground. None of the animals were seen. It was concluded that the entire population of this variety of tortoise consisted of only a very few individuals at most. The presence of pumice in the crotches of trees and fresh lava flows on the slopes of the crater was ample evidence of recent volcanic activity. This was believed to be responsible for the reduction of the tortoises to what may, even now, be the point of extinction.

One of the giant tortoises of the Galapagos Islands, *Testudo elephantopus*. R. T. ORR

The green turtle (*Chelonia*) has long been considered a choice food delicacy. RUSS KINNE

The largest of all chelonians are the sea turtles, which are grouped into two families. One of these contains a single species, the leatherback turtle, which is widely distributed over the tropical seas of the world. The leatherback, the largest of all turtles, may attain a length of seven or eight feet. It derives its name from the fact that the outer horny shell is missing and the underlying plates of bone are embedded in a tough skin. The remainder of the sea turtles, including the famous green turtle that often ends up in a soup bowl, are in the second family.

All of the truly marine turtles have become adapted to life at sea. Their limbs have become flipper-like, and their heads cannot be retracted into the shell. They all must come to land, however, to lay their eggs. These are deposited in holes dug by the females in sandy beaches. When the young hatch out, they must force their way to the surface and crawl down to the sea. This is a time of great danger, because these tiny turtlets are preyed upon by different sea birds. Many survive, however, for marine turtles are not rare.

The tuatara.   Inhabiting a number of islands along the coast of New Zealand is a reptile that looks like a lizard but really is not one. Its native name is the tuatara, and scientifically it is called *Sphenodon punctatum* and placed in a separate order by itself, the Rhynchocephalia.

The tuatara has no close living relatives. It belongs to a very ancient group of reptiles that flourished long before the dinosaurs arose. An interesting feature of this strange animal is the presence of a third eye on the top of the head. This character is shared with some of our modern lizards and was also a peculiarity of many of the ancient amphibians.

Tuataras occurred on the mainland of New Zealand until about one hundred years ago. Today they survive on the offshore islands partly because they take advantage of the protection afforded them in the numerous burrows of a group of sea birds known as shearwaters that nest there and partly because they are protected by the Australian Government. Although I regret to say it, biologists have been one of their principal enemies. Because of their rarity and the fact that they are "living fossils" or relicts of an ancient group of animals, museums, universities, and other centers of scientific learning are always anxious to secure specimens of the tuatara.

The crocodilians.   These are rather well-defined reptiles of large size that inhabit swamps, rivers, lakes, and estuaries in tropical parts of the world. They are classified into three major groups—the alligators, the crocodiles, and the gavials. The caimans, which are broad-snouted crocodilians from South America, are placed in the same family as the alligators.

The crocodile- and alligator-like reptiles have no close relatives living today. They belong to a long extinct, but once exceedingly important, group known as the archosaurs. These were the ruling reptiles of the Mesozoic. They developed into the many dinosaur groups, gave rise to birds, and are now represented by a few species of crocodilians. The ancestors of crocodiles and alligators were bipedal like many of the dinosaurs, but their living descendants have reverted to walking or crawling on all four feet.

Crocodiles and alligators are rather closely related and are even considered by some scientists to belong to the same family. The crocodiles, however, have more slender snouts, upper and lower teeth that are rather closely aligned, and a constriction near the end of the snout resulting from

The male nurse frog (*Phyllobates bicolor*) guards the eggs and then transports the tadpoles on his back. EDWARD S. ROSS

A colorful frog of the genus *Rana* from Malaya. EDWARD S. ROSS

One of the many kinds of true frogs of the family Ranidae inhabiting the Congo forests of Africa. EDWARD S. ROSS

chlegel's pit viper *(Bothrops schlegeli)* is a rehensile-tailed species inhabiting Central merica. JOHN TASHJIAN

he marine iguana *(Amblyrhynchus ristatus)* of the Galapagos Islands is he only lizard known to feed on gae in the sea. R. T. ORR

(Opposite) The collared lizard *(Crotaphytus collaris)* is an inhabitant of the deserts of western North America. JOHN TASHJIAN

Many tropical snakes, like this green pit viper, are arboreal. JOHN TASHJIAN

Flamingos are among the most beautiful birds in the world. Even in captivity they build their nests on pedicels of mud. JOHN TASHJIAN

The regent bowerbird (*Sericulus chrysocephalus*) uses a tuft of leaves to paint the inside of its bower. The "paint" is made of saliva mixed with various pigments. JOHN TASHJIAN

The Australian cassowary (*Casuarius casuarius*). JOHN TASHJIAN

The crowned pigeon (*Goura victoria*) was once sought for its plumes which were used in the millinery trade. JOHN TASHJIAN

The lesser panda (*Ailurus fulgens*) of eastern Asia is related to the raccoons of North America. JOHN TASHJIAN

(*Opposite*) The fulvous lemur (*Lemur fulvus*) of Madagascar exhibits great variation in color. EDWARD S. ROSS

A California sea lion (*Zalophus californianus*) is recognized by his dark body color and the prominent crest on the head. R. T. ORR

The gemsbok is one of the most beautiful of the African antelopes. EDWARD S. ROSS

the presence of a notch on each side into which the large fourth pair of lower teeth fits.

Crocodiles are found in many parts of Africa, southern Asia, the East Indies, South America, and north along the west coast of Mexico to Sinaloa. Although primarily reptiles of fresh water, they are capable of living a marine existence and have arrived at many offshore islands, especially in the Indian Ocean. In western Mexico they inhabit saltwater estuaries.

Many instances have been recorded of these big reptiles attacking man, although their principal food consists of fishes, amphibians, and reptiles, supplemented by birds and mammals. Some species may attain a length of more than twenty feet. Any carnivorous animal this large, and armed with formidable spikelike teeth, is to be feared.

Most Americans are familiar with alligators. They are common in the lakes and swamps of Florida and are often seen on reptile farms and in zoos. They occur in both the New and Old World but are best represented in South America. There are several species there with very broad snouts that are commonly called caimans.

Alligators, unlike crocodiles, have the teeth of the upper jaw overlapping those of the lower jaw. Their skin, like that of the crocodilians, is exceed-

The tuatara (*Sphenodon punctatum*) of New Zealand is not closely related to any other living group of reptiles.
EDWARD S. ROSS

ingly thick on the back and overlies bony plates beneath. Alligators have long been hunted for their skin, which, when tanned, is made into leather handbags and shoes. Young alligators are often sold for pets, although they can inflict a severe bite even when quite small and become a problem as they grow.

All crocodilians lay eggs. The American alligator constructs a nest made of mud, plant material, and various kinds of debris. The eggs are arranged in the bottom of this pile of material in two layers and remain there during the nine- or ten-week incubation period. Sometimes the female guards the nest and even assists the young in emerging when the eggs are hatched.

The gavials are quite different from crocodiles and alligators in a number of respects anatomically. Their most obvious difference lies in their extremely long slender snout. Gavials live on fish. They inhabit the rivers of India and southeastern Asia.

The American alligator (*Alligator mississipiensis*). R. T. ORR

The lizards. All but about 5 percent of the reptiles of the world are lizards and snakes, of which there are about an equal number of species. As regards numbers of individuals, however, lizards are the most numerous. There are few places in warmer parts of the world where lizards of one kind or another cannot be seen in numbers almost daily. Most of them are small, but the giant lizard of Komodo in the East Indies attains a length of ten feet. Lizards, in general, have well-developed legs and often can run with great rapidity, but some species are limbless and superficially look like snakes. About nineteen families of lizard-like reptiles are known.

Geckos are small, relatively soft-scaled lizards that have large eyes and are, for the most part, nocturnal. They are represented in most of the warmer parts of the world. Their remarkable ability to cling to vertical surfaces is made possible by the presence of large pads on their toes equipped with numerous small hooklets. We have watched them come out after dusk in Mexico and gather on walls and ceilings of buildings near lights. They have learned that lights attract insects, and these insects are their food.

Another family of night lizards, ranging from southwestern United States to Central America and Cuba, is known as the Xantusidae. One species is found in the deserts of California, where it lives under fallen yuccas. These bayonette-leaved plants provide the small lizards with considerable protection. It is interesting that members of both these families of night lizards have immovable eyelids that have been fused together and become transparent like those of snakes. The "window," as it may be called, is actually formed from the lower lid.

Although it has no representatives in the Americas, there is a large family of lizards known as the Agamidae that has some very unusual-looking members in Australia, Africa, and southern Asia. One of these is the famous *Draco,* or flying lizard, which occurs in the East Indies. These colorful reptiles have membranes that extend from the front to the hind legs somewhat like those of flying squirrels. Like the latter, they are able to leap from the upper part of a tree and glide to an adjacent one. It is not true flight.

One of the most peculiar agamids is the frilled lizard of Australia, which has a large membranous collar that is usually folded back in pleats around the neck. When needed this collar can suddenly be raised to surprise an enemy so that the lizard may escape. The bearded lizard of Australia makes use of a somewhat similar device for the same purpose.

There is one Australian agamid, known as the moloch, which has gone to even greater extremes in the development of spines than the American horned toads. Molochs are harmless lizards about eight inches in length but so covered by horny protuberances that they present a weird sight.

There are few lizards better known than the chameleons. This, in itself, is rather surprising since the family to which they belong is found almost exclusively in Africa and on the island of Madagascar. Their fame in legend and history comes from their ability to change their color. This is a protective device that tends to produce a body color somewhat like that of the background. A chameleon on a green plant is green, while one on

About half of the eighty known species of chameleons live on the Island of Madagascar. EDWARD S. ROSS

brown leaves is brown. This is a result of the movement of pigment granules within certain cells of the skin under the influence of light. There are other reptiles that can change color the same way. This ability is also shared with certain amphibians and fishes as well as some invertebrates.

Certain chameleons have developed remarkable horns, knobs, shields, and other excrescences on part of the body. Some species look like miniature rhinoceroses or ancient dinosaurs because of the elongation of spines on the head. One of the most amazing things about some chameleons is their ability to extend the tongue out a distance equal to, or greater than, the body in order to capture an insect. This has been recorded many times in motion pictures and demonstrated on television programs relating to natural history.

In the Americas the best-known lizards are members of the iguana family. Outside the New World, iguanas are known only from Madagascar and a few Pacific islands. They correspond to the agamids of Africa, Asia, and Australia, and to the lacertids of Europe.

Among our commonest iguanas are the fence lizards of the genus *Sceloporus*. A number of species occur over North America. Most of them like areas where there are rocks, logs, or fences exposed to the sun. The males often have conspicuous blue patches on the sides of their bellies, which they display to scare away other males from their own territory. Their well-known push-up exercises aid in this.

Fence lizards, like all reptiles, are so-called cold-blooded animals. By this is really meant that they are incapable of producing appreciable body heat and must depend for this on their environment. When they are in the shade, their body temperature approaches that of the surrounding air, but as soon as they go out sunbathing on a rock, it rises rapidly. To prevent being overheated, a lizard must frequently move out of sunlight.

Fence lizards make interesting pets. One can easily capture them by slowly approaching them with a noose made of hair, thread, or fine wire

The three-horned chameleon (*Chamaeleo oweni*) is an inhabitant of African rain forests.
JOHN TASHJIAN

and slipping it over their neck. We kept three fence lizards in our home in a glass aquarium partly filled with sand. They had a peculiar habit of resting one on top of the other during the day. As it grew dark in the evening, each lizard buried itself in the sand and remained there until morning.

There are many iguanid lizards that have adapted themselves to the deserts of the West. Among the better known are the desert iguana, the zebra-tailed lizard, the fringe-toed lizards, and the so-called horned toads. The first two species are able to run across the sand at a very rapid rate. They do this by raising the front part of the body from the ground and using the hind feet only for locomotion. The fringe-toed lizard has scales that extend laterally from the toes, which function like snowshoes.

Horned toads, on the other hand, move quite slowly. Their protection is derived in part from their color, which blends with their background, and partly by the presence of elongated scales, which look like horny protuberances. In this respect they bear some resemblance to the Australian moloch, which is a member of a very different family. A most unusual feature of horned toads is their ability to squirt a drop of blood from the corner of the eyes when they are in danger. It is possible that this might hit an enemy in the eye and momentarily blind it while the lizard escapes.

The horned toad (*Phrynosoma*) is not a toad but a lizard with a flattened body and scales that have become enlarged and hornlike in appearance. EDWARD S. ROSS

Horned toads can quickly bury themselves in sand by moving their very flat bodies rapidly from side to side.

Throughout Mexico and Central America the commonest iguanids are the anoles. These lizards are mostly tree dwellers and often very colorful. Like chameleons, many of them have the ability to change color.

The largest iguana in the United States is the chuckwalla. This is a desert species that lives around large rocky outcrops. It sleeps in rock crevices. When not in hibernation it lives on the leaves and flowers of desert plants.

The largest of all iguanids are members of the genus *Iguana,* which extends from northern Mexico to South America, and several closely related genera including a land and a marine iguana on the Galapagos Islands.

The Galapagos land iguana (*Conolophus pallidus*) of Barrington Island in the Galapagos Archipelago. R. T. ORR

In tropical Mexico one becomes accustomed to seeing large green or mottled orange, brown, and black iguanas on trees in patios and even grazing on lawns. In mangrove swamps and riparian vegetation these giant lizards are commonly seen sunning themselves high up on the exposed limbs of the trees. They are quite wary, however, and will quickly move out of sight if not approached very cautiously. In most places they are highly regarded as items of food.

The marine iguanas of the Galapagos Islands are famed for the fact that they secure their food in the sea, living on algae. They may attain a length of five feet. No other lizards are known to feed in the sea. During my visit to these islands early in 1964 as a participant in the Galapagos International Scientific Project, these strange reptiles were often my only companions while I spent days along the lava-lined shores studying sea lions.

Another very large family of lizards is that to which the skinks belong. They are found on all continents except Antarctica but are most abundant in Africa. Most skinks have cylindrical bodies with relatively short legs. Some species are entirely limbless. The group is largely terrestrial, but they

The stump-tailed skink (*Tiligua rugosa*) is a native of Australia. EDWARD S. ROSS

are not adapted to rapid movement. In fact, a number of species have taken to life underground.

The surface-dwelling species often have the body striped lengthwise. Their tails are frequently short and blunt. There is an Australian species known as the stump-tailed skink, which has the posterior part of the body shaped like the head. One has to look carefully to determine which end is which.

In Europe, parts of Asia, and parts of Africa the lacertid lizards are in a sense the counterparts of the American iguanids. The European fence

The flying lizards (*Draco*) of southeastern Asia and the East Indies have a winglike membrane on each side of the body that enables them to glide when expanded. EDWARD S. ROSS

lizard is of the family Lacertidae, but this family shows none of the many specializations seen in iguanids.

As already mentioned, some species of skinks are limbless. This apodous condition occurs in several other lizard families. One of these is represented by but two species and is limited to coastal sand-dune areas from central California south to northern Baja California. Here they stay underground until nightfall. I have been with collectors who have spent days digging up dunes in search of these reptiles. They have been delighted to capture one or two a day. Members of this family give birth to live young.

The worm lizards, which occur in both the Old and the New World, either have no hind limbs or else are without both pairs of legs. Much of their time is spent underground, where they feed largely on ants and termites.

Worm, or two-legged, lizards (*Bipes*) lack any hind limbs. These subterranean reptiles occur along the west coast of Mexico and Baja California.
JOHN TASHJIAN

One of the famous limbless lizards is erroneously known as the "glass snake." Glass snakes are members of the alligator lizard family and, like most of this group, have the ability to break off their very long tails and confuse their enemies. The enemy will watch the wiggling tail or pounce upon it while the lizard itself escapes and later regenerates a new tail. The slowworms of Europe and Asia are closely related to the glass snakes.

Alligator lizards of western North America are heavy bodied, slow-moving lizards that forage for animal matter over the surface of the ground in forested or brushy country. They have powerful jaws, and one must exert care in handling them.

The largest lizards in the world are the monitors of Australia, Africa, Asia, and the East Indies. Some of these "dragons" may attain a length of ten feet and weigh several hundred pounds. They may live in holes in the

The scheltopusik or glass snake (*Ophisaurus apodus*) of southwestern Asia and southeastern Europe is actually an anguid lizard that has lost all its limbs. JOHN TASHJIAN

ground or in logs; others may inhabit trees. Monitors live on animal matter or carrion. Because of their size they can capture birds and mammals of fair size. In the desert areas of central Australia the aborigines are fond of monitor flesh.

There are quite a few venomous snakes but only two venomous lizards. These are the Gila monster and the Mexican beaded lizard. Both are members of the genus *Heloderma* and occur in the desert areas of the southwestern United States and Mexico. Both are rather sluggish animals, with scales somewhat elevated so that they look like beads. They are variously banded with blackish and pink, white, or yellow. Both are fairly large and stocky for lizards and may reach a length of two feet.

These venomous lizards lack fangs. Their poison glands are in the back of the lower jaw. When biting, they grasp an animal in a bulldog grip and then roll over on their backs so that the poison will run down the grooved back teeth and penetrate the wound. In captivity they are usually very docile and easily kept. A favorite food is an egg broken in a dish. This they will slowly lap up with the tongue.

The snakes.   Snakes, like lizards, are relatively modern reptiles compared to the turtles, the tuatara, and the crocodilians. Nevertheless, they are very specialized. The limbs have disappeared, and only in the boas are tiny vestiges of hind appendages to be found. Since snakes live on animals which they must swallow whole, their jaws have become specially modified. The lower mandibles will separate from one another anteriorly and will essentially detach from the skull posteriorly. I once watched in amazement while a rattlesnake swallowed a jackrabbit whose body had a considerably greater diameter than that of the snake.

Snakes, like lizards, have scales that are continually being produced from beneath. As a result they shed their skin periodically. The old skin is usually shed in one piece, while that of a lizard comes off in fragments.

Snakes progress by crawling. This may be accomplished in several different ways, but most frequently it involves lateral undulatory motion.

The gila monster (*Heloderma suspectum*) shown here and its close relative, the Mexican beaded lizard (*H. horridum*) of western North America, are the only known venomous lizards. R. T. ORR

The scales on the underside of most snakes are very broad and overlap one another from posterior to anterior. The little ridges resulting from this overlap give the snake a sort of grip on the ground.

Many snakes lay eggs, but some species give live birth to their young. One is occasionally surprised to find thirty or forty snakes in a container that held but one the day before.

There are two families of large snakes. One contains the boas and the other the pythons. Both are primitive in that they possess paired lungs and small stumps near the vent that are remnants of former hind legs. In all the higher groups of snakes only the right lung develops, and all external traces of hind limbs are gone. Boas give birth to their young, while the pythons lay eggs.

The boas are primarily snakes of the New World, although a few species are found in Madagascar, Africa, part of Europe, southern Asia, and the South Sea Islands. There are two small boas that occur in California. From Mexico southward the species become larger and more colorful. The largest is the giant anaconda of South America, which is known to attain an extreme length of twenty-nine feet. Anacondas live along rivers in the jungle and prey principally upon mammals when they come to drink.

In parts of Mexico the natives keep boas around their homes and in their gardens to keep down rats and mice. All of the boas kill their prey by constriction. The victim is first grabbed in the mouth of the snake which then rapidly coils about it and crushes it to death. This method of capturing food is also employed by pythons as well as by many colubrids.

There are many tropical boas that live in trees. Some of these are colored just like the vegetation. One of the most beautiful is the emerald tree boa.

Pythons are entirely restricted to the Old World. They are found in tropical parts of Africa, Asia, the East Indies, and Australia. The longest species is the reticulated python of southeastern Asia, which reaches a length of nearly thirty feet.

Pythons feed on rodents, small antelopes of various kinds, pigs, birds, and other fair-sized vertebrates that they can capture. The female lays eggs, which she gathers into a pile and encloses in the coils of her body with her head covering them on top. Though snakes are regarded as cold-blooded animals, they are (because they are living) burning up a certain amount of body fuel, thereby creating some heat. Even a tree in winter produces enough heat to melt the snow about it. The eggs of the python, therefore, may be raised a few degrees above the temperature of the environment at night or in cold weather.

There are a number of families of burrowing snakes. This is not surprising, because it is believed that the typical snake body was developed primarily as an adaptation to subterranean life. This accounts for the loss of limbs, the elongation of the body, and the fusion of the eyelids with their developed transparent windows. When a snake sheds its skin, the dry plates covering the eyes are also shed.

Although the five known families of burrowing snakes show no close relation to one another and are found in many of the warmer parts of the world, they exhibit many similar structural adaptations to life in the ground. Their heads are small, as are their eyes. The eyes may even be concealed and nonfunctional in the blind snakes. The body scales are all very smooth to reduce resistance in moving through sand or soil, and the broad ventral scales are often reduced or sometimes no different from those on the sides and back. The tail is usually short.

Some of these snakes obtain their food, which consists of insects and reptiles, by burrowing through the ground. Others come to the surface at

The New South Wales blind snake (*Typhlops nigrescens*), like other so-called "worm snakes," is a subterranean species. EDWARD S. ROSS

night. One time I was camped with a herpetologist on the San Felipe
Desert of Baja California. Just after dark one evening when we were sitting
around a lantern talking, he made a lunge toward the sand and came up
with an unfortunate burrowing snake that is now catalogued as *Leptoty-
phlops humilis*. This was my first experience with these reptiles.

Most of the common snakes of the world belong to the family Colubri-
dae. It is by far the largest family of serpents, with representatives almost
every place where snakes are to be found.

Many colubrids are associated with water. This is especially true of
snakes of the genus *Natrix*, as well as the garter snakes of the genus *Thamno-*

Garter snakes (*Thamnophis*) are often called water snakes because of their liking for aquatic
situations. EDWARD S. ROSS

phis. Strictly speaking, however, the real water snakes belong to a separate
family that is found from southeastern Asia to the Solomon Islands. The
American garter snakes, which commonly live near streams or ponds, feed
upon small amphibians, fish, and insects. They are capable swimmers,
moving through the water by lateral undulatory motion. Although most
colubrids lay eggs, garter snakes, like racers, give birth to live young.

Eggs and hatching young of the egg-eating snake (*Dasypeltis*). JOHN TASHJIAN

The milk snake and king snakes are well-known, colorful members of the colubrid family. Their bodies are generally banded in shades of yellow, red, or white on a black background. Legend has it that milk snakes suck the udders of cows, but no one has ever witnessed such an event. The king snakes are famous for their ability to prey on other snakes, especially rattlers. They are immune to the venom of the latter and invariably win in a contest. King snakes kill their prey by constriction, like the boas and pythons. This method of killing is employed by a number of kinds of colubrids.

The fastest-moving members of the family are aptly called racers. Some of them can move quite rapidly, although a man can easily outwalk the fastest. They can also climb trees with ease. When captured, most racers will bite their captor viciously, but they are nonvenomous. One time when I was collecting animals near the Colorado River in southern Nevada, I came across a racer that I wanted. The feeling, however, was not mutual, and the snake went up a mesquite tree. Mesquites are very thorny, but this

Vine snakes of the genus *Oxybelis* barely get as far north as southern United States. JOHN TASHJIAN

did not daunt me at the time. I went up too, and finally caught my prize, but by the time I reached the ground again my arms were badly lacerated by the teeth of the snake as well as torn by mesquite thorns.

While most colubrids are harmless, there are some venomous species. The venom generally is rather weak except in the boomslang. A snake of this African species was responsible for the death of one of America's outstanding herpetologists a few years ago. Venomous colubrids differ greatly, in their poison apparatus, from rattlesnakes and other pit vipers. The latter have hollow fangs in the front of the mouth, which are capable of injecting poison into a victim. Venomous colubrids have rear fangs which are not hollow. These fangs are grooved, and the poison flows down these teeth from modified salivary glands in the upper jaw.

Some colubrids are aquatic, many are terrestrial or partly subterranean, a large number are aboreal, and in Malaya there are a few species that are capable of gliding through the air. These are so-called flying snakes, although they are no more able to fly than the flying fish, flying lizards,

One of the largest puff adders (*Bitis*) is the Gaboon viper from the forests of Central Africa.
JOHN TASHJIAN

flying phalangers, or flying squirrels. Gliding is accomplished by flattening their light bodies as they move through the air from tree to tree or bush to bush.

There are several families of very venomous snakes. These contain the cobras, the sea snakes, the true vipers, and the pit vipers. The cobra family, which is known as the Elaphidae, contains such deadly species as the mambas, the Egyptian asp, the death adder, and the coral snakes, as well as the many kinds of cobras and kraits. The great majority of these poisonous snakes occur in southern Asia, Africa, and Australia. There are a few representatives known as coral snakes in the New World. They are found locally from Arizona south to northern Argentina.

The fangs of cobras and their relatives are situated in the front of the upper jaw. Unlike those of pit vipers, the jaws are not hinged, and therefore cannot be folded back when not in use.

Cobras have achieved fame for these reasons among others: (1) Snake charmers in India and the Far East use them in their shows. (2) They have the remarkable ability to extend the sides of the body behind the head so that it forms a sort of hood. This is accomplished by lateral extension of riblike structures in this region. (3) The death fight between the cobra and the mongoose described by Kipling has been reenacted many times and recorded on film. (4) Cobras take a large toll in human life in Asia. It is estimated that ten thousand persons die each year as a result of bites by these reptiles.

For the most part cobras are not aggressive, but they live in countries where the human population is very high and where the cobras are afforded protection by religious custom. Furthermore, they are nocturnal and bite usually when stepped upon by barefoot natives. Some of the largest of the cobras reach a length of nearly fourteen feet.

There is an entire family of serpents that have adapted themselves to life in the ocean. They must, of course, breathe air, so they must live close to or on the surface. Some come into sea caves to breed, but others bear their young alive in the open ocean.

Sea snakes occur in the eastern Pacific, but they are most abundant along the coasts of Australia and eastern Asia. They are not aggressive reptiles, yet their bite is regarded as more deadly than that of a cobra. It must be remembered that snakes have developed venom glands, not for the purpose of killing human beings, but to enable them to secure food. Sea snakes live on fish, and many of the fish when bitten might escape or swim into the protection of coral or rock crevices if they did not succumb quickly to this toxin.

The true vipers are entirely restricted to the Old World, while the pit vipers are essentially New World inhabitants except for a few genera that get into Asia and one genus that reaches northeastern Europe. Both true vipers and pit vipers have hollow fangs of similar structure, situated in the front of the upper jaw, like those of the cobra family, but differing in that they are hinged and can be folded backward when not in use.

The pit vipers differ from the true vipers by the presence of special sensory pits on each side of the head below a line running from the eye to the nostril. Although the presence of the pits was known for generations, their function was not discovered until 1937. Now we know that they serve to detect heat and are properly called radiation organs. A pit viper in total darkness or with its eyes covered can accurately locate and strike a warm object. This has been demonstrated in the laboratory. Under natural conditions these sensory organs enable the snake to locate small mammals, which constitute its principal food, at night. These pits also enable the snake to strike at enemies when it is molting and temporarily blind, since the skin covering the eyes is shed.

The rattlesnakes, the copperhead, and the water moccasin are the major North American members of this family. There are many more species in Central and South America, where the most deadly are the fer-de-lance and the bushmaster. Rattlesnakes derive their name from the presence of rattles on the end of the tail. These rattles are derivatives of the skin; a new rattle is added each time a rattler molts. They give no specific information on the age of the snake, nor do they accurately indicate the number of times it has molted, since rattles are often lost.

Rattlers use the rattles as a warning and will rarely attack except when alarmed during the molt. They are really very beneficial in controlling

The western diamondback rattlesnake (*Crotalus atrox*) is one of the largest of the New World pit vipers. R. T. ORR

rodents, on which they largely live. Their prey is bitten and then allowed to die before being swallowed. I have surprised my zoology students on field trips by finding a rattlesnake, demonstrating some of its characteristics, then releasing it unharmed to continue on its way.

BIRDS

Birds and mammals share two major features in common. They are the most recent groups of backboned animals to have developed in the world, and both are basically warm-blooded in contrast to the rest of the animal kingdom. Birds, like mammals, developed from the same reptilian ancestors that gave rise to the dinosaurs. The oldest bird known is *Archaeopteryx,* whose fossil remains were found embedded in slate in Bavaria many years ago. This bird, which was contemporary with the larger dinosaurs more than one hundred and fifty million years ago, had true feathers but differed in many respects from birds as we know them today. It possessed rows of teeth in each jaw and had a long lizard-like tail on which there were feathers. The wings possessed claws and were probably used primarily for gliding.

From these reptile-like ancestors arose a great variety of feathered animals. Because of their powers of flight, birds have become widely distributed over the world. There are about eight thousand five hundred living species.

All birds possess feathers, which cover most parts of the body. These soft and often beautifully colored structures serve many purposes, but they are most important in conserving body heat. All the lower forms of life have body temperatures that vary with the temperature of the environment. A fish or a snail living in a lake where the temperature is 60° Fahrenheit will have a body temperature that is approximately the same as that of the water. A lizard may sit in the sun and raise its temperature to 100° Fahrenheit and then move into the shade where it is 70° Fahrenheit. As soon as it leaves the sunny place, it begins to cool off, and if it stays in the shade a little while it will have a body temperature approximately that of the air around it.

Birds and mammals, unlike these lower organisms, tend to maintain constantly high temperatures. In fact, the temperature of most birds is higher than that of most animals. To maintain body heat means high metabolic activity. More fuel, therefore, in the form of food is needed, as well as more oxygen for combustion. Much of the bird's day is spent in searching for food. The food is rarely stored before being eaten. Later it may be stored as fat in various parts of the body to be utilized when needed.

The thick outer covering of feathers on a bird's body is filled with numerous pockets of still air, which act as insulation to prevent heat loss. Feathers function for birds much as clothes do for us. In cold weather we usually put on more clothing so as to have a thick layer of insulation. Birds accomplish this merely by raising the feathers and fluffing them out. In warm weather they tend to draw the feathers tightly across the body so as to reduce the layer of insulation.

Feathers, of course, serve many other purposes, one of the most important of which is flight. Some of the most primitive birds, however, are unable to fly. It is not that their ancestors were always flightless, but rather that they have secondarily lost this power.

The ostrich is a good example of such a species. Hummingbirds, on the other hand, have the most remarkable powers of flight. They not only can fly with considerable speed forward, but also are able to hover, dive, and even fly backward. It has been found that some of these diminutive birds beat their wings more than fifty times per second.

Another interesting avian character is the possession of a horny bill. The bill of a bird in many ways reflects its habits. For example, a thick conical bill, such as is characteristic of finches, usually indicates a seed-eater; a slender tubular bill, like that of a hummingbird, is a sign of a nectar-eater; and a sharply hooked bill, such as the eagle possesses, indicates a flesh-eater.

The living birds are divided into twenty-seven orders. The majority of these orders have one or more well-known representatives.

The penguins. These strange birds are primarily antarctic in distribution. Because of their upright posture and black-and-white coloration, which gives them the appearance of a man in formal attire, they have been subjects of caricature as well as symbols of various commercial products. There are several species that occur outside of antarctic and subantarctic regions. Three of these are rather closely related: the jackass penguin of South Africa; the Humboldt penguin, which is principally found along the west coast of southern South America; and the Galapagos penguin, which inhabits the islands of the same name off the Ecuadorian coast. The latter species occurs on the equator, but the Galapagos shores are far from tropical because of the cooling effect of the northwardly flowing current that comes up from the antarctic along the west coast of South America.

Penguins, like some of the other large land birds, have lost the power of flight. Their wings, unlike those of any other birds, have developed into flipper-like structures, which are used in swimming. There are a number of

The king penguin (*Aptenodytes patagonicus*) of the Arctic is the second largest of all penguins.
Courtesy SAN FRANCISCO ZOOLOGICAL SOCIETY

diving birds that use their wings for propulsion under water, but none can even closely approach the efficiency and speed that penguins have developed in this respect. This, of course, is essential because most of their traveling is in the water. They cannot fly, and walking is a slow process for these short-legged birds. Under some circumstances, however, they can make fairly good speed on ice by propelling themselves along in a toboggan-like manner on their bellies.

The largest of the penguins is the emperor, which attains a height of about four feet. The smallest is the little blue of New Zealand and southern Australia, which is not much more than a foot in height. It has bluish-gray feathers in its upper parts, rather than the black characteristic of most of the other species.

The feathers of penguins are very dense and close together. Furthermore, these birds have a relatively thick layer of fat beneath the skin. These two features serve to keep out the antarctic cold and to conserve warmth produced within the body.

Penguins obtain all their food from the sea. Their great speed and agility under water enables them to secure fish and squid with ease. In the south polar seas, myriads of tiny crustaceans called krill provide them with food.

One or two eggs are laid by the females, the number depending upon the species. Two kinds nest in burrows, and a few make simple nests of pebbles, mud, or vegetation. The two largest penguins, the king and the emperor, differ from all the others in nesting habits. No nest is constructed. Instead, the single egg is placed on top of the feet and then covered above by the belly for protection against temperatures that may go far below zero. The young are fed regurgitated food.

The ostriches, rheas, cassowaries, and emus. These large flightless birds were once thought to be related to one another. For this reason the term ratite was applied to them collectively, because of their simplified breastbone. Ratite is a word derived from the Latin *ratis,* meaning a raft; in other

The Humboldt penguin (*Spheniscus humboldti*) occurs along the coast of South America. R. T. ORR

words, flat-bottomed. In birds that fly we find that there is a deep keel, or carina, on the breastbone for the attachment of flight muscles. Flightless birds have no keel to the breastbone. (This is the structure that divides the breast of a chicken into right and left halves.) The birds with a carina are called carinate.

Although we often use the term ratite for these flightless avian giants, it is now believed that they are not closely related to one another but have evolved independently in widely separated parts of the world and represent distinct orders.

There is only one living species of ostrich, and it is presently restricted to Africa. Here it inhabits relatively arid, open regions, where enemies may be detected at a distance. Until very recently a few of these birds were found in the desert areas of southwestern Asia, but this population is said to have been exterminated during World War II.

Although the ostrich is truly the largest living bird in the world today, it was once exceeded in size by the great moas of New Zealand, the largest of which attained a height of thirteen feet, and by the elephant birds of that island. The moas and elephant birds became extinct six or seven hundred years ago, so the ostrich, whose maximum height may reach eight feet, now holds the record.

Ostriches have been domesticated by man for generations, and even used as work animals. They are best known, perhaps, for their plumes, which have been used as articles of feminine decoration. These plumes, which are possessed only by the males, are the wing and tail feathers. They are purely decorative.

There are many stories written about ostriches, but the best-known trait attributed to these birds concerns their habit of hiding the head in the sand when alarmed. This is far from true, as they are formidable fighters if cornered, using their almost hooflike feet as weapons. However, their principal means of escaping enemies lies in their ability to run very rapidly.

The rheas are the South American counterparts of the ostriches of Africa. Like the latter, the rheas inhabit open country, including the pampas of Brazil and Argentina and the eastern foothills of the Andes. Rheas travel in groups consisting of a male and several females. The male is a good father. He not only incubates the eggs, which the females deposit in a common nest, but also cares for the young for some weeks after they hatch.

Cassowaries, unlike ostriches and emus, are forest dwellers. They inhabit the dense jungles of New Guinea and northern Australia. The top of the head is adorned with a large horny protuberance referred to as a casque, and the skin of the head and neck is colored somewhat like that of a turkey, with red and blue predominating. As is true of most ratite birds, the male is an excellent father. The incubation of the dark green eggs, which superficially resemble avocados, is his duty. Both the male and the female care for the young. The latter have light and dark stripes extending the length of the body, which effectively serve to camouflage them from their enemies. The adults are fierce adversaries in a fight, making use of their powerful feet, which are armed with sharp nails.

Emus are strictly Australian at present, although they formerly occurred on several adjacent islands including Tasmania. Like the ostriches and rheas, they are inhabitants of open, semiarid country, where they travel in small flocks. In size they are exceeded only by the ostrich. Males may

The emu (*Dromiceius novae-hollandiae*) of Australia is exceeded in body size only by the ostrich among modern birds. R. T. ORR

attain a height of six feet and weigh up to one hundred and twenty pounds. In former times emus were sought after for their meat, which is said to be fairly good eating although a bit tough. In recent years efforts have been made to control emus in agricultural areas because of damage they are said to do in various crops.

The kiwis. These strange flightless birds are considered to be very primitive. They are confined to New Zealand, where several species occur. Kiwis are about the size of domestic fowl but have hairlike feathers and a long tubular bill with nostrils at the tip. The latter feature is unique among birds. Being flightless, kiwis necessarily are ground dwellers. They live in rather dense, damp forests and are nocturnal. Their nests are situated in burrows. The egg of a kiwi is remarkably large, being about five inches in length.

The tinamous. From southern Mexico south throughout most of South America there is a group of ground-dwelling, dull-colored, brown or gray, fowl-like birds whose relationship is rather obscure. These are the tinamous. In some respects they resemble the ratites, but they have a well-developed keel on the breastbone and are capable of grouselike flight.

Tinamous are shy birds and are protectively colored. They are highly sought after for food, since they make excellent eating. Some live in dense jungle, while others are adapted to open grassland. All are ground-nesting. There is great variation in the color of the shiny eggs, which range from blackish to yellow, green, or blue in different species.

The loons. The name of these birds is much better known than are the birds themselves. To observe loons, one must live for a while along a sea-coast in the Northern Hemisphere or spend a summer in the far north, where these birds nest on the shores of lonely lakes.

There are only four species of loons. Each is primarily arctic or subarctic in distribution during the nesting season. The yellow-billed loon tends to stay in the far north all year round, but the other three species—the arctic, the red-throated, and the common loons—all come south along the shores of the Atlantic and Pacific oceans.

In winter all four species of loons are very drab in appearance, being grayish above and whitish below. In breeding-plumage they become strikingly colored. The common, arctic, and yellow-billed loons are boldly barred or dotted in patterns of black and white on the back at this season. The red-throated loon is not so conspicuously marked, but it does have a reddish throat and its spearlike bill is more upturned than that of the other three.

Loons are powerful flyers, but they are most noted for their diving ability. When alarmed they can go beneath the surface of the water so rapidly that the eye cannot follow them. Under water they swim with considerable speed by means of their webbed feet.

The legs of these birds are situated far back on the body. In fact they are so far back that a loon is unable to walk any distance on land. If one is forced into such a situation, it will raise its body upright, take a few steps, then fall on its breast, only to repeat this process again and again until it reaches water, where it is at home. Much of the leg of a loon is actually encased in the body.

In the spring of the year great flights of loons moving northward may be observed from suitable vantage points along the coasts of North America and Europe. At such times the birds form lines and follow one behind another.

Loons nest on small islands or along isolated shores of northern lakes. The young are heavily covered with down and are capable of swimming immediately after hatching. This enables them to escape land predators, but many of them fall prey to large freshwater fish.

The grebes. These birds are also divers like the loons, but the two groups are not closely related. Grebes are relatively poor flyers, and only a few species undergo any extensive migratory movements. Although they are excellent swimmers under water, their toes are not connected with one another by webbing as in ducks and loons. Instead, each toe possesses a series of compressed, scalloped lobes similar to those found in coots. These lobes perform the same function in swimming as webs do in certain other kinds of water birds. Their legs, like those of loons, are situated far back on the body and are not suited for walking much on land.

Grebes are rather widely distributed over the world, being found on lakes and rivers and along the coasts of major continents. Their nests are made of aquatic vegetation; they float in the water, usually close to shore, where they are anchored to reeds that hide them. The young are able to swim after hatching, but, like young mergansers, they spend much time riding on the backs of their parents.

Some grebes are restricted to freshwater lakes, while others are equally at home on either salt or fresh water. Their food consists primarily of fish. Perhaps as a means of protecting the digestive system from being pierced by the bones of the animals on which they feed, grebes have developed the habit of consuming feathers removed from their own bodies. Their feathers are very soft and dense and are swallowed in quantity, even by the young.

An arctic loon (*Gavia arctica*) on its nest. JOHN KORANDA

Another interesting feature of these birds is their ability to eliminate air from their bodies and gradually sink in the water until only the upper part of the head is above the surface. Loons and anhingas are also capable of this submarine-like submersion.

The tube-nosed birds. These are the true birds of the ocean—the albatrosses, fulmars, shearwaters, and petrels. They are strictly marine species that come to land only to rear their young.

These birds exhibit great diversity in size. The wandering albatross of the oceans of the Southern Hemisphere has a maximum wingspread of more than ten feet, and shares with the two American condors the honor of being the largest of flying birds. By way of contrast, some of the small storm petrels are no bigger than a swallow.

Most members of the group have proportionately long, slender wings that are adapted to gliding above the surface of the ocean. The updraft that provides them with the necessary lift is thought to result in part from air compression caused by the ocean waves.

Another outstanding character of these birds pertains to the nostrils, which are in the form of tubes, either on the sides or on the top of the bill. Because of these peculiar tubelike nostrils, this group used to be called the Tubinares. These nostrils not only serve for the intake and outlet of air but are also connected with salt-secreting glands situated on the top of the skull above each eye. For many years no adequate explanation was found to account for the ability of these sea birds to survive the dehydrating effect of salt water, which is the only kind that is available to them. Recent studies, however, indicate that these glands on the head can start removing salt from the system within a few moments after ingestion. The concentrated salt exudate passes down a duct to each nostril and drips out rapidly, thereby eliminating the need for fresh water.

Albatrosses are principally birds of the Southern Hemisphere, where they are most abundant in the roughest seas. It is there that the wind is strongest, and, since these birds are gliders, the air currents are essential for their flight. Their presence is also associated with an abundance of plankton in the water. They are well known to sailors because of their habit of following ships for days at a time, and to kill or injure one is considered an ill omen.

The name "gooney" or "gooney bird" is often applied to albatrosses. This may be a result of their lack of fear of man or may have originated from the peculiar nuptial dances that the males and females participate in at the beginning of the nesting season.

Like other members of the order, albatrosses nest on islands—usually oceanic islands, where the birds aggregate in great numbers. Recently the United States Navy had considerable difficulty with albatrosses on Midway Island in the Pacific area. Large numbers of these big birds are a hazard to planes, but it is difficult to get them to change their habits just because man decides to build an airfield in the midst of their nesting ground. One solution to the Midway dilemma was to change the conformation of the surface of part of the island near the runway so that the updrafts, on which albatrosses depend for gliding, were eliminated. This caused them to desert that particular area.

The nests of albatrosses may be either depressions in the ground or mounds that the birds construct. Shearwaters and petrels do not nest in the open like their larger relatives but lay their eggs in burrows or sometimes under rocks, and at this time they become largely nocturnal. By carrying on their activities at night, they avoid conflict with such predatory birds as gulls and skuas.

Most shearwaters nest in the Southern Hemisphere, but many migrate to northern seas after the breeding season. One of the most amazing migrations is that of the slender-billed shearwaters, which breed off southern Australia and Tasmania. There they are known as "mutton birds," and the young are used for food. Following the breeding season in February or early March, the adults migrate eastward to the vicinity of some of the South Pacific Islands, then veer to the northwest so as to pass along the Asiatic coast. By midyear they are in the North Pacific, where they move eastward to Alaskan waters and then south along the Pacific coast of North America. By August they may sometimes be observed by the millions as they move south along the California coast, often within a mile of shore. From southern California or northern Mexico they fly diagonally to the southwest so as to cross the Pacific and arrive back at the nesting area by early November.

Storm petrels, commonly known to sailors as "Mother Carey's chickens," are more widely distributed over the world during the nesting season than any other group of tube-nosed birds. There are nearly two dozen species of these small oceanic birds. In the Southern Hemisphere, ranging all the way down to the antarctic, there is another limited group of petrels, known as the diving petrels. These birds differ from others in the order by having relatively short wings that are capable of rapid movement. Under water they are proficient swimmers, and it is here, rather than from the surface, that they secure their food.

The pelicans and their relatives. These are moderately large birds with proportionately long bills. They are strictly aquatic and largely marine in occurrence. Most of them have a large, unfeathered throat pouch, such as we are familiar with in the pelicans. The principal members of this group in addition to the pelicans are the cormorants, anhingas, frigate birds, gannets, boobies, and tropic birds. One or more representatives of this order are to be found in most parts of the world.

In North America the white pelican nests principally on the shores of rather alkaline inland lakes. Brown pelicans are coastal in occurrence and frequent offshore rocks and islands in the nesting season. Anyone who has watched these birds feed is impressed both with their apparent clumsiness and with their actual skill. Alternately flapping and gliding in a manner that seems barely sufficient to keep them aloft, they sail a few feet above the water just beyond where the waves break. When a fish is spotted below, the pelican drops into the water with a great splash, but it usually makes a successful capture despite its seeming awkwardness.

Pelicans are generally gregarious birds. They nest in colonies, and even during the nonbreeding season they are most often seen flying in orderly lines.

Cormorants, like pelicans, occur in freshwater lakes as well as along the coast, but the majority of species are marine. Coastal species nest on cliffs or ledges along shore or else on offshore islands. They are quite colonial and may occur in very large aggregations. The well-known guano islands along the Peruvian coast of South America owe their fame to the guano produced by the vast numbers of cormorants, locally known as guanays.

In the Orient there is an age-old custom of training cormorants to fish. Tame birds have rings or collars temporarily placed around their necks to prevent them from swallowing any large object. During the fishing operation the birds are released so that they may dive for fish. When the fish is secured the bird returns to the boat with its catch, which it cannot swallow and which is removed from its bill by the owner.

Most interesting relatives of the cormorants are the anhingas, which are also known as snake birds or water turkeys. Anhingas occur in warmer parts of the Americas, southern Asia, Africa, the East Indies, and Australia, where they are found along rivers, around lakes, and in swamps. They resemble cormorants but have much more slender heads and necks, which give them a snakelike appearance.

I associate these birds with the bayous of Louisiana and the mangrove-lined esteros and lower river systems of tropical Mexico. By moving along quietly in a dugout canoe, I have occasionally approached them closely as they were sunning themselves with outstretched wings on stumps or branches. Suddenly, when they became aware of me, they just dropped into the water and submerged with remarkable speed and without so much as a dive.

Unlike cormorants, anhingas have the habit of soaring in great circles quite high in the air. When indulging in such flight, they will flap for a few moments, then glide for some distance before flapping again.

The frigate, or man-of-war, birds are among the most striking birds of the ocean. They are restricted to tropical or semitropical waters. They usually remain within sight of land but are not limited to coastal waters. Frigate birds also occur about oceanic islands in the Pacific, Atlantic, and Indian oceans. They are very inept on land but in the air can seemingly soar almost indefinitely on their long slender wings without a perceptible flap.

Frigate birds nest on islands. During the courtship period the male inflates its huge reddish throat pouch until it looks like a balloon. Perhaps this serves to attract a mate.

A young brown pelican (*Pelecanus occidentalis*) on a rocky, cactus-covered islet in the Gulf of California. GEORGE E. LINDSAY

Boobies are often found with frigate birds. Like them, they are inhabitants of tropical or semitropical seas, where they nest on remote coastal islands. Their feet and bills show much variety in color and have been responsible for the common names of some of the species—such as the blue-footed, the red-footed, and the blue-faced booby.

Very closely related to the boobies are the gannets, large sea birds that inhabit the colder waters of the north and south temperate zones. Gannets nest in great colonies on cliffs. Some of the most famous nesting colonies in North America are on Bonaventure and Bird islands in the Gulf of St. Lawrence.

The most aberrant members of this order are the tropic birds, which, as their name implies, are restricted essentially to tropical seas. These trim birds, whose plumage is patterned principally in black and white, possess two elongate, slender tail feathers that may be white or red, depending on the species. They are poor swimmers and, like the frigate birds, usually stay within sight of land. Their food consists of fish, which they secure by diving from the air in a ternlike manner.

The heron-like birds. There are more than one hundred kinds of birds belonging to this order. As a group they are very widely distributed over the world, and many species are quite well known. In addition to the

The red-footed booby (*Sula sula*) is a species of the tropical seas of the world. R. T. ORR

herons, the order includes the bitterns, storks, ibises, spoonbills, and flamingos.

Practically all these birds have long legs and necks, and all are associated with water. In or along the water they secure most of their food, which consists principally of small fish, frogs, crayfish and other crustaceans, mollusks, insects, small reptiles, and even small mammals. The flamingos are the only members of the group that eat smaller organisms; these they obtain by straining mud and water through their bills, which have sievelike laminations on each edge.

Most of the heron-like birds are of medium or large size, and many are quite brilliantly colored. Some of the most beautiful of the herons are the egrets, whose pure white plumes were so avidly sought after for hat decorations in the nineteenth century that the birds were brought close to extinction. Other herons are various shades of blue-gray, green, or reddish.

Shades of pink or red are found in the spoonbill, the scarlet ibis, and the flamingos. It is difficult to appreciate the vivid colors of these birds unless they are actually seen. Any written description gives the impression of exaggeration.

My first experience with spoonbills was along the mangrove-lined waterways of Nayarit in western Mexico, where I was conducting a university class on jungle life one winter. The area was extremely rich in heron-like birds. Almost daily we encountered as many as eleven species of herons, including the rare boatbill, and three kinds of ibises. We searched continually, however, for spoonbills. Finally, early in the morning on our last day we saw a flock of these beautiful, pink-tinted birds with long spatulate bills flying overhead. Shortly afterward, as we came around a bend in an estero, we found ourselves within one hundred feet of a spoonbill that was perched among a group of white ibises and egrets. The color combination was so stunning that we forgot about our cameras until it was too late to use them.

The herons have long, straight bills that make good fishing spears. This is also true of the storks, but their bills tend to be thicker and, in some species like the shoe-billed and maribou storks, are very large. Ibises have long curved bills that are proportionately rather slender in contrast to those of herons and storks. Flamingos have relatively short, bent bills, which, in certain respects, are ducklike with their marginal strainers. Flamingos, because of their long legs and extremely long necks terminating in a bent bill, use the bill in an upside-down position. Most of us will re-

(Above) Young egrets not yet ready to fly. CECIL TOSE

(Left) The common egret (*Casmerodius alba*) was once almost exterminated for its plumes. R. T. ORR

member that this was the way they held their heads in the croquet game in *Alice's Adventures in Wonderland.*

The waterfowl. For all practical purposes one can divide the majority of the waterfowl into three major categories—the swans, the geese, and the ducks. The swans are the largest of the group from the standpoint of size, but smallest as far as number of species is concerned. Seven different kinds are known. Five of these occur either in the northern parts of Europe, Asia, or North America. The black swan is native to Australia and Tasmania, and the black-necked swan inhabits southern South America.

Swans, because of their grace and beauty, have been domesticated for centuries. The commonest species in parks over much of the world is the

The white ibis (*Guara alba*) with its red face is a familiar sight along waterways in tropical America. R. T. ORR

mute swan, which is native to Europe. These large white birds with knobs on their bills are well known to most persons. Almost equally widespread, but under domestication for a much shorter time, is the black swan.

Because of their size and the edible quality of their flesh, swans have long been pursued by hunters. The result has been a great reduction of these birds in the wild, and in some instances almost complete extinction. The trumpeter swan of North America was reduced to a population numbering but a few individuals not many years ago. Rigid protection, however, has seen the species make a steady comeback. Today summer visitors may observe nesting trumpeter swans under natural conditions at Jackson Hole in Wyoming, Yellowstone National Park, and other places in western United States and Canada.

Geese and ducks undoubtedly are our most important game birds. In the United States millions of dollars are expended annually by hunters in equipment, travel, and gun clubs to enable them to participate in water-fowl shooting. Ducks are more numerous, but geese because of their size are the choicest reward for the hunter.

Geese differ from ducks in a number of technical ways, but they are most readily recognized by their larger size, longer legs, and longer necks. There are about twice as many species of geese as swans, and they are more widely distributed than the swans.

Geese, like most waterfowl, are flocking birds except during the mating season. The southward flights of great flocks of geese flying in formation is a familiar sight in parts of western North America in the autumn. Frequently they are heard calling at night as they pass overhead in migration.

The largest and most beautiful of these birds in North America is the honker, or Canada goose. It is recognized by its black neck and head with a white band extending from one side of the head, back of the eye, down under the chin and up the other side. Larger forms of this bird may weigh up to fourteen pounds.

Some geese, like the Hawaiian goose or nene, are sedentary, while others have remarkable migratory habits. One of the most amazing migrations is made by the blue goose. This species nests in Baffin Land and winters in the marshes of Louisiana. Its migration is believed to be made with but a single stop en route.

Various kinds of ducks are found from the Arctic to the tropics. They are abundant wherever there is water, but they do not go far to sea. The total duck population has been greatly reduced by man, partly by hunting but mostly by changing the land in various ways. The draining of potholes

The Canada goose (*Branta canadensis*) is one of the finest game birds in America.
JAMES MOFFITT

and marshes and the pollution of streams, rivers, and lakes are among the factors that have adversely affected these birds. However, one can still see fairly large numbers of certain species in many parts of the world.

Man's association with these smaller members of the waterfowl group goes far back beyond recorded history. No doubt the caveman was dependent in part on many kinds of waterfowl for food. And the domestication of certain species goes back so far that one cannot state with surety when it began.

The majority of common wild ducks are generally classified as either surface or diving ducks. The former would include such common species as the mallard and pintail. These birds do not dive for their food but have the habit of tipping over so that the head may reach a foot or so below the surface while the rear end of the body and the tail are directed vertically. Their principal food is aquatic vegetation.

By way of contrast, the diving ducks secure their food under water, often at considerable depths, as a result of diving. The pochard, canvasback, and goldeneye are good examples of this group. Many of them occur in salt water during the winter season.

There are, of course, a number of other groups of ducks—such as the tree ducks, a peculiar group showing some affinities with the geese; the mergansers, or fish ducks, characterized by long, slender "toothed" bills; the wood ducks, whose beauty is difficult to exceed; and the various kinds of sea ducks.

The vultures, eagles, hawks, and their relatives. These are the carrion eaters and diurnal birds of prey. Their food consists of animal matter, which, with the exception of the vultures, they capture alive with their powerful talons and strong hooked bills. All have a fleshy base to the bill in which the nostrils open.

Vultures live on carrion. Though their food habits are repulsive to us, they perform a very important service as nature's scavengers. The New World vultures include the two largest flying land birds in the world—the Andean condor and the California condor. Both are reported to have a maximum wingspread of slightly more than ten feet, a distinction held by

The turkey vulture (*Cathartes aura*) with its black plumage and red head is well known to most persons in North America. Courtesy CALIFOR-NIA ACADEMY OF SCIENCES

the wandering albatross among sea birds. In North America the turkey vulture is the best-known species. These large blackish birds with naked red heads are frequently seen soaring in great circles in the sky in search of food. Their vision, like that of all members of this group, is extremely keen and responsible for their finding the carrion on which they feed.

From southern United States south, the black vulture is one of the common birds of towns, villages, and even cities. It is a familiar sight to see groups of these birds on houses, utility poles, or other suitable perches.

The Old World vultures, which are so abundant in Africa and southern Asia, are not closely related to the vultures of the Americas. In fact, they are much closer to the eagles and hawks. They resemble their New World counterparts, however, in having mostly naked heads, relatively dull claws for a bird of prey, and a dependence on dead animals for food. In lion country in Africa, flocks of vultures of several kinds seem invariably to be waiting for the carcasses of zebras, antelopes, and other big game left by the large cats.

With the exception of the secretary bird, a strange long-legged ground hawk of Africa, whose food consists principally of snakes, small mammals, and insects, the rest of the members of this order, which is known as the Falconiformes, are divided into three families. One of these contains a single species—the osprey, or fish hawk.

Ospreys are found wherever there are large bodies of water or rivers. To me they seem equally at home along the shores of high mountain lakes and on the shores of desert islands in the Gulf of California. Their food consists primarily of fish, which they catch by plunging downward, often from a considerable height, into the water below. Along the northwest Pacific coast it is not uncommon to see a bald eagle pursuing an osprey and forcing it to drop its catch. This the eagle usually grasps before it hits the ground or water below.

The largest of the true hawks are the eagles, of which there are a number of species in different parts of the world. The golden eagle occurs all around the Northern Hemisphere. Best known, perhaps, is the bald eagle, whose head is not bald but covered with white feathers. This is the bird whose figure adorns many United States coins. In recent years these eagles have become very scarce over most of North America, and serious efforts are being made to protect them. Two of the largest and most powerful eagles in the world are the monkey-eating eagle of the Philippines and the harpy eagle of Mexico, Central America, and South America. Both are jungle dwellers, and both are armed with extremely powerful talons.

In the same family with the eagles are the kites, the many medium to large broad-winged soaring hawks, and the long-tailed, forest-inhabiting bird hawks. The largest of the bird hawks is the goshawk, a species that occurs in the northern coniferous forests of North America, Europe, and Asia. The principal food of these birds consists of various kinds of grouse.

The Galapagos hawk (*Buteo galapagoensis*) is rapidly becoming a rarity because of its lack of fear of man. R. T. ORR

The remaining hawklike birds are members of the falcon family. The falcons have long, slender, pointed wings suited for very rapid flight. Their bills, unlike those of others of this order, have a conspicuous notch or tooth on each side. The largest of the falcons is the gyrfalcon of the Arctic, but the most famous is the peregrine. This species, which is nearly worldwide in distribution, has been the principal hawk used in falconry since medieval times. In North America this bird is commonly known as the duck hawk, probably because it often frequents seacoasts, where it nests on inaccessible ledges and preys upon various kinds of marine ducks.

Smaller but almost equally well-known falcons are the merlin, the kestrel of Europe, and its close American relative the sparrow hawk. All these birds tame very readily and make lovely pets.

Another group of the falcon family is represented by the caracaras. These are long-legged hawks that spend much of their time on the ground, where they walk a great deal. Caracaras range from extreme southern United States to South America. They resemble vultures in their liking for carrion. I associate the caracaras with the black vultures, or *zapalotes*, in Mexico, because the two are often seen gathered together along the highways where cattle or burros have been killed by automobiles.

The gallinaceous birds. These are the fowl-like birds, whose best known representatives are the quail, pheasant, chicken, turkey, grouse, and ptarmigan. There are, however, other very interesting but lesser-known members of this order. The mound-builders of the Australian and East Indian region come into this category.

Mound-builders, or megapodes as they are often called, have solved the problem of incubating their eggs in a most remarkable way. The adults, which are chicken-like in appearance, rake leaf litter from the forest floor into a great pile when the breeding season begins. The wet, rotting vegetation generates heat, and the females lay their eggs in this mass. Incubation is effected by the heat of decomposition. The young birds, when they hatch after two months, are completely able to care for themselves. There is no parent-offspring relationship, which is unique for birds.

In tropical America there is another group of gallinaceous birds—the chachalacas, guans, and curassows, which are highly sought after as game birds but little known to most persons in other parts of the world. Most of these are forest dwellers.

Turkeys are entirely North American in origin. The bronzed or wild turkey that is under domestication originally occurred from northeastern United States south to Guatemala, but in its wild form it has long been extinct throughout much of its former range in the United States. Another species, the ocellated turkey, is restricted to the Yucatan peninsula, British Honduras, and Guatemala. It is smaller and colored somewhat differently from the common turkey. Recently it too has been raised in captivity.

Apart from the several kinds of guinea fowl native to the African continent and a strange South American bird called the hoatzin, the remainder of the gallinaceous birds are placed in either the grouse or the pheasant family. The former contains some of our finest game birds and is restricted entirely to the Northern Hemisphere, where representatives are found from the prairies north through the coniferous forests to the arctic tundra. Members of the grouse family all have the lower leg at least partly feathered, and in many species it is entirely feathered, as are sometimes even the toes.

The largest and one of the most highly sought-after grouse is the capercaillie of northern Europe and northern Asia. This choice game bird, whose size almost equals that of a turkey, inhabits coniferous forests. Because of its shyness it has been able to survive in less settled areas despite centuries of hunting.

In North America the blue grouse, although much smaller, is more or less the counterpart of the capercaillie and is also very shy and elusive. It inhabits the western coniferous forests. During the breeding season in the spring of the year the male blue grouse utters a series of ventriloquial sounds referred to as hooting. In the Sierra Nevada, the Cascades, and Coast Ranges of the Pacific coast the hooting is done from fairly high in a pine or fir and may be heard under favorable circumstances a mile away. Despite this I have often spent more than an hour trying to locate one of these calling birds, whose body is as large as a good-sized chicken, even after I have determined in which tree it was located. Its concealing coloration, quiet demeanor, and ability to produce a ventriloquial call, all serve for protection.

The spruce grouse of Canada, by way of contrast, shows practically no fear of man. It has aptly been called the "fool hen." Because of its trusting behavior, it has been eliminated in many parts of its former range.

Other important related game birds belonging to this group are the black cock of Europe and Asia, the prairie chicken, sage grouse, ruffed grouse, and sharp-tailed grouse of North America. All these birds have interesting types of courtship behavior.

On sagebrush-covered slopes in parts of western North America, sage grouse gather at what are referred to as strutting grounds in the spring of the year. The sites are usually clearings where there is little vegetation. One spring an associate and I built a blind on the edge of one of these areas, just as the Indians had done for centuries before. The Indians, however, constructed their blinds of rocks and shot their birds with arrows. We made our blind of canvas and did our shooting with a camera. Each morning for a week in early April we made our way in the freezing pre-dawn hours to our observation post to watch a strange ritual.

Long before daylight more than one hundred male sage grouse quietly came onto our stage. Each spaced himself a few feet from his nearest neighbor and began displaying. The display consists of inflating large air sacs in the throat so that the breast becomes greatly expanded, fanning the tail, and dropping the wings like a turkey gobbler. The air sacs are then so moved as to produce a series of strange sounds—like the sounds produced by large bubbles of air rising to the surface of the water. A few steps may be taken by a strutting male, but he does not move far unless vanquished in a fight. Many conflicts arise regarding territorial boundaries between adjacent birds. Little attention is paid to the females, who may move about the display area. Strutting ceases, and the males leave shortly after sunrise. They return in the late afternoon to perform until dark.

On the treeless tundra of northern regions the grouse are replaced by several species of ptarmigans. These interesting birds have two plumages a year. In summer they are brown, but in autumn they molt into a white plumage that makes them difficult to see against the winter snow. In spring the white plumage is replaced by the brown one of summer. Consequently at all times of the year they blend well with their environment.

Members of the grouse family usually possess rather dull plumage, colored various shades of gray and brown. It may even be black. In the pheasant family, by way of contrast, we find some of the most colorful birds known. It would be difficult to find brighter plumage than that of the male golden pheasant, with his velvety red underparts, his golden head, and the back plumes bordered with orange, black, green, and blue feathers. Perhaps the peacock, a member of the same family, might be considered equally colorful.

The males of many other kinds of pheasants show remarkable color patterns, but the females generally are quite dull. This, of course, makes them less conspicuous and less likely to be the target for predatory animals. This is important in view of the fact that they usually have the responsibility of caring for the young.

Pheasants are native to central and southern Asia. A number of species have been semidomesticated. The ring-necked pheasant has been widely introduced into many parts of the world as a game bird.

There is only one true pheasant that is not native to Asia—the Congo peacock, a shy, beautiful species that was not discovered until the 1930's. This bird inhabits the dense jungles of the Congo in central Africa.

The domestic fowl or chicken is really a pheasant. Its ancestors are the jungle fowl of southern Asia, but man has been keeping these birds in captivity for more than five thousand years. Today they play an important part in the economy of most countries.

The smaller members of the pheasant family are the partridges and quails, of which there are many kinds in the Americas, Europe, Asia, and Africa. They tend to be much duller than their larger relatives, the pheasants. Throughout much of the year they travel in flocks or coveys, usually made up of one or more family groups. During the nesting season these flocks break up and the birds pair off. Quails, unlike many other gallinaceous birds, are monogamous.

The cranes and rails.   These birds belong to an order known as the Gruiformes, which contains a number of species that superficially show great diversity. Some of the larger cranes stand five feet high, while the smallest rails are not much larger than a sparrow. Certain species, like the whooping crane of North America, undergo very extensive migrations, while other species are sedentary and, in the case of some rails, have even lost the power of flight.

Cranes are large, conspicuous birds that to me have a certain air of dignity about them. Most zoos have several species on exhibit. Those

The crowned crane (*Balearica pavonina*) of Africa possesses ornate head feathers. JOHN TASHJIAN

most commonly seen are the small demoiselle, the sarus, and the crowned crane. Two species are found in North America—the sandhill and the whooping crane. Most cranes, however, are Eurasian and African.

In the Orient, especially in Japan, cranes are looked upon with great favor, and many superstitions revolve about them. In many parts of the world they have long been a target for hunters, and their populations have been greatly reduced. In 1963 it was estimated that there were only twenty-eight whooping cranes in existence in North America. Despite years of rigid protection, this species verges on extinction.

Cranes are often confused by many persons with herons, to which they are not at all closely related. Herons feed on animal matter while cranes are omnivorous, eating grain, berries, roots, and fruit as well as various small animals ranging from snails to mice. In flight a crane has its neck extended, while a heron draws its head back so that the neck is in an S-shaped curve.

One of the characteristic features of cranes is their dancing. Though the dance is performed most frequently during the breeding season, it is not restricted to that time of year nor even to adult birds. Occasionally all members of a flock may indulge in the dance, which consists of leaping high into the air with the wings partly extended and at times bowing.

Rails, crakes, and moorhens, as they are sometimes called, are world-wide in distribution. They not only occur on all the continents aside from Antarctica, but on most oceanic islands of any size. Some of the island species have lost the power of flight, and a few of these have become extinct, directly or indirectly because of man.

In general, rails are shy birds that inhabit marshy vegetation. Their bodies are proportionately very narrow to permit them to move rapidly between the stems of rushes and reeds. What will happen to our rails in the world of the future is problematical. They live in a habitat that man seems determined to eliminate, yet one which is most fascinating to the naturalist. I fear that the rate at which our marshes are being drained and filled in is greatly endangering the future of these birds.

Most rails are good swimmers. The gallinules and coots, which are really rails, spend much of their time in the water. The toes of coots are lobed somewhat like those of grebes.

Related to the cranes and the rails are the limpkins, the trumpeters, the finfoots, the sunbitterns, and the bustards. The latter are large running birds found on the plains of Asia and Africa. Bustards are capable of flying like cranes but usually avoid danger by running. Because of their edible qualities they have been hunted for centuries and presently survive only in remote areas.

The waders, gulls, and their relatives.   Birds belonging to this order are found from the Arctic to the Antarctic. They are most abundant along continental shorelines, where they frequent tidal marshes, mudflats, sandy beaches, headlands, and offshore rocks. There are some species, however, that live inland and others that spend much of the year on the open ocean.

In the temperate zones of the Northern Hemisphere the appearance of numerous shorebirds, ranging from small sandpipers to large curlews, is a familiar sight during the spring and autumn periods of migration. Many species nest in arctic or subarctic regions, but their movements to and from the breeding areas are somewhat leisurely. Freshwater marshes and even the shores of alkaline ponds in the desert appear to be alive with a variety of wading birds at these seasons of the year. Along the coast they must synchronize their lives with the changing actions of the tides each day. As the tide goes out, the mudflats and sandy shores and even the reefs are invaded by a variety of shorebirds, whose bills may be long or short, straight or curved, depending upon the food habits of the species and the zone in which it forages. As the tide returns, these birds leave the feeding areas to rest in secluded places or else continue on their journey

Oyster catchers are strictly coastal shorebirds that are most often found, usually in very small numbers, on rocky headlands, small offshore islands,

Dowitchers (*Limnodromus griseus*) feeding in a rain pool. R. T. ORR

Marbled godwits (*Limiosa fedoa*) in flock formation even while at rest with a few coots (*Fulica americana*). R. T. ORR

and remote beaches. They are very noisy, especially during the nesting season. While their plumage ranges from somber black to various combinations of black and white, their large, bright-red chisel-like bills often make them relatively conspicuous.

Plovers are stocky shorebirds with fairly short bills and legs. They are represented in nearly every region of the world where there is land. One of the most extensive migrants is the golden plover, a species that nests in the American and Asiatic arctic regions and winters as far south as Argentina and New Zealand. The eggs as well as the meat of certain species of plovers were long considered a table delicacy.

The avocets and stilts are medium-sized shorebirds with extremely long legs. It is said that the stilts have longer legs, in proportion to body size, than any other bird. Both avocets and stilts also have long slender bills, but in the former the bill is curved upward. In feeding, this upcurved bill is swung from side to side in the water.

The only true swimming shorebirds are the phalaropes, of which there are three species. Two of these breed in the Arctic, and the third nests in central and western North America. Phalaropes have bodies resembling moderately small sandpipers, but their toes are lobed like those of coots

The avocet (*Recurvirostra americana*) has extremely long legs and a slightly upturned bill. Courtesy CALIFORNIA ACADEMY OF SCIENCES

and grebes. This is an adaptation for swimming. They are rarely seen on shore except during the nesting season. They swim in circles or arcs as they feed on small crustaceans in the water. The two arctic species winter southward in the Atlantic and Pacific oceans.

Unlike most birds that show a plumage difference between the sexes, the female phalarope is the one that possesses the brightly colored feathers during the nesting season. In keeping with her malelike plumage, she leaves the problem of nest-building, incubation, and care of the young to her duller-colored mate.

Gulls of various kinds are probably the best-known representatives of this order of birds. Although they do not look like shorebirds, they are related to them in many anatomical characters. Gulls are found along continental shores and on most medium or large lakes and rivers. They are scavengers to a large degree and have learned that man can often supply them with food. Consequently they abound around coastal cities and harbors. They have also developed the habit of following ships and ferryboats, waiting for scraps that may be thrown overboard. Another interesting habit that many kinds of gulls have developed is to follow farmers who are plowing in the spring. In the newly turned soil they capture many worms and insects.

Terns are closely related to gulls but can be recognized by certain structural and behavioral differences. Gulls have rather heavy, hooked bills and their tails are essentially square at the end, while terns have more slender, pointed bills and forked tails. Terns have the habit of diving into the water for their food as they fly along, whereas gulls do not do this. In fact, it is rare for a gull to capture live food.

Many terns have very extensive migrations, but the record is held by the arctic tern. This species breeds all around the northern polar area. The northernmost nesting region is northern Greenland and the southernmost is Cape Cod in eastern United States. After the nesting season is over, these

Western gulls (*Larus occidentalis*) nest on most rocky islands along the Pacific coast of North America. R. T. ORR

terns move southward and winter along the edge of the Antarctic. It is estimated that many individuals make a round trip annually of twenty-two thousand miles.

One of the most beautiful members of this group is the fairy tern of the central Pacific Ocean. This diminutive bird is pure white with a black bill. It nests on oceanic islands and has the strange custom of laying its single egg on a bare branch, where it is balanced and incubated by the adult without the aid of a nest.

The auks, auklets, murres, murrelets, and their relatives constitute another major group belonging to this order. They are all restricted to the Northern Hemisphere, where they inhabit rocky coasts and offshore rocks. They are mistaken by many persons for penguins because of their stocky bodies, upright posture, and black-and-white color patterns.

My favorite among these birds along the Pacific coast is the pigeon guillemot. This species is about the size of a pigeon, is black in color with a white patch on each wing, and has brilliant coral-red legs and feet.

During recent summers, while watching the social behavior of sea lions from a blind on an island along the central California coast, I have had two major distractions. One of these has been from nesting western gulls that resent a strange presence and continually dive-bomb one in a threatening attitude, although they have never come closer than about three feet from my head. The second distraction has been the behavior of the guillemots, which nest in holes in the banks and rocks all along the island shore. These birds begin the season by performing what might be termed a nuptial dance consisting of bowing, nodding, and head-moving. Their shrill cries are constantly heard. When the young are hatched there is a steady stream of adults flying back from the sea with curious small fish in their bills which are greedily consumed by the babies.

The most famous member of this group of birds was the great auk, a large flightless species that formerly occurred on the shores of Iceland and Greenland as well as a number of other islands in the North Atlantic. Its lack of fear of man and inability to fly led to its extinction. Great auks were slaughtered for food. The last one was killed in 1844.

The pigeons and doves. Like the gallinaceous birds and waterfowl, members of this order have long been associated with man. The wild rock pigeon of Europe and Asia has been under domestication for thousands of years and is now found over most parts of the world where there are cities or agricultural activities. Many varieties have been bred—some for show, some for food, and others to be used for carrying messages. The ability of birds to return to their home base when transported some distance away is by no means confined to the homing pigeon. We now know that many birds navigate very accurately by means of star patterns or by the sun. In the domesticated pigeon, this ability has been made use of by human beings for centuries.

Pigeons and doves are fundamentally alike. The former term is used for the larger species and the latter for the smaller kinds. Both have stocky bodies, small heads, loose feathers, and bills that possess a fleshy base. The group is worldwide in distribution but most abundant in southeastern Asia, the East Indies, New Guinea, Australia, and the Pacific Islands.

The largest pigeons in the world are the crowned pigeons of New Guinea. These pheasant-sized birds have long been sought after for their crown feathers, which until recent years were of considerable value in the millinery trade. Many of the fruit pigeons of the tropics are very brilliantly colored in shades of green, blue, red, and yellow.

In North America the mourning dove is one of the most important of all upland game birds. Despite persistent hunting for centuries, it still occurs in large numbers from the east to the west coast.

One member of this order whose individual numbers were once thought to exceed those of any other species of bird is now extinct because of man's greed. This is the passenger pigeon, which was formerly so numerous that flocks of them literally darkened the sky in passing. These birds nested in large colonies consisting of millions of individuals. It was here that they were slaughtered and shipped by the trainload to be sold in the markets of the larger cities. Years of such practices left their toll, and the passenger pigeon population ultimately reached a minimum that inhibited reproduction. The last one died in captivity in 1914.

Related to the pigeons and doves are the sand grouse of Eurasia and Africa. These are birds of open grassland or desert. Like other members of the order, they are good eating and hence hunted considerably. Some species are migratory.

The dodo, so well known from Lewis Carroll's *Alice's Adventures in Wonderland,* was also a relative of the pigeons and doves. Dodos of several species formerly occurred on the Mascarene Islands in the Indian Ocean off the east coast of Africa. They were very large flightless birds, utterly defenseless. Consequently, they were easily killed by sailors, and those that survived direct human attack were eliminated by hogs that were introduced on those islands by the Portuguese. Several dodos were shipped to Europe in the late sixteenth and early seventeenth century. One species became extinct before the end of the seventeenth century, and the last one was exterminated before the close of the eighteenth century. Our knowledge of the appearance of the dodo is based largely on the paintings of Roelandt Savery, a famous seventeenth century artist who showed these birds among others in some of his works. A few years ago it was my privilege to see Savery's original sketches in pencil when they were discovered in the collections of the Crocker Art Gallery in Sacramento, California.

The parrots. These noisy, colorful birds are found in tropical regions all over the world. They vary greatly in size from the tiny lovebirds of Africa and the parrotlets of tropical America, whose bodies are not much larger than those of sparrows, to the large macaws of Mexico, Central America, and South America, whose length from head to tip of tail may be as much as three feet.

Members of the order all have proportionately large hooked bills, which might superficially resemble those of birds of prey but are really adapted to eating fruit and seeds. The base of the bill is fleshy as in birds of prey and in pigeons, and the feet have the toes arranged with two in front and two behind. This type of foot is very useful in manipulating food.

There are two remarkable parrots that are found in New Zealand. One of them is the kea, a high-mountain form that has developed the habit of killing sheep to secure their fat. The other is a nocturnal species known as

The kea (*Nestor notabilis*) is a unique parrot that inhabits the highlands of New Zealand. JOHN TASHJIAN

the kakapo. The kakapo lives in subalpine forests and has lost the power of flight.

Most parrots are excellent flyers. Some of the smaller species resemble doves in their rapid flight. Even the large macaws, which most persons associate with zoos where they perform on their perches like acrobats, are wonderful flyers. A flock of military macaws flying in formation high over the jungle is a thrilling sight that one long remembers.

Parrots make excellent pets. They are long-lived in captivity and generally are easily tamed. In recent years the grass parakeet, or budgereegah, of Australia has proved to be one of the most popular caged birds.

Macaws (*Ara*) are the largest parrots in the New World.
R. T. ORR

The cuckoo-like birds. This order includes a number of very interesting and seemingly unrelated types of birds. The cuckoos themselves are widely distributed over the tropical and temperate parts of the world. The Old World species, however, are best known. The common cuckoo of Europe, Asia, and Africa is the one whose call is responsible for the name of the group as well as the sound that is imitated by the cuckoo clock.

The cuckoos of Europe, Africa, and Asia are famous for their parasitic habits. They never build nests of their own, nor do they incubate their eggs or care for their young. Long ago they solved the problem by laying in the nests of other birds. The female cuckoo, when laying, removes an egg from the nest of the host. The host is usually a member of a much smaller species. When the young cuckoo hatches, it pushes the eggs or young of the other species out of the nest so that they perish, and all the food brought in by the unsuspecting foster parents goes to the intruder.

The American representatives of this family do not show this parasitic habit. In western North America one of the better-known species of the cuckoo family is the roadrunner, or chaparral cock. This rapidly running, crested, long-tailed bird is often seen on the desert, where it has won fame for its ability to capture and kill snakes.

Other American members of the family include the anis, a group of tropical birds of black somber plumage with deep, laterally compressed bills. Anis are very social in their behavior. They live in small flocks and build communal nests in which several females may lay. The eggs are incubated and the young fed by various members of the flock, who protect their territory against invasion by other anis.

In Africa there is another family of birds belonging to the order to which the cuckoos belong. These birds are known as plantain eaters. They dwell in forested areas, and almost all have rather brilliant plumage. They have two unique types of copper pigments in their feathers, one of which is a red that may be dissolved in water. Plantain eaters are almost squirrel-like in the way they rapidly run along branches, in this respect resembling the squirrel cuckoo of the American tropics.

The owls. Owls are large-headed, soft-feathered, nocturnal birds of prey that are found in nearly all parts of the world. They take the place of hawks at night and play a very important role in curbing the populations of many kinds of rodents and other small animals.

One of the best-known species is the barn owl, so called because of its liking for barn lofts as well as attics and towers. Barn owls, of which there are several species, are placed in a separate family by themselves and are recognized by their heart-shaped face and long legs. They occur over most of the world. Although I have kept barn owls in captivity, I have never felt that they make particularly attractive pets. My birds, even after a year in an aviary, maintained a somewhat disturbing habit of lowering the head as soon as I approached and slowly moving it from side to side while uttering a series of threatening clicks.

The roadrunner (*Geococcyx californianus*) is a familiar sight on the deserts of western North America. JOHN TASH-JIAN

The remaining more than one hundred species of owls vary in size from the diminutive, sparrow-sized elf owl of the deserts of western North America to the snowy owl of the Arctic and the great gray owl of the conifer forests of the Northern Hemisphere, both of which exceed two feet in length.

The prey of owls is consumed entire, and the fur, feathers, and bones that are indigestible are regurgitated in the form of pellets. These accumulate beneath their daytime roosts. An analysis of the contents of these pellets will usually provide adequate proof of the skill of owls as rodent catchers.

Most owls are some shade of brown or gray, which tends to make them inconspicuous while sleeping during the day. In the Arctic, however, the snowy owl is almost pure white in winter, so as to blend with its environment. During some winters conditions in the Arctic, such as shortage of food, seem to force large numbers of these owls to move far south of their normal range, even into the United States. Occasionally they enter other areas, where they become very conspicuous. I once saw one of these birds sitting in a Sitka spruce in the snow-free Pacific Northwest. It not only seemed out of place but could be seen nearly half a mile away.

The goatsuckers. This is an odd name, given to a group of nocturnal

(Above) The Galapagos short-eared owl (*Asio flammeus galapagoensis*), like most endemic birds on that oceanic archipelago, shows little fear of man. R. T. ORR

(Left) The snowy owl (*Nyctea scandiaca*) is a resident of the Arctic. JOHN KORANDA

birds that were suspected by the superstitious in ages past of sucking the milk of goats with their large mouths at night. The whippoorwill, night-hawks, and nightjars, are some of the better-known representatives. The plumage of members of this order resembles that of owls in its soft shades of gray and brown. Again, this would appear to make these birds very incon-spicuous during the day. Most species sleep during this time on the open ground or on stumps or branches, where bright coloration would be detri-mental.

With one exception, the goatsuckers feed entirely on animal matter, principally insects, which are captured by most species while in the air. Whippoorwills, poorwills, and their near relatives fly up from the ground to catch their insect food in glades and clearings and even along roads. Others, such as the potoos of Central and South America, fly out from stumps and branches to secure passing insects and then return to these perches. Nighthawks, which are not related to hawks and are more active in the daytime than at night, forage fairly high in the air. Their long pointed wings and harsh calls are familiar to most persons in the United States. They frequently forage over cities and even nest on the gravel roofs of buildings.

One of the strangest birds of this order is the oilbird of northern South America and the island of Trinidad. The oilbirds inhabit caves, are strictly nocturnal, and live primarily on the fruits of palm trees. They were dis-covered by the naturalist Baron von Humboldt and named oilbirds be-

The oilbird or guacharo (*Steatornis caripensis*) of South America is strictly nocturnal and nests in the darkness of caves. EDWARD S. ROSS

cause the young became exceedingly fat from the palm oil prior to being fledged. The natives used to collect these young birds just for their fat and, even though the birds are now protected, still do so on occasions.

Oilbirds navigate in the total darkness of caves at night by means of sound, much like bats. They produce clicking noises with great rapidity as they fly and depend upon these sounds being reflected from adjacent walls or other objects to determine their location.

Goatsuckers of one species or another are found over most of the temperate or warmer parts of the world. They are absent from New Zealand, most oceanic islands, northern North America, extreme northern Europe, northern Asia, and South Africa.

To me there is something intriguing about nocturnal birds. Perhaps it has to do with their vocalization. In the still of the night the call of an owl or a whippoorwill always stirs excitement. In the mountains of western North America the call of the poorwill at late dusk is a sign that day is over and that the creatures of the night are ready to emerge.

One June my wife and I, while camping in the high Sierra Nevada, were informed by a ranger friend of a poorwill nest within about one hundred yards of our camp. The nest was not much to talk about, since it consisted of a slight depression in the ground containing two eggs whose shells were white with a faint pinkish tinge. The nest was in a small clearing next to brush on a gentle slope in an open fir and pine forest. An adult bird was on the nest when we first looked at it, and so beautifully did its plumage blend with the color of the ground that it was difficult to distinguish even a few feet away.

That evening at dusk we heard a series of calls that started near the nest and gradually moved down the mountain slope. They sounded like the words "pool duck." Having heard this call for years in the summer months while camping out, we decided that here was an opportunity to learn something of its significance. As a consequence each evening from about sunset until after dark for a period of two weeks was spent in quiet observation near the nest.

On the first night just before dusk, we were watching the nest site, which we had carefully marked, when something hopping over the ground in a toadlike manner began approaching the nest very slowly and cautiously. When it was about one foot from its goal, the poorwill on the nest suddenly flew up and the newcomer took its place on the eggs. The bird that left glided down the slope a short distance and began calling. After a few calls it fluttered up and glided a bit farther and repeated another series of calls.

This was continued until the calls grew faint and far away. Obviously the bird that had been sitting on the nest all day was being relieved by its mate so it could go out and forage for insect food. Later the bird returned and approached the nest in the same manner until it was near enough for another exchange of positions.

Each evening we watched this same behavior, even after the young hatched. After that, each bird returned with insect food in its esophagus which it regurgitated into the mouths of the babies. Since that interesting experience I never hear the call of a poorwill at dusk without wondering if there are not two white eggs somewhere on the ground nearby.

The swifts and hummingbirds.   These two groups of quite dissimilar birds probably arose from a common ancestor many millions of years ago. Since they still show some similar anatomical traits, they are classified together in the same order.

Swifts are worldwide in distribution, while hummingbirds are restricted to the New World, where they occur in greatest numbers in northern South America. Apart from the fact that both are remarkable flyers, they share little in common as regards habits and appearance.

Swifts bear a superficial resemblance to swallows and, like the latter, secure insect food in the air, but their wings are proportionately longer and narrower, producing a silhouette in the sky shaped somewhat like the crescent of a new moon. The wing strokes are extemely rapid when the birds are not gliding, which also distinguishes them from swallows.

Most swifts are rather somberly colored, in shades ranging from black to dark gray, occasionally broken up by white on various parts of the body plumage. Their feet are generally small in proportion to body size and adapted to clinging to cliffs, tree trunks, the sides of caves, and even chimneys, so that the body is held in a vertical plane. Most swifts nest in these situations, although the palm swifts and the crested swiftlets are exceptions.

Many kinds of swifts have developed the remarkable habit of using saliva in nest construction. Sometimes the saliva serves to hold mud and vegetation together and glue it to a cliff, cave wall, or ledge. It may be used to hold small twigs together so as to form a shallow cup. Or the nest may be made entirely of saliva, which hardens into a semitransparent, amber-like shell in which the egg or eggs are deposited.

The edible birds' nests are used in making the well-known "birds' nest soup" of the Orient. They are the pure saliva nests of a species of swift that occurs in great numbers in caves in southeastern Asia, principally in Malaya and Indo-China.

Several years ago my life became intimately involved with swifts at a time when I was studying the interrelationship of a New World group of these birds. An associate with whom I had been collaborating in this project had discovered the first nest of a relatively rare and large species of swift in Mexico. The following year he returned to the cave containing the nest. While I was attending an International Ornithological Congress, he secured one live young bird. On my return to San Francisco I had not been in my office more than twenty minutes when I received a long-distance call from Mexico City. The following morning "Junior" was making his way northward in a plane and I was involved with airline companies, brokers, departments of Public Health, and friends in the bird importing business. I found out that live birds traveling alone in commercial planes across international borders have certain problems, but in spite of a great deal of red tape, our prize was destined to land at International Airport at midnight.

Not certain as to the age or size of the visitor, my wife and I arrived at the air freight office equipped with a fair-sized cage and exerted all the caution one would take with a wild falcon about to be uncrated. All the doors and windows in the office were closed and the cage was made ready before we proceeded to open the carton marked "Live bird, handle with care." We had quite an audience of clerks, customs officials, and bondsmen, as well as an airline representative. We were somewhat embarrassed, therefore, when upon opening the box we were faced with a tiny creature clothed in heavy gray down which could hardly balance itself on its legs, much less fly away. Its bill was open for food, and we promptly fed it the mealworms we had brought.

"Junior" soon became a major part of our lives. He had to be hand-fed several times a day for the eight and a half months he lived. During the first six weeks, feedings were quite frequent. He came home at night with me and slept in a shoebox on my bedside table. We came to learn much about his development and behavior and made many photographs of him as he acquired his plumage. But despite the best of medical care, provided by the University of California Medical Center, he succumbed to pneumonia the following winter.

Hummingbird's are among nature's most marvelous creations. Although they occur as far north as Alaska and as far south as Tierra del Fuego, by far the majority of the more than five hundred species are inhabitants of the New World tropics. They range in size from the diminutive bee hummingbird of Cuba, which is only about two and a half inches long from tip

"Junior," a young white-naped swift (*Streptoprocne semicollaris*) looking over the top of the ladder to which he usually clung. R. T. ORR

of bill to tip of tail, to the giant hummer of the Andes, whose overall length reaches eight and a half inches. The bee hummingbird is the smallest bird in the world.

Hummingbirds all have long tubular bills that are adapted to securing nectar from flowers. This is their principal food. Many species supplement their diet with small insects, obtained mainly from cobwebs. The bill may be straight or curved. The South American swordbilled hummer, whose length is eight and a half inches, has a bill five inches long.

The beauty of hummingbirds is difficult to describe. The brilliant, shiny plumage of the males covers all the colors of the rainbow. Most species possess considerable irridescence, especially on the brightly colored bib, or gorget. There are also some species that have greatly elongated tail feathers. The streamertail of Jamaica is one of these. This little bird, whose overall length is nine and a half inches, has a tail that constitutes seven inches of this total.

Hummingbirds are noted not only for their small size and beauty but also for the rapidity of their wing movement and their ability to fly backward. Slow-motion pictures of some species have shown that they take more than fifty wing strokes per second. This gives them the appearance of a sphinx moth.

Most, though not all, of our species in the United States are migratory. In central California we have two nesting species. One of these, the Anna hummer, is resident the year around, but the Allen hummingbird is classi-

A female Allen humming-bird (*Selasphorus sassin*) on her nest. R. T. ORR

fied as a summer visitant, though it is our earliest visitor to arrive, coming back to its nesting area around the middle of February. When I hear the buzzy sound produced by the outer tail feathers of these little birds in flight, I know that spring is just around the corner.

Once I was fortunate enough to have a hummingbird nest just outside my office window. The female does not allow the male anywhere near the nesting territory once the eggs are laid. I set up a camera in the window and each day for the ensuing weeks had a chance to record on film the behavior of the female during incubation as well as the daily changes in the young from the time they were hatched until they flew away.

The trogons. There are fewer than three dozen species of trogons, and they inhabit the tropics of the Americas, Asia, and Africa. They are brilliantly colored birds with plumage that may be irridescent green, blue, yellow, or red, usually combined with black and white. Despite this coloring, they are not easily seen in the tropical forests in which they live.

The trogons are thought to be an old group of birds that once ranged much more widely over the world. The New and Old World species show great similarity and are all placed within a single family.

The most famous trogon is the quetzal. This is a large, beautiful species whose body is brilliantly green and red. The male has green tail plumes that may attain a length of two feet. The quetzel is the state bird of Guatemala and was revered by the ancient Aztecs and Mayas. Quetzalcoatl, or the feathered serpent, was the principal god of the Mayas. The symbol of a reptile clothed in quetzal feathers is seen on many art treasures unearthed in southern Mexico and Central America.

The mousebirds.   There are six closely related species of birds that comprise this order. They occur only in the southern half of Africa and show little relationship to any other groups of birds. Their plumage is dull gray or brown, their bills are red, and their tails are long. Their bodies are about the size of a small jay. They derive the name "mousebird" from the fact that they may run up a tree limb in a somewhat mouselike manner. In this respect they resemble plantain eaters and certain kinds of cuckoos.

The kingfishers and their relatives.   This is a wide-ranging order containing a number of seemingly very different groups of birds. However, they all have certain anatomical characters in common. One of these is a partial fusion of the front toes. Their bills are relatively long. All members nest in cavities or holes.

The order is best represented in the tropics. Kingfishers occur in both the New and Old World but are most abundant in southeastern Asia, Australia, and the Pacific Islands. In North America the belted kingfisher, with its rattling call, is a familiar sight wherever there are rivers, creeks, or lakes. Another well-known member of the kingfisher family is the kookaburra, or laughing jackass, of Australia, an attraction in many zoos.

Young belted kingfishers (*Megaceryle alcyon*) just out of the nest. Courtesy CALIFORNIA ACADEMY OF SCIENCES

Many tropical kingfishers are beautifully colored, and their large bills make them even more striking in appearance. Their food consists of various kinds of animal matter, ranging from insects to fish, amphibians, and even small mammals.

The largest members of the order are the hornbills, whose enormous beaks are responsible for their name. These birds occur in Africa, southeastern Asia, and adjacent islands. They are omnivorous, eating fruit, berries, insects, frogs, and various other small animals. One of the most unusual features of these large-billed birds relates to their nesting habits. They generally nest in cavities in trees, and here the female is imprisoned by the male from the time she is ready to lay until the young are about half grown. The nest entrance is sealed with mud or dirt, leaving only a narrow vertical aperture sufficient to allow the bills of the birds to pass through when food is being transferred from the male to the female. He is responsible for feeding her during the period of egg-laying and incubation and also provides for the young for another one to two months.

There are three other Old World families related to the kingfishers and hornbills. These are the hoopoes, the bee-eaters, and the rollers. In Central and South America there are two additional families, the todies of the West Indies and the motmots, whose range extends from Mexico to Argentina. Motmots are colorful birds with soft green, blue, and brown feathers. Their tails are very distinctive; in some species the central feathers are quite elongate with webbing only at the tip, so that they appear racket-shaped. Furthermore, they have the peculiar habit of wagging their tails from side to side instead of up and down as so many other birds do.

The woodpecker-like birds.   Like the previous order, this one also consists of a number of families that superficially seem to bear little resemblance to one another. Related to the woodpeckers are the barbets, the honey guides, the toucans, the puffbirds, and the jacamars.

Woodpeckers occur in forested parts of all the continental land masses except Australia. They have strong, sturdy bills for drilling into wood and very long tongues, which may be extended for a considerable distance. Most woodpeckers feed on insects, many of which are excavated by the birds from the bark of trees. There are species, such as the Lewis woodpecker of western North America, that fly out from perches and secure insects in flight. Flickers do much of their feeding on the ground, where they consume quantities of ants. Other species feed to a large extent on sap, fruit, and nuts.

One of the most interesting birds of this group is the acorn-storing woodpecker of western North America. These birds drill holes in trees, posts, and even houses, and store their acorns for future use.

The storage of food is not a common avian custom, but it goes a long way back with this species. One day in 1942 we received at the museum a section of redwood log that had a cavity crammed full of acorns deep in the heart of the wood. It seemed at first to present a mystery, but before long a plausible explanation was deduced. About two hundred years before the Norman Conquest and shortly after the death of Charlemagne, a woodpecker had started excavating a nest hole in the redwood in north-

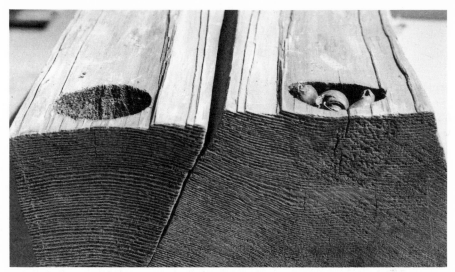

The storage chamber of an acorn-storing woodpecker (*Balanosphyra formicivorus*) with acorns that were placed there shortly after the death of Charlemagne. Courtesy CALIFORNIA ACADEMY OF SCIENCES

western California. The job was only half finished and then abandoned. The tree continued to produce new wood each year, and in time the opening into the cavity became smaller and smaller. When it was reduced to a diameter of about three-fourths of an inch, it probably resembled one of the numerous holes that the resident acorn-storing woodpeckers drill for storage, and no doubt was used for just that purpose. When an acorn was inserted, it fell into the cavity and thus left the opening free to entice further storage. Finally the hole was filled, and in time the opening was closed over. The tree continued growing for well over a thousand years more, adding another layer of wood over the storage chamber each season until it was cut down in 1942. At that time we counted 1,080 growth rings between the acorn pocket and the bark.

Barbets occur in tropical parts of Africa, Asia, Central America, and South America. They are somewhat like woodpeckers in appearance, being stocky birds that often move about on the trunks of trees in search of insects. They also feed on fruit, seeds, and flowers. Their bills, unlike those of woodpeckers, are rather thick and surrounded by conspicuous, bristle-like feathers.

Three other families in this order, found only in the New World tropics ranging from southern Mexico to South America, are the puffbirds, the jacamars, and the toucans. The first two are known to few persons except ornithologists outside their native areas. Toucans, however, are familiar birds in zoos and aviaries and are pictured in many books. Like the horn-bills of Africa and Asia, toucans have enormous bills, which are sometimes as long as the birds themselves and proportionately quite deep. The bills, which are often more colorful than the plumage, may be emerald green, chartreuse, or orange, and often boldly marked or striped with black, white, blue, or red. The cutting edges are toothed. This aids in manipulating fruit, their principal food. Toucans are nonmigratory and rather weak flyers. They nest in cavities in trees, and both parents care for the young.

Another remarkable group of birds related to the woodpeckers are the honey guides. These are dull-colored little birds primarily of Africa, although two species occur in Asia. Their fame comes not from their appearance but rather from an unusual habit that several species have developed.

Honey guides are insectivorous, and all of them are particularly fond of various kinds of bees and wasps. In Africa some species have acquired the trick of luring both the ratel, or honey badger, and man to the bee hives by their chattering. After the mammalian honey-eater has completed his destruction of the hives, the birds move in and have their feast. However, instead of consuming the bee larvae or the honey, they eat the wax. Wax itself is quite inert and essentially indigestible to most animals, but the honey guide possesses special bacteria in its digestive system which produce enzymes that break down the wax into substances that the bird's body can utilize. In many ways this is similar to the action of symbiotic intestinal protozoa on wood in the digestive system of termites.

The perching birds. This order contains more than five hundred species, or about three-fifths of the birds of the world. It includes all those that are commonly referred to as songbirds, such as finches, wrens, warblers, orioles,

The large bill of the toucan enables it to handle fruit with ease. Courtesy SAN FRANCISCO ZOOLOGICAL SOCIETY

vireos, troupials, tanagers, and many others, as well as a good many that are not really songsters, like flycatchers, crows, jays, shrikes, and swallows. Birds of this group have developed a perching-type foot with three toes in front and an opposable toe behind. They are all of small or medium size. None has become adapted to aquatic or marine life. Some build open, cup-shaped nests, while others nest in holes or have elaborate covered nests, but a few have actually lost the nest-building habit and have become parasitic, like certain of the Old World cuckoos.

The perching birds, because of their abundance and dominance, are more widely distributed over the world than members of any other order. The only major land mass from which they are absent is Antarctica. They have even established themselves on many remote oceanic islands such as the Hawaiian group in the central Pacific, the Galapagos Islands off the west coast of South America, and the Tristan da Cunha Islands in the South Atlantic. Some species are of extremely limited distribution. Kirtland's warbler in North America breeds only in parts of central Michigan. There are island species of even more restricted range. The raven, by way of contrast, is found all over the Northern Hemisphere; and the English sparrow, or house sparrow, which was originally native to Europe and parts of both Asia and Africa, has become established accidentally or otherwise in most cities of the world and now is essentially cosmopolitan.

It is impractical here to attempt to name the more than fifty families of perching birds, but mention can be made of a few with unusual habits. I think most persons would include the swallow, the crow, the thrush, and the finch-sparrow families among the best known of these birds. There are a few parts of the world where none of these is represented, but in general they are of widespread occurrence and are known to many people.

Swallows, like bluebirds, which are members of the thrush family, have long been looked upon as harbingers of spring. They make their appearance each year in many parts of the Northern Hemisphere when the vernal season starts to get under way. They are always conspicuous on their arrival because of their habit of foraging for insects in the open sky in loose flocks. A number of species have taken to nesting on man-made structures such as bridges, barns, and other buildings.

Many tales and superstitions have arisen regarding these birds. In past ages their sudden disappearance from Europe in the fall of the year was accounted for in several ways. Some thought that they congregated in great numbers on marsh reeds and gradually sank into the mud below, where they stayed until spring. Others even claimed that they went to the moon to spend the winter. In western North America there are well-known stories of swallows returning to the same place on the same date each year. Although they do return to the same place, we know that the date may vary by as much as two weeks. Their arrival is largely dependent on climatic conditions encountered during migration.

Many swallows nest in colonies. Their nests may be open cups made of mud, lined with feathers and grass, and plastered onto a vertical surface or on a ledge. This is the type built by the common barn swallow. Others, like the cliff swallow, make a covered mud chamber that has an opening near the bottom; this type is attached to a cliff or wall. Some species, such as the bank swallow, nest in holes in banks, while tree swallows and martins make use of holes in trees.

Less liked than swallows, but equally well known, are members of the crow family, which includes the jays and magpies. The largest member of this group is the raven. In fact, it is about the largest of the perching birds. Ravens occur all around the Northern Hemisphere. They can be distinguished from the various kinds of smaller crows by their hoarse croak. Crows and ravens are considered to be among the most intelligent of birds. Despite their persecution by man because of some of their bad habits, they still survive successfully. Captive birds can be taught many tricks and may even learn a few words.

Jays and magpies are more widely distributed than their larger relatives, the ravens and crows, and more brilliantly colored, often in shades of green and blue. Most species have moderately long tails. Jays are primarily forest-dwellers and, while common in the Old World, they are especially well represented in Central and South America. Even in the coniferous forests of the far North, the Canada jay, or camp robber, is a familiar bird.

Also belonging to this family are the nutcrackers. Clark's nutcrackers are

Clark's nutcracker (*Nucifraga columbiana*), a bird of the high mountains of western North America, was named after the early explorer, William Clark, who with Captain Meriwether Lewis discovered the source of the Missouri River. ROBERT AMES

birds of the high mountains of western North America. Here their harsh cries are commonly heard as they fly from one rocky crag to another at or near timberline. Their food consists largely of the seeds of coniferous trees, some of which they cache for future use. Anyone who visits Crater Lake National Park in Oregon will find these dove-gray birds with black and white wings all about the resort area.

The thrush family is a fairly large one and well represented in most parts of the world, including many oceanic islands. Thrushes are strong flyers, and many species are migratory. Perhaps this accounts for their wide distribution. Some species, such as the bluethroat, the bluebirds, and the rock thrushes, are quite colorful, but many of the forest-dwelling types are clothed in soft shades of gray and brown. Their food consists of animal matter, especially insects, and berries.

Thrushes are most famous for their song. In North America the wood thrush, the veery, the hermit, and the Swainson thrush are among the top songbirds. In Mexico the solitaires and, southwardly, the nightingale thrushes have songs of remarkable beauty. In Europe and Asia the most famous songbird is the nightingale, which is also a thrush.

Not only are thrushes melodious, but they are familiar figures in many places. Throughout much of North America the robin is one of the com-

A western meadowlark (*Sturnella neglecta*) with hungry young. Courtesy CALIFORNIA ACADEMY OF SCIENCES

monest and best-liked birds. The European robin, although very different, is well known in parts of the Old World.

The finches and sparrows constitute the largest group of all the perching birds. They are usually divided into two families, one of which is restricted to Europe, Asia, Australia, and Africa, while the other is worldwide. Some of the better-known members of the Old World group are the weaver finches of Africa and the waxbills of Africa, Asia, and Australia. The former are famous for their highly complex, colonial nests, while the small, colorful kinds of waxbills are common aviary birds. One of the best-known and least-liked members of this family is the English sparrow, whose worldwide distribution has been brought about largely through man's activities.

The second family contains all the native finches and sparrows of North and South America as well as many species found on other continents. The buntings, grosbeaks, tree finches, ground finches, goldfinches, towhees, cardinals, juncos, and crossbills are some of the more familiar kinds. As is true of members of the previously mentioned family, these birds are primarily seed eaters and all have strong conical bills suited to this purpose. Most of our common garden birds, and birds of the hedgerows, are members of this group.

Among the most exotic birds belonging to the order are the famed birds of paradise, found primarily on the island of New Guinea. There a family of birds has developed whose strange and colorful plumes are unequaled elsewhere in the world. These plumes adorn the male, who uses them to display before the females.

Members of this family were killed by the thousands each year during the latter part of the nineteenth century in order that their plumes might be used on ladies' hats in Europe and America. In fact, a number of species were described and known for many years only from millinery items. Some of these plumes look as if they were made from cellophane, and others resemble colored wires or beautiful fans. For several decades now, trade in wild bird plumes has been prohibited by most countries. As a consequence, certain kinds of birds of paradise whose populations had been greatly reduced have shown an increase in numbers.

Perhaps the strangest birds in the world are the bowerbirds of New Guinea and northern Australia. The males of many members of this family have developed the amazing habit of constructing elaborate bowers in the jungle, in which they dance, display, and seek to attract a female for mating. These bowers may look like small jungle huts made of leaves and

The entrance to a bower with its decorations of bones, seeds and even bottles in northern Australia. EDWARD S. ROSS

sticks, or they may resemble a stage surrounded by a woven curtain. Each bower is decorated with fresh flowers, leaves, shells, or other objects, which are continually being replaced. Some bowers are worked on by a male for years. I have seen male bowerbirds building complicated settings in captivity and decorating them with flowers that were placed in the cage.

MAMMALS

Mammals are the class of vertebrates to which man belongs. We like to think of ourselves as the dominant backboned creatures on land today, but, as a group, we had a lowly beginning about two hundred million years ago. The first mammals were small, and, far from being rulers, they originated from reptiles when the latter were reaching their peak of development. Reptiles, at that time, were not only dominant on land but also occurred in the sea, and others were capable of flying through the air. Mammals did not begin to rise to their present position until the Age of Reptiles was nearly at an end, about one hundred million years ago.

Today we find mammals from the mountaintops to the sea, and from the Arctic to the Antartic. They are probably the best-known group in the animal kingdom.

All mammals feed their young on milk for a certain period of time. In fact, the presence of the mammary glands that produce this milk is responsible for the name Mammalia, which is applied to this group of animals. The period that young mammals are dependent on this food may vary from just a few days in some species to many months in others.

The body of most mammals is covered with hair, which is somewhat comparable to feathers in birds. Hair provides warmth and protection, among other things. Like a feather, hair, once it is formed, is a nonliving structure that is subject to wear, oxidation, and fading. Consequently it must be replaced periodically. This is effected by the process of molting, during which the old hairs are shed and replaced by new ones.

Mammals, like birds, are warm-blooded animals. Their body temperatures tend to remain fairly constant and high. Some mammals become dormant at certain seasons of the year. In winter we refer to this as hibernation, and in summer as estivation. At such times these animals, in a sense, cease to be warm-blooded and let their temperatures drop to approximately that of caves or burrows in which they are living. These deep sleeps, with lowered bodily activities, enable them to survive during periods of inclement weather and food scarcity.

It is estimated that there are about seven thousand species of living mammals. These are classified into nineteen different orders.

The monotremes. The most primitive of living mammals belong to an order known as the Monotremata, a group found only in Australia, Tasmania, and New Guinea, and represented by the duck-billed platypus and the spiny anteaters, or echidnas. These strange animals lay eggs, like birds and many reptiles, and the mothers incubate the eggs. The young, when they hatch, are dependent on milk, which seeps from glands on the abdomen of the female. There are no nipples, so the young must lap the milk from the hair on the surface of these glandular areas. The young are blind and helpless at the time of hatching and completely dependent on the parent for some months. The mouths of monotremes are very modified and

lack teeth. The platypus has developed a horny, bill-like structure somewhat resembling that of a duck, while the echidnas have an elongated
cylindrical mouth. Their food consists principally of insects and worms.

The platypus, which is probably one of the most famous of Australia's
strange animals, is semiaquatic, inhabiting streams and living in holes in
banks somewhat like a beaver. The feet are webbed. In the male, each
hind limb possesses a vicious spur that is connected with a poison sac.

The marsupials.   Another primitive order of mammals whose center of
distribution is primarily in Australia is the Marsupiala. These are the
pouched animals, such as the various kinds of kangaroos and wallabies,

The duck-billed platypus (*Ornithorhynchus anatinus*) is one of the most primitive of living
mammals. NEW YORK ZOOLOGICAL SOCIETY

the koala, and the Tasmanian devil. Marsupials also occur in limited numbers in tropical America, where they are represented by several kinds of opossums, one species of which ranges northward into the United States.

The young in all members of this group are born in a very premature state. They are able, nevertheless, to climb into their mother's pouch, or marsupium, where they remain attached to her nipples for a long period

The Tasmanian devil (*Sarcophilus harrisii*) is a carnivorous marsupial from the Island of Tasmania. Courtesy SAN FRANCISCO ZOOLOGICAL SOCIETY

of time. Even after they are old enough to get about by themselves, I have often seen young kangaroos hop into the pouch of the female when frightened or tired.

In Australia marsupials have had little competition from other mammals for millions of years and have adapted themselves to many different kinds of habitats. As a consequence some species have become very specialized. Koalas, for example, are confined to eucalyptus forests, where their sole

Wallaroos (*Osphranter*) inhabit rocky situations in their native Australia. A young one may be seen here with the front part of its body out of the mother's pouch. Courtesy SAN FRANCISCO ZOOLOGICAL SOCIETY

food consists of the leaves of certain species of these native trees. This is one of the problems that zoo keepers in other parts of the world have to worry about if they are to maintain these animals alive and healthy for display.

The aforementioned fact was responsible for my involvement in an international argument early in the year 1959. At that time some members of our San Francisco Zoological Society thought that it would be desirable to secure several koalas for our zoo. Being the only member of the Board of Directors of the Society who was a mammalogist, I was somehow prevailed upon to prove to the Australian authorities that sufficient eucalyptus trees of the correct species were available locally to support a small koala population. After determining that this was true, I transmitted the information to the proper persons "down under." For reasons unknown to me this had an unfavorable effect on the Australian public, with the result

The koala (*Phascolarctos cinereus*) probably is the most famous of Australia's marsupials. Courtesy SAN FRANCISCO ZOOLOGICAL SOCIETY

that one Australian paper went so far as to say that sending koalas to California "would be like a sentence of death."

The arguments continued, with Evangelist Billy Graham, who was in Melbourne at the time, joining me in a plea for live koalas to be shipped to America. I even had the temerity to write a respectful letter to Her Majesty Queen Elizabeth II asking for her intervention in the matter. The receipt of this communication was announced in London with great reserve, following its acknowledgment by Buckingham Palace. Finally, on April 11, 1959, as a result of the efforts of many persons and through the great generosity of Sir Edward Hallstrom, Australian philanthropist and head of Sydney's famous Taronga Park Zoo, the koalas arrived at San Francisco's

A female tree kangaroo (*Dendrolagus*) with a baby poking its head out of the pouch. Courtesy
SAN FRANCISCO ZOOLOGICAL SOCIETY

International Airport. It was an exciting moment when Sir Edward stepped out of the plane with an armful of living "teddy bears." Sometime later one of the females gave birth to a baby, thus justifying our contention that koalas would not only survive in California but would thrive there.

While koalas and kangaroos are the best-known marsupials, there are a great many other kinds of pouched mammals in Australia. Many have developed in a manner that parallels the development of different groups of mammals in other parts of the world. Some have become rodent-like in appearance and habits, others superficially resemble carnivores. There is even a so-called "marsupial mole," which has become adapted to life beneath the surface of the ground. Flying phalangers are marsupials that are capable of gliding from tree to tree much like the flying squirrels of North America, Asia, and Europe.

The insectivores. Though more advanced than the egg-laying and pouched mammals, the insectivores are the most primitive of the higher Mammalia. It is from the ancestors of these small mammals that both bats and primates are believed to have evolved. The better-known representatives are moles, shrews, and hedgehogs. Three of the eight known families of the order Insectivora are confined to Africa. The giant water shrew, which attains a length of about two feet, occurs in the equatorial forested areas of that continent, where it lives in streams and rivers. It has an otter-shaped body and a laterally compressed tail that no doubt aids in swimming.

In South Africa there are several species of subterranean insectivores known as golden moles. Like the true moles, they have minute eyes, lack external ears, and have short but powerful front limbs for digging. They derive their name from the beautiful color of their soft fur. More widespread over arid parts of the African continent are the elephant shrews. These peculiar little animals have long hind legs and a tail somewhat like that of a kangaroo rat or a jerboa. The nose, however, is elongate like that of most insectivores and, because of its resemblance to a trunk, is responsible for the name "elephant shrew."

Two families of insectivores are insular in occurrence. One of these includes the tenrecs, which are confined to the island of Madagascar, and the other the solenodons of the West Indies. The tenrecs vary greatly in structure. The largest species are tailless and may measure up to eighteen inches in length. The small tenrecs have remarkably elongate tails. The solenodons are large for insectivores and resemble enormous rats.

The three remaining families are much more widespread. One of these contains the hedgehogs. Hedgehogs occur throughout most of Europe, Asia, and Africa. Their small, round, and essentially tailless bodies are covered with short stiff bristles. When alarmed, hedgehogs curl themselves into a ball, so that any attacking enemy must risk injury by these sharp spines. Like other insectivores, hedgehogs live largely on insects. However, they will also eat fruits and vegetables and are great scavengers.

The two most widely distributed families of insectivores are those containing the shrews and moles. Neither is found in Australia, and moles are absent from Africa and southeastern Asia, but both groups are well represented in other parts of the world.

Typical moles have naked, sensitive snouts; minute eyes that are obscured by the short, dense fur of the body; and short but powerful front legs whose huge claws enable the animals literally to swim through the ground. They lack external ears. In places moles are somewhat of a nuisance to gardeners because of their underground burrow system and their habit of pushing up mounds of dirt from their excavated tunnels. They do not, however, eat vegetable matter and frequently are beneficial in controlling certain kinds of insects on which they feed.

Shrews are the most abundant insectivores in the world, both as regards numbers of species and numbers of individuals. They range from the Arctic to the tropics and from desert to timberline in the higher mountains. There are no large shrews. The smallest living mammal is believed to be the pygmy shrew of North America, whose body weight is no more than that of a small coin.

Despite their small size, shrews are ferocious little animals. They will attack and kill other species many times their own size. They are voracious eaters and can easily consume an amount of food equal to their own body weight within a twenty-four-hour period. Some shrews will starve to death if they are deprived of food for even a few hours.

One morning some years ago while duck hunting, I was sitting quietly in a blind at sunrise. My eyes were on the horizon, but suddenly I became aware of the presence of a small visitor walking on dry reeds by my knee. It was a long-tailed shrew, so I edged it into an empty cartridge box, replaced the cover, and decided I had a new pet. When I arrived home about five hours later, the shrew was dead. Many others have had this same experience. For many years such deaths were attributed to fright. Now we know that shrews have such a high metabolic rate that they require food very frequently in order to live, and may die of starvation in a very short time.

Shrews feed on insects. To chew the tough chitinous covering that the majority of insects possess, shrews have highly developed and complex teeth, which are sometimes pigmented red or orange. They have few enemies because of their ferocity and also because they possess glands whose secretions are obnoxious to other animals.

The bats. Bats presumably developed from ancient insectivores back when the modern orders of mammals were first appearing. They are the only mammals that have developed the true power of flight. This has been

The pallid bat (*Antrozous pallidus*) has large external ears and moderately large eyes. R. T. ORR

accomplished by elongation of the bones of the palm and fingers, which are encased in a tough double flight membrane. The latter is responsible for the technical name Chiroptera that is given to this mammalian order. It literally means "winged hand." The flight membranes extend posteriorly and are joined at the ankle. In many kinds of bats another double membrane extends between the hind legs and may encase the tail.

Because of their powers of flight, bats are more widely distributed over

The hoary bat (*Lasiurus cinereus*) is a migratory species in North America. R. T. ORR

the world than any other group of terrestrial animals. They occur on all the continents except Antarctica and also on most oceanic islands of any size.

There are two major groups of bats—the fruit bats of Africa, Asia, Australia, and the Pacific Islands; and the so-called insectivorous bats, which are widespread over most of the world. The fruit bats are sometimes called flying foxes because of their relatively large size and somewhat foxlike faces. Large species may have a wingspread of up to four or five feet. As their name implies, they live principally on fruit; since they sometimes occur in flocks of tens of thousands of individuals, they are not looked upon with much favor by agriculturists.

The wings of bats consist of thin living membranes stretched over a delicate skeletal frame-work. R. T. ORR

The insectivorous bats have more complicated teeth than the fruit bats, and this enables them to break up the tough covering of insects on which most of them feed. Since bats are nocturnal, they serve to control the populations of certain night-flying insects, just as insectivorous birds control day-flying insects.

Some bats have developed very specialized food habits. In semidesert and tropical regions of North America there are nectar- and pollen-eating bats. There are species that eat fish, catching their food by impaling it on enlarged, talon-like claws as they fly over the surface of the water. One such species is found only on small islands in and along the shores of the Gulf of California.

Although I had observed these strange bats on such islands, it was not until 1954 that I had an opportunity to study this species in captivity. In April of that year I received several of these bats from a friend and succeeded in keeping one of them for almost ten years. Its diet consisted principally of small fish, which I kept frozen until feeding time each evening.

My serious involvement with bats really began in May, 1947, when my

Lesser white-lined bats (*Saccopteryx leptura*) from British Guiana. FRANCIS X. WILLIAMS

wife and I were guests at the ranch of some friends who had a keen interest in natural history. While exploring cliffs on the last day of our visit, we came upon a colony of pallid bats living in a rock crevice. It was not long before we had collected several dozen individuals, all of which proved to be females in advanced stages of pregnancy. The following morning we left for home with our live cargo in an improvised cage. As we approached San Francisco late that afternoon, our expectant mothers began to have their young. At least three baby bats were born while we drove across the Golden Gate Bridge, which I am sure was, and still is, an all-time record for that engineering masterpiece.

On reaching our home, we devoted most of the night to acting in the capacity of midwives for mother bats. Our interest was deeply aroused at watching the naked young emerging tailfirst, rather than headfirst like most other mammals. The reason seemed obvious, because the large tail membrane that extends from each hind foot to the tip of the tail in this species serves to cover the rather clumsy wings, which would hinder the delivery if the head came first.

For the following ten years much of my research was concerned with bats, especially their reproductive habits. We constructed many cages, which were referred to as "bateries" at the California Academy of Sciences, and succeeded not only in keeping some individuals alive and healthy for more than nine years but also in having captive animals breed and success-fully rear young.

The food bill was high, since these bats were fairly large and thrived on mealworms, which are expensive. However, this cost could be eliminated for three or four months each year by placing the bats in a refrigerated room where the temperature was maintained at about 40° Fahrenheit. Here they became dormant and remained in this induced state of hiber-nation until they were returned to a warm room again.

Several times each year subsequent to 1947 we visited the area where we had found the first colony and succeeded in locating a number of other bat roosts. One of these was situated in the loft of a barn on a ranch owned by a lady farmer. She welcomed us on our arrival on each occasion and was delighted to have us remove what she considered to be pests from her property. What she never knew was that while my wife and friends were with her capturing bats in the barn, I was usually outside releasing the bats that we had taken the previous year and had kept in captivity for study. The released animals were all banded so that we might learn something about their movements and longevity. I had no feeling of guilt about the matter, because these animals are very beneficial.

One of the most interesting and perhaps best known of the bats is the vampire, which ranges from Mexico to South America. Most of us have read or heard of the story of Count Dracula by Bram Stoker. The fact is that the basis for this legend which concerns the dead leaving their graves at night and feeding on the blood of human victims originated in southeastern Europe long before vampire bats, which are strictly inhabitants of the New World, were discovered.

Vampires live entirely upon blood. Their teeth are greatly reduced in number but sharp as a surgeon's scalpel. At night they stealthily approach their victims, which are frequently domestic animals, and make small incisions in the skin. The bitten animal's blood flows freely because of a nonclotting material in the bat's saliva. Since vampire bats may transmit rabies to animals or man, they are feared in certain regions.

The ability of bats to fly about at night without hitting obstacles in their environment was long a mystery to man. However, even as far back as 1793 an Italian scientist named Spallanzani showed that the ears and the mouth were essential to navigation in the air for these animals. He proved this by stringing piano wires across a room as obstacles and observing that bats could avoid hitting them in flight even though he covered their eyes so that they could not see. However, when he plugged the ears or sealed the mouths of the bats they seemed unable to detect the wires. The exact explanation of this was not discovered until around 1940, when it was determined that bats produced sounds of very high frequency with great rapidity when flying and that they depended upon the echo of these sounds to reveal the presence of nearby objects, large or small. Since then it has been found that there are a number of other kinds of animals that also use echolocation as a means of navigating either in the air or in water.

There are a few solitary kinds of bats, but most species are quite gregarious and live together in large colonies. Colonies of fruit bats roost during the daytime in trees in the tropics, but most colonial insectivorous bats inhabit caves, hollow trees, mine tunnels, or attics. Sometimes the females separate from the males when they are having their young, which usually number one or two. Later these nursing colonies break up.

The flying lemurs.   There are several very limited orders of mammals, and one of these is the Dermoptera which contain a most peculiar and primitive type of gliding animal found in the Philippine Islands, Malaya, Borneo, Sumatra, Java, and Siam. One of the common names applied to the several species contained in this order and placed in the genus *Cynocephalus* is the flying lemur.

Flying lemurs do not fly, nor are they lemurs. They glide because of the presence of fur-covered membranes that extend on each side of the body from the neck to the tail and encase the front and hind limbs exclusive of the webbed feet. These membranes provide a broad surface for gliding from tree to tree. Members of the order Dermoptera are not closely related to any living mammals but are thought to show a distant relationship to the most primitive primates, the tree shrews.

Flying lemurs are squirrel-like in size, and feed upon leaves and fruit. When sleeping they usually hang from a branch, to which they cling with all four feet.

The primates. The order Primates is the one to which man belongs. It not only contains the most intelligent of living creatures but also some very primitive species. Primates are believed to have originated from a basic insectivore-like stock far back in the early age of mammals. Even today the lowest members of this order are thought to be the tree shrews, a group that many consider to be somewhere between the insectivores and primates and which bear no close resemblance to higher monkeys and apes.

Apart from the primitive tree shrews, the primates are frequently divided into the lemurs and tarsiers, the Old World monkeys, the New World monkeys, and the great apes. The true lemurs are restricted to Madagascar and associated islands. They differ very much from the higher primates in appearance. In most species the tail is long and bushy, and the muzzle is often fairly elongate, as in an opossum or a fox. They vary also in size, the smallest having a body about four inches in length, while the largest is more than four feet long. Some species are strikingly colored. The bush babies, or galagos, of Africa and the lorises of southeastern Asia are lemur-like animals. They make interesting pets, but one must remember that they are nocturnal. If you are to enjoy their company, you must adapt your life to theirs.

Several years ago I received a slow loris from a friend who had returned from a collecting trip in southeastern Asia. We named him Boris, for the simple reason that it rhymes with loris. Boris was extremely deliberate in all his movements. In climbing about in his cage he never released his grasp with one hand until he had firmly latched on to the next object with his other hand. All his actions were in the slowest tempo one could imagine. He was very fussy about his food. While fond of fruit, he not only required that his grapes be peeled before he would eat them but they also had to be pink grapes and over-ripe as well. Boris was very lonely, so I gave him to my secretary, who had two bush babies from Africa. The presence of other lemurs, even though they were very active compared to a slow loris, was just what he needed. He is still alive and well today.

Some species of lemurs are strictly vegetarians, subsisting entirely on

"Boris," a slow loris (*Nycticebus coucang*) from southeastern Asia, has very large eyes for use at night. EDWARD S. ROSS

leaves or leaves and fruit. Other species are very fond of insects and are more or less omnivorous. Because most lemurs are restricted to Madagascar, their future is very uncertain. Extreme deforestation could easily result in the extinction of many kinds.

The tarsiers are strange little animals inhabiting the forests of the Philippine Islands, Java, Sumatra, Borneo, and the Celebes. They are nocturnal and live upon insects, which they capture in the treetops. Their most outstanding feature is their enormous eyes, which seem to be out of proportion to the small size of their bodies.

The true monkeys of the Old World are found throughout most of Africa and southern and eastern Asia, and on the Gibraltar peninsula in southern Europe. They vary greatly in appearance, since they include such diverse types as the baboons, the barbary ape, the colobus and Diana monkeys, the guenons, the macaques, the langurs, and the grotesque proboscis monkey of Borneo. Some have long tails and some short tails, but none have prehensile, or grasping, tails like the New World monkeys. Furthermore, unlike the latter group, they have nostrils that are separated by a rather narrow septum and directed downward, much as in our own nose.

Most monkeys are vegetarians, although some species are omnivorous. Their food is picked up with the hands and placed in the mouth, a characteristically primate trait and one that no doubt has been of great significance from the evolutionary standpoint. Some monkeys live in trees, rarely ever coming to the ground, while others, such as the baboons, are primarily ground-dwellers, although they may occasionally climb rocks or trees. Most monkeys are social animals, living in family groups or larger organizations in which an old male holds the position of dominance.

The New World monkeys range from southern Mexico south through Central America and much of South America. They include the tiny marmosets, tamarins, titi, and squirrel monkeys, as well as the larger capuchin, woolly, howler, and spider monkeys. Many of these primates have prehensile tails, which serve more or less as a fifth hand. Their noses, unlike those of the Old World primates, have the nostrils widely separated by a broad septum and opening laterally.

The New World monkeys often make excellent pets. They are usually seen in zoos. Best known, perhaps, are the capuchins or organ-grinders' monkeys, which in former years were frequently seen begging with a cup while the master ground out a tune. Marmosets, because of their diminutive size, appearance, vocalization, and friendliness, have often been among the most fashionable of pets.

The anthropoids are the most advanced and, to us, the most interesting of the primates because this is the group to which man belongs. The smallest are the gibbons and the closely related siamangs. These apes are remarkable acrobats, with very long arms that enable them to swing from limb to limb in their native forests of southeastern Asia.

The great apes consist of the gorilla, the chimpanzee, and the orangutan. The gorilla is the largest and most powerful of all the primates. It is con-

An immature Chacma baboon (*Papio porcarius*). NEW YORK ZOOLOGICAL SOCIETY

fined to remote and isolated forests in west-central Africa, particularly in the Cameroons, Gabon, and parts of the Congo. Some live in the lowlands, while others inhabit mountain areas. Gorillas are vegetarians and live in family groups. Despite their enormous strength, they rarely attack man, although I can vouch for one instance in which one did.

One of the least enjoyable experiences in my life took place in the San Francisco Zoo with two young gorillas named Bwana and Missy. Missy was the larger of the two, weighing about ninety pounds at the time. I had been in the cage with the gorillas, along with several other persons, for about two hours one morning in an attempt to secure some motion pictures of the animals in action for a television show. Both the apes were fairly friendly. They sat on my lap and ate ice cream. After performing with human beings for such a long time, I suppose Missy became irritable or possibly jealous of attention paid to Bwana. At any rate, while I was looking away from her, Missy landed on my back and attached herself there with her teeth. The following minute was one of the longest that I can recall, but she was eventually persuaded to let go. I had black and blue

"Big Daddy," an eleven-year-old male orangutan (*Pongo pygmaeus*) in the San Francisco Zoological Garden. R. T. ORR

marks on my back for some time to come but received no serious injury. The most regrettable part of the whole episode was the fact that the shutter of the motion picture camera was defective, and all the film taken that day was spoiled.

The chimpanzees, though smaller than gorillas, are considerably more dangerous and much more destructive. They are rather widely distributed over the deciduous forests of equatorial Africa. Chimpanzees exhibit a high degree of intelligence and, if started young, can be trained to perform

"Missy," a captive gorilla (*Gorilla gorilla*) on the occasion of her fifth birthday. Courtesy SAN FRANCISCO ZOOLOGICAL SOCIETY

many tricks, some of which seem almost human. They can be taught to ride a bicycle, smoke a cigarette, and even eat with a fork.

The orangutans are confined to the islands of Borneo and Sumatra. Unlike the gorillas and the chimpanzees, they spend most of their lives in trees, through which they can move with great dexterity because of their long and extremely powerful arms. They are reddish in color, in contrast to the blackish-brown color of the other great apes, and have faces that bear a certain resemblance to those of human beings. With age they develop huge throat sacs that give them a grotesque appearance.

The armadillos, anteaters, and sloths.   These animals are classified together in the order Edentata, which literally means "without teeth." Not all edentates are really toothless, but some are, and others have teeth that are reduced to uniform peglike structures.

The armadillos of North and South America are among the few living mammals that have their bodies covered with an armor of skin plates. When an armadillo rolls up like a pill bug, it presents an almost impenetrable outer surface to potential enemies. Hair is essentially lacking in these peculiar creatures. Like most members of this order, the armadillos reach their peak of development in South America, where they are believed to have originated. Some of the species in that continent have fur on the under parts of the body, with plates of armor on the head, back, and rump. The armor plate on the rump may serve to block the entrance to a burrow, keeping enemies out.

The giant, the lesser, and the pygmy anteaters are distributed variously over parts of Central and South America. The giant anteater is probably the best-known species, often being exhibited in zoos. It may attain a length of six feet and has a very long, slender head. The forearms are extremely strong, and the tail is long and plumelike. These anteaters lack teeth. Their food consists principally of termites, which they secure by breaking up the nest of these insects with their front claws and then inserting their long tubular tongue into the mass. The tongue is coated with a sticky saliva, which acts somewhat like flypaper to hold the termites. Although toothless, a giant anteater can prove a formidable opponent in battle by using its strong front limbs and claws.

There are two kinds of sloths that inhabit the New World tropics. One possesses two fingers on each foot, while the other has three. Sloths are strange animals, with enormous recurved claws by means of which they hang upside down from the limbs of trees. They not only sleep in this

The three-toed sloth (*Brady-pus griseus*) sleeps hanging in an upside-down position.
JOHN TASHJIAN

reversed position but also move about and feed the same way. Sloths are vegetarians, living on the leaves and flowers of certain trees. Their fur often has a greenish tinge, which makes them difficult to see when they are sleeping in the daytime. This color is the result of the presence of algae, which becomes established in their grooved hairs.

The pangolins. These odd animals belong to a very small order known as the Pholidota. There are only a few species of pangolins known, and they are found in the equatorial parts of Africa, Asia, and on the islands of Indonesia.

Superficially pangolins resemble the armadillo-like edentates. The upper parts of the head, body, and tail are covered with very large, hard scales that overlap one another like shingles. These scales serve for defense. When a pangolin is attacked, it curls up with the tail covering the head.

Pangolins have powerful limbs armed with long curved claws. They are often referred to as scaly anteaters, because their principal food consists of termites and ants, whose nests they tear apart with their front claws. As in the New World anteaters, the tongue is long and very protrusible and serves to gather the insects.

The pikas, hares, and rabbits.   The name Lagomorpha is applied to members of this order. In some respects the lagomorphs resemble rodents, but they are readily distinguished from these gnawing animals by the presence of four instead of two incisors or front teeth in the upper jaw. The second pair of incisors is small and situated behind the large front pair. Furthermore, these teeth are surrounded by enamel, while in rodents the enamel is restricted to the front of the incisor teeth.

The least-known members of the order are the pikas, or conies as they are sometimes called. Pikas are found in the northern parts of North America and Asia, barely getting into far-eastern Europe. They are moderately small, short-bodied animals, lacking any obvious tail. Their ears are rounded, somewhat like those of a rat.

Some of the Asiatic pikas live in burrows in forests, but most species are rock inhabitants, showing special preference for alpine talus slopes. To me pikas are a symbol of our western wilderness. They live high in the mountains in piles of rocks where bushy-tailed woodrats and pine martin are at home. To hear their little bleatlike utterances and see them scurrying among the boulders, one must get away from the highways and climb toward timberline. During the summer months they forage on vegetation growing close to the rock slides in which they live. In summer and autumn they harvest and dry plants for their winter food supply. These hay piles are quite apparent at these times of the year. Before the winter snows come, the cured hay is brought under the protection of overlying rocks. Pikas are active all winter.

Unlike hares and rabbits, pikas are rather vocal. They can often be heard calling from far down in rock piles in winter when deep snow on the surface seals them from the outer world.

Hares are generally larger than rabbits and usually depend upon escaping from their enemies by running rather than hiding in burrows or thickets. The newborn hare is fully furred and has its eyes open. It is capable of hopping around at a very early age. Newborn rabbits are essentially naked and do not open their eyes until they are some days old. They are entirely dependent upon maternal care for a few weeks.

The so-called "jack rabbit" of western North America is one of the best-known hares. It is a familiar figure on the prairies and deserts of the West.

One of the most interesting inhabitants of the coniferous forests of the North is the varying hare, sometimes called the snowshoe rabbit. These hares, like certain other northern animals, have fur that is brown in the summer and white in the winter. This change is accomplished by two molts a year, one in spring and the other in autumn. Since varying hares live in regions where the ground is generally covered with snow in the winter, it is easily seen that this seasonal change in color is decidedly protective. In Canada the principal enemy of the varying hare is the lynx.

Since the early days of fur trading, records have been kept by the Hudson's Bay Company on the annual take of lynx by trappers. These records show that the lynx population is dependent on the number of varying hares. When these hares are abundant, the animals that use them for food are abundant. Conversely, when the hare population undergoes a marked

"Billy," a varying hare (*Lepus americanus*) beginning to lose his brown summer coat. R. T. ORR

decline, a condition that occurs about every nine or ten years, the lynx population drops.

For years I had observed these interesting animals in the mountains of western North America, but my contact had never been too close. One day, however, I received a telephone call from a local banker who said he had found an abandoned litter of young snowshoe rabbits the previous year at Lake Tahoe and had reared them to maturity. Three were still alive and healthy and would be turned over to me for study if I wished. I gladly took them, because an interesting line of research occurred to me.

Lake Tahoe is at an elevation of over 6,200 feet in the Sierra Nevada and is covered with deep snow during the winter months. San Francisco, where our three varying hares were to reside, is essentially at sea level. The question in my mind of course was whether an animal that normally

"Billy" as he appeared a little more than two weeks after the preceding picture was made.
R. T. ORR

molts from a brown coat to a white coat in a high, cold environment do so in a locality where frost is newsworthy and the roar of the sea can be heard. The answer was definitely in the affirmative. Not only did the hares assume a brown pelage in the spring and a white one in the fall, but each individual began its spring and fall molt at a different time and did so consistently at about the same date during all the years that I had them.

In winter it was always a thrill to see those beautiful white animals, with dark eyes unlike those of a white domestic rabbit, move about silently on great padded feet, which are truly nature's snowshoes.

The domestic rabbit is a well-known species that is native to Europe and North Africa. It was introduced into England at the time of the Norman Conquest. European colonists introduced it into Australia, where it increased prodigiously because of favorable conditions and the absence of any natural enemies. Millions of dollars have been spent in trying to control rabbits in that country.

Hares and rabbits are widely distributed over the world. Various species occur in Asia, Europe, Africa, and North and South America. They are adapted to many different environments. Some live in the Arctic; others in mountains, deserts, and the tropics. There are also a few species of very limited distribution, such as the short-eared rabbit of Sumatra; the pygmy rabbit, which occurs locally in a small part of western United States; and the volcano rabbit of the high grassy slopes of Mount Popocatepetl in Mexico.

The rodents. The order Rodentia is an enormous one, containing more than half of the living species of mammals. Furthermore, many of these species are represented by vast numbers of individuals. Rodents occur from the arctic regions of Europe, Asia, and North America, south to the tip of South Africa and South America. They even occur in Australia, where the native mammalian fauna consists principally of monotremes, marsupials, and bats. Many Pacific islands are also inhabited by native rodents.

These animals are variously specialized to live on a great many kinds of plant life. They may consume lichens, fungi, ferns, grasses, annual and perennial flowering plants, and parts of deciduous and coniferous trees. Their food may consist of roots, tubers, stems, bark, leaves, flowers, fruits, seeds, or nuts. Some species show extreme specialization, such as the red-backed tree mouse of the Pacific coast of North America, whose food consists principally of parts of the needles of the Douglas fir. Others, like the Norway rat, are omnivorous. These animals, in turn, serve as food for many kinds of carnivores, and therefore represent an important part of a food chain.

Rodents are small- to medium-sized mammals. The smallest species are even more diminutive than the well-known house mouse and the largest, the capybara, is about three feet long and may weigh over two hundred pounds. It is a native of the rivers of South America. In North America the beaver is the largest rodent. All members of the order are characterized by the presence of only two incisors or front teeth above and two below. They lack canine teeth and have a large space between their front and back teeth.

The order is broadly divided into three major groups, based upon technical anatomical characters. These are the squirrel-like forms, the mouse-like forms, and the porcupine-like forms, technically known as the Sciuromorpha, the Myomorpha, and the Hystricomorpha. These divisions, however, are of little help to the nonprofessional because of the great diversity in appearance and habits exhibited by various members of these groups.

The sciuromorphs, or squirrel-like rodents, consist not only of the squirrels, ground hogs, and prairie dogs but also include such animals as the pocket gophers, the kangaroo rats, the pocket mice, the beaver, and the aplodontia. Of all of these mammals the squirrels are probably the best known, since they are found on all the continents. Some squirrels live in the ground in burrows, which they usually dig themselves. Certain species are colonial. This is especially true of the prairie dogs, which may have very large "cities."

Many kinds of squirrels are tree dwellers. They are found in coniferous, deciduous, and tropical forests in various parts of the world. The flying squirrels have even gone beyond this arboreal adaptation and have developed lateral folds of skin on either side of the body so that when their front and hind limbs are extended they present a broad, flat surface for gliding from tree to tree. Flying squirrels, unlike ground squirrels and tree squirrels, are nocturnal in habits.

I have kept both species of our North American flying squirrels and found them to be charming pets. My favorite is named Skitter. He is a member of the large northern species. What happened when he was a baby no one knows, but he was picked up by a Siamese cat one day. The cat's mistress lived in a trailer in the Giant Sequoia country, and Skitter was taken in and reared on a bottle. About a year later the family had to move and asked me if I would take him, which I did. He was a favorite

Flying squirrels (*Glaucomys volans*) do not really fly, but they are capable of gliding a considerable distance. R. T. ORR

with all visitors at the museum. I finally gave him to a friend who later took him back to Connecticut when her husband received an appointment to Yale University. It is a long way from a Big Tree forest to the Ivy League.

Beavers are aquatic rodents that were once widespread over North America, Europe, and Asia. Today the range of the beaver is very restricted. Under natural conditions beavers may live in dens, which they dig into the banks of rivers and streams, or else they construct dome-shaped houses of branches and mud in ponds. These houses are usually produced by the beavers themselves as a result of the damming of streams with fallen trees and mud. This serves to provide them with permanent water and to encourage the growth of aspen, willow, birch, and other trees on whose bark they feed.

Pocket gophers, kangaroo rats, and pocket mice are small mammals occurring in western North America. All possess fur-lined cheek pouches. Pocket gophers are subterranean in habits. The kangaroo rats have long hind tails and, when moving rapidly, progress in a bipedal manner like a kangaroo.

Some kangaroo rats and pocket mice have the ability to survive without free water. This does not mean that their bodies do not need water, but they acquire it indirectly, such as through the breakdown of fats. Also, they live in such a manner that their water loss is reduced to a minimum. Many years ago I captured a small silky pocket mouse in the center of what is presently the Atom Bomb Test Range in Nevada. Cactus, as I named him, since he came from Cactus Flat, lived for seven years and during that time ate nothing but air-dried bird seed and an occasional walnut. He could not be induced to eat greens or consume water. I have never had an easier pet to keep. A handful of seed would last him for a month.

Kangaroo rats (*Dipodomys heermanni*) are adapted to life in desert areas of western North America. R. T. ORR

The majority of the rodents of the world are myomorphs, the group containing the house mouse and the Norway rat as well as the many species of voles and field mice. It is estimated to consist of nearly two thousand species, many of which are of considerable importance to man. The European house mouse and also the Norway, roof, and black rats have spread to many parts of the world. Their populations are concentrated principally in cities and towns, although there are few ranches and farms that do not have some representatives about their barns. The food they consume, or make useless by contamination, amounts to many millions of dollars annually. Furthermore, they are a potential danger because of disease that they may transmit to man by way of such ectoparasites as fleas. Rat fleas are the chief vector of the dreaded bubonic plague that was a threat to all Europe in the Middle Ages.

In the Northern Hemisphere voles are among the better-known members of this group of rodents. These little animals are principally inhabitants of grasslands and meadows, both in the lowlands and mountains. They tend to have rather blunt muzzles, tails of only short or moderate length, and relatively long, coarse hair. Many kinds make runways in the vegetation that lead from one burrow to another. They are active all year round.

Voles are important sources of food for many kinds of carnivorous mammals, birds, and reptiles. Some species undergo marked cyclic fluctuations in numbers. This phenomenon, however, is best known among their arctic relatives, the lemmings. The lemmings of Europe, Asia, and North America experience periodic population increases which finally result in so many individuals being present in a given region that reproduction ceases. Large-scale emigrations then may occur, and vast numbers die from various causes, including disease, starvation, shock, and other factors not yet known.

A relative of the vole that has become aquatic in habits is the muskrat. This species lives in ponds and rivers where there is an abundance of vegetation. Its tail, unlike that of most rodents, is laterally compressed and serves somewhat as a rudder in swimming. The underfur in muskrats is very soft and thick and keeps the animal warm and dry. In many places muskrats make rounded nests from the leaves and stems of water plants. These nests, rising domelike out of the water, are used for the rearing of the young.

Lesser-known myomorph rodents of wide distribution are the jumping mice of North America, Europe, and Asia. These are small, trim animals with remarkably long tails and rather long hind legs for jumping. Their fur is somewhat harsh and often of an orange color on the sides and pure white below. They inhabit grassy areas in or close to woodlands and forests and hibernate in winter. They are related to the jerboas of Asia and North Africa, a group of small mammals that have developed remarkable hind legs and long tails much like the kangaroo rats of western North America. The jerboas are adapted to life in desert country.

There are many other myomorph groups that are much more restricted than those already mentioned. A few examples are the hamsters of Asia and Africa; the rice rats, whose range extends from southern United States through much of South America; the deer mice and wood rats of North America; and the water rats of the Australasian area.

The third group of rodents, the Hystricomorpha, is one that developed in South America. Because of submergence of the Isthmus of Panama during much of recent earth history, it is represented outside of Central and South America by only a few species, all of which are porcupines. Porcupines are found over forested parts of North and South America, and in parts of Europe, Africa, Asia, Sumatra, Java, and Borneo. All these animals have hairs that have developed into stiff bristles that serve for protection against enemies. However, the New and Old World porcupines have developed independently and are not closely related. The North American porcupine is a slow-moving rodent of moderately large size. It is primarily an inhabitant of coniferous forests, although by no means restricted to such a habitat. Because it feeds largely on the bark of trees at certain seasons of the year, the porcupine is looked upon with disfavor by many foresters. In Central and South America there are species of porcupines that have prehensile tails.

The remaining hystricomorphs are largely South American, with a few species ranging northward as far as southern Mexico. Although most of them are little known outside their native land, some are world renowned. The guinea pig is one of these. Guinea pigs were one of the few native South American mammals that were domesticated prior to the discovery of the New World. In the wild they are known as cavies.

Another famous hystricomorph is the chinchilla. It may come as a surprise to many that these little animals, whose extremely fine silky fur commands such a high price, are relatives of the bristly haired porcupines. Chinchillas are native to the higher parts of the Andes in Chile, Bolivia, and Peru. Today they are raised on farms in many parts of the world for their fur. Other related South American rodents are the capybara, which is the largest member of the order; the coypu, or, as it is more commonly known in the fur trade, nutria; the viscacha; the hutia; the paca; and the agouti.

The cetaceans. The cetaceans are the porpoises, dolphins, and various kinds of whales. Although they are living in the sea, which is the ancestral home of animal life, they are really descendants of land animals that have moved into an environment where they have little competition from other members of the class. These mammals have torpedo-shaped bodies that glide smoothly through the water. Beneath their skin is a thick layer of fat, or blubber, which helps to insulate them against the cold of their environment. Many species inhabit arctic and antarctic waters during the summer months.

Most of the big whales lack teeth. Instead they have long strips of a substance called baleen hanging down in rows from either side of the upper jaw. The edges of these strips have hairlike fringes and function as strainers. The food of these whales consists of small floating or swimming marine organisms, especially a type of crustacean known as krill. Huge masses of these tiny animals are taken into the whale's mouth with seawater. The water then flows out through the baleen, leaving the food material behind.

The largest animal that has ever lived on earth is the blue whale, a species found in most of the oceans of the world today. The blue whale may attain a length of one hundred feet and weigh as much as one hundred twenty-five tons.

The sperm whale, the killer whale and its relatives, the beaked whales, and the porpoises and dolphins possess teeth. Their food consists principally of various kinds of fishes and squid. The sperm whale is the largest of the toothed whales and may reach sixty-five feet in length. Sperm whales have teeth in the lower jaw only and have a huge head that contains oil compartments. These animals are capable of diving to great depths. They are known to feed at times on giant squid, which occasionally challenge them to mighty battles. Killer whales may attack and eat seals, sea lions, and even other kinds of whales.

The porpoises and dolphins come into bays and rivers. There are freshwater species that inhabit certain of the larger rivers of the world—the Amazon, the Ganges, the Yangtze, and others.

Since cetaceans are mammals, they must come to the surface periodically

The spout of a whale represents the exhalation of air from the lungs along with some water vapor and a certain amount of external water that may be over the blowhole. JOHN TASHJIAN

to breathe air. When they surface they usually exhale, or spout. The spout has a certain amount of vapor in it, and, of course, some of the water outside the nasal valve is blown into the air at such times. For these reasons it was erroneously believed in former times that whales spouted water.

Man has learned a great deal about the smaller whales, porpoises, and dolphins in recent years. One of the most interesting discoveries is the fact that they produce a great many underwater sounds. The echos of these sounds enable them to find their way around in the sea, much as bats make use of echolocation in the air. The echos are actually used somewhat as a ship uses a sonar depth finder. The time required for the echo to bounce back from an object—the shore, the bottom, food, or other members of their own species—provides a means of determining the location and distance of the object. These animals have developed this amazing sense to such a high degree that they are capable of distinguishing small particles of food from nonfood particles of the same size.

Cetaceans are very intelligent animals. Their brains are proportionately larger than those of the great apes, and their ability to learn in captivity is remarkable. At Marineland in Florida and Marineland of the Pacific in California, trained dolphins perform many tricks and are taught in a very short time to play complicated games.

Cetaceans have a high degree of intelligence. This pilot whale (*Globiocephala*) leaps high out of the water to hit a ball suspended in the air at Marineland in Florida. R. T. ORR

Bottlenosed dolphins (*Tursiops*) can readily be trained to perform complicated tricks in captivity. R. T. ORR

I have read accounts of dolphins and porpoises that reportedly saved the lives of swimmers who were drowning by nosing them to the surface and pushing them toward shore. How true this is I don't know, but mothers of newborn dolphins have been seen pushing their young to the surface to breathe. I also remember a sick captive porpoise that we kept for a few days in the Steinhart Aquarium. It had been injured by a ship, and we tried to save its life. The animal had difficulty surfacing to breathe, and soon learned that I would hold its head above water by placing my hand under its chin. Thereafter, every time I came to the tank the porpoise immediately came to me for assistance.

A bottlenosed dolphin leaping high out of the water in the Gulf of California. BRUCE MARKHAM

The carnivores. These are the so-called flesh-eating mammals belonging to the order Carnivora. Carnivores are very widely distributed over the world, even being represented in Australia by the doglike dingo. The smallest species is the least weasel of northern North America, whose body is no larger than that of a field mouse, while the largest is the brown bear of Alaska, reported to attain a maximum weight of fifteen hundred pounds.

The living carnivores are grouped into seven different families generally separated into two groups by scientists. The first group contains the cats, the hyenas, and the civets. The second group contains the dogs, the bears, the raccoon-like animals, and members of the weasel family.

The cat family has representatives on all the major continents. They fall into three or four natural groups. One of these comprises the large cats, such as the lion, the tiger, the leopard, the snow leopard, the clouded leopard, and the jaguar. The cheetah is distinct from all other living cats in its ability to run at remarkable speeds. It has unusually long legs and lacks the retractile claws so characteristic of cats in general. The cheetah is native to parts of Africa and Asia. The smaller cats are either grouped together or divided into two tribes—those with tufted ears, often referred to as the lynxes, and those without, such as the many other small species found in various parts of the world. One of these is the wild cat of Europe and North Africa, which is believed to be the progenitor of the house cat.

For many persons cats have a great attraction. Perhaps it is because of

The male lion (*Panthera leo*) on the Serengetti Plain. EDWARD S. ROSS

their independence and refusal to obey orders. I have always attributed this seeming aloofness to the fact that cats in general are not pack animals, which many members of the dog family are. As a result cats will not be led and insist on doing only what they want to do.

The story of the domestic cat goes far back in antiquity. The ancient Egyptians honored them and had the cat god Bastis. So highly prized were cats in Egypt that the killing of one was a crime punishable by death. There was a practical reason for this. The cats kept down the mice and permitted the storage of grain.

The hyenas, despite their somewhat doglike appearance, are rather closely related to cats and civets. The family is represented by three species: The striped hyena occurs in parts of India and Africa; the spotted hyena

Tigers (*Panthera tigris*) are strictly Asiatic, ranging far north into Siberia. Courtesy SAN FRAN-
CISCO ZOOLOGICAL SOCIETY

(Right) Even as a kitten, the serval (*Felis serval*) has proportionately large ears. ED-WARD S. ROSS

(Below) Leopards (*Panthera parrdus*) are still found in the wild in many parts of Africa and in southern Asia. Courtesy SAN FRANCISCO ZOOLOGICAL SOCIETY

The ocelot (*Felis pardalis*) is the common cat of the New World tropics. It is frequently kept in captivity but cannot be regarded as domesticated. Courtesy SAN FRANCISCO ZOOLOGICAL SOCIETY

is restricted to Africa; and the third member is the aard-wolf of Africa. Hyenas have the forequarters of the body much larger than the hind parts. The head is large, and the jaws are extremely powerful and capable of crushing large bones. Hyenas are mostly scavengers, although they will kill when given the opportunity. The aard-wolf, unlike its two relatives, has rather small teeth, and, though it will consume carrion, its principal food consists of insects, particularly termites.

The civets are small- to medium-sized carnivores restricted to Africa and Asia, except for one species that gets into southern Europe. Members of this family have scent glands that may exude a strong-smelling substance. Although there are a great many species of civets, few of them are well known, with the exception of the mongooses. Mongooses have been

The spotted hyena (*Crocuta crocuta*) is a carrion feeder that occurs over much of Africa. Its jaws and teeth are extremely powerful. JOHN TASHJIAN

domesticated for thousands of years and have achieved fame for their ability to defeat cobras and to control rat populations. Unfortunately, the latter attribute has been responsible for their introduction into certain islands, including Cuba and the islands of Hawaii, where it was hoped they would eliminate rats and mice. Instead they have tended to prey upon more readily accessible native species and have been responsible for the extinction of certain ground-dwelling birds.

There are few parts of the world where one does not find members of the dog family. They are represented in the Northern Hemisphere principally by the wolves, coyotes, and various kinds of foxes. Jackals range widely over the drier parts of Africa, southeastern Europe, and southern Asia. The raccoon-dogs and dholes are found in eastern Asia, the hunting dogs in Africa. In South America there is a group of jackal-like animals whose relationship to other canines is somewhat obscure.

Many kinds of carnivores tend to lead solitary lives, but this is generally not true of members of the dog family. Some species hunt in packs and have a rather well-established social order.

In North America wolves have been eliminated over much of the range that they originally inhabited except in remote subarctic regions. Several species of native foxes, however, have survived the inroads of civilization

The maned wolf (*Chrysocyon*) is a long-legged member of the dog family that occurs in southeastern South America.
JOHN TASHJIAN

fairly well. These include the gray fox, the red fox, the kit fox, and the arctic fox.

Bears are much more restricted in distribution than any other carnivores. In North America they are represented by the polar bear, the black bear, the brown bear, and the grizzly. The grizzly has been eliminated throughout much of its former range. Bears are presumably absent in Africa. In South America there is the spectacled bear of the Andes. The sun bear and sloth bear both occur in Asia, as do brown bears, closely related to those found in North America and northern Europe.

The black bear of North America is one of the best-known species and is often in evidence in certain national parks. Its name is misleading, because it has several different color phases, including brown and cinnamon. In colder parts of North America black bears den up in winter and enter into partial hibernation. It is not a complete hibernation, since their body temperatures do not drop much at such times, and they can easily be awakened.

Most bears are omnivorous, feeding on berries, grass, roots, insects, and honey as well as meat. This is especially true of the smaller kinds. Polar bears depend to a large extent on seals for food, and the brown and grizzly bears are very adept at catching fish, particularly salmon when they are moving upstream to spawn.

The black bear (*Ursus americanus*), which comes in many other colors, is still fairly common in the mountains of North America. R. T. ORR

(Left) The polar bear (*Thal-arctos maritimus*) is strictly an arctic species. Courtesy SAN FRANCISCO ZOOLOGICAL SOCIETY

(Opposite) While the grizzly (*Ursus horribilis*) appears to be a comic in the zoo, it is a dangerous animal to encounter in the wild. Today it is gone from most of its former range. Courtesy SAN FRANCISCO ZOOLOGICAL SOCIETY

The raccoon family is well known in North and Central America, where raccoons, cacomistles, or ring-tailed cats, coatimundis, and kinkajous occur. Some of these animals are also represented in parts of South America.

Two strange and not very closely related members of this family occur in the Himalayas of Nepal and western China. These are the lesser panda and the giant panda. The lesser panda, in certain respects, resembles the North American raccoon, even having a banded tail. The giant panda, however, is more bearlike in appearance. Although it is a carnivore, its native food consists entirely of bamboo shoots. Only a few of these odd black-and-white animals have ever been exhibited in zoos.

The weasel family is a large one, containing many important fur-bearing species. The smallest members are the various kinds of weasels that occur throughout the Americas, Asia, and Europe. Weasels are known for their cunning and strength. While they may do great damage to domestic fowl, they are extremely valuable in curbing small rodent populations in many parts of the world.

One of the most interesting members of this family is the sea otter of the north Pacific coast. This species was responsible for the Russian exploration of North America, from Alaska south to California, in the eighteenth and early nineteenth centuries. Single pelts are reported to have brought as much as $1,500 to $2,000 in the European fur market in

The raccoon (*Procyon lotor*) uses its front feet in feeding.
EDWARD S. ROSS

Raccoons soon become accustomed to human beings and learn to make nightly visits to the kitchen door.
EDWARD S. ROSS

those days. Their value, however, almost brought about their extinction in the nineteenth century. Rigid protection in recent decades has saved them from this fate. Sea otters rarely come to land. In the sea, just beyond the surf, they float and swim on their backs unlike other marine mammals. Their food consists of shellfish, and they have a most remarkable habit of opening various mollusks and sea urchins with the aid of a rock, which they bring up from the ocean floor and use as a tool on their bellies while they float.

These little animals have recently moved into the waters surrounding an island where I have been studying seals and sea lions. They show little fear of the larger marine mammals, which often come up to them as they float on their backs. One might wonder why they don't drift away with the tides, but they have solved this problem by wrapping about their bodies

The sea otter (*Enhydra lutris*) swims on its back in the sea. R. T. ORR

the long stems of seaweed attached to the ocean bottom. Thus they anchor themselves.

Among the better-known members of this family are the minks and martens. Because their furs are highly valued, they are now raised commercially on fur farms. The pine marten of North America is a beautiful animal that is associated with the northern coniferous forests. On the few occasions that I have come across marten in the high country, my first impression has been that I was looking at a red squirrel. They are nimble animals and can move with great rapidity up the trunk of a tree or from limb to limb in a squirrel-like manner.

Less valuable as fur-bearers, but equally well known, are the several kinds of skunks, whose strong scent provides them with effective protection against their enemies. Scent glands are characteristic of all mustelids but

The river otter (*Lutra canadensis*) tames readily in captivity. R. T. ORR

are perhaps most highly developed in skunks whose fur is patterned variously in black and white.

The largest and most ferocious member of the family is the wolverine, which occurs over forested parts of the Northern Hemisphere. It is said that wolverines are even avoided by bears. They are often referred to as gluttons because of their appetites and perhaps because they will follow a trap line and destroy the catch. Despite their ferocity, they can be tamed.

Badgers, the ratels, the grisons, the zorilles, and the tayras are some of the other members of the weasel family.

The pinnipeds. The seals, sea lions, and walruses belong to an order known as the Pinnipedia, which literally means "feather feet." Their name is derived from the fact that their front and hind limbs are modified as flippers. These animals are mostly marine in occurrence, although there are some species found in fresh water. The Lake Baikal seal, which occurs in the huge Siberian lake after which the seal is named, is one of these. Most pinnipeds, however, are found along continental coasts or the edges of the polar ice caps. A few, like the Hawaiian seal, are inhabitants of oceanic island shores.

Walruses are restricted to arctic or subarctic waters, where they spend much of their time on floating masses of ice. Their food consists principally of shellfish of various kinds, especially oysters and clams, which they secure from the ocean floor. They have been known occasionally to eat small seals. The greatly enlarged canine teeth, which are tusklike in form, are distinctive features of adult walruses. They have been hunted for centuries by the Eskimos for their ivory, which is carved into tools, weapons, and ornaments. Today the conservation of these animals is a considerable problem, since they are easily decimated by modern weapons.

The walruses comprise one of the three families of pinnipeds. The other two are the eared seals and the so-called "earless" or hair seals. The eared seals include the sea lions, which are represented by several species in both the Northern and Southern Hemispheres, and the fur seals. All members of this family have small external ears, which can easily be seen, and hind flippers that are reversible and can be used more or less as feet to travel on land. The sea lions are the largest members of the family. They may have derived their name not only from their size but also from the fact that the hair on the neck of the males is often somewhat shaggy, perhaps vaguely resembling the mane of a lion. At least one species roars in a lionlike manner.

Several species of fur seals nearly became extinct in the nineteenth century as a result of being sought for their pelts. Following rigid protection, however, some have made a fine comeback. The Alaskan or northern fur seal is one of these. Presently about two million of these animals migrate annually to the breeding rookeries on the Pribilof Islands in Bering Sea, Alaska, and a number of the nonbreeding males are harvested each year for their fur under government supervision.

The "earless seals," or hair seals, can really hear very well, but they lack a prominent external ear such as the sea lions and fur seals possess. Furthermore, their hind flippers cannot be turned forward and therefore are of little use for moving about on land. The harbor seal is fairly common along both coasts of North America in temperate and subarctic waters and is well known to many people. It also occurs along the coasts of northern Europe and Asia. Most of the hair seals, however, are found in the Arctic and Antarctic. The largest seals in the world are the elephant seal, of which there are two species. One occurs on islands bordering the Antarctic, and the other on several islands along the Pacific coast, from northwestern Mexico to central California. Large bulls, as the adult males are called, may measure nearly twenty feet in length and weigh as much as seven thousand pounds.

The Guadalupe fur seal (*Arctocephalus philippi townsendi*) was barely saved from extinction. Even today only a few hundred living individuals are known to exist. GEORGE E. LINDSAY

Some pinnipeds, such as the Alaskan fur seals, the sea lions, and elephant seals, have a very interesting social organization during the reproductive season. The breeding males come to the rookery areas and, after vying for favorable locations for some days or even weeks, space themselves out on the beaches or reefs. There they attempt to secure harems of females, referred to as cows, when these arrive. They are very belligerent at such times. I have been chased on several occasions by Steller sea lion bulls, but I have no desire to engage in any argument with these big animals, whose weight may be as much as two thousand pounds. Even on the Galapagos Islands, where native animals are remarkably tame, I have been chased by bull California sea lions. Elephant seal bulls are also belligerent during the breeding season, but they are so awkward on land that I have never had any fear of being outrun by one when it charged.

Some years are required for the males to attain maturity, so the sub-adults, or "bachelors" as they are called, are kept out of the harem areas and must stay by themselves. The bulls protect their harems of cows against invasion by unestablished males. Within several weeks after the young are born, the adults mate. About six to eight weeks after the arrival of the females, the harems break up and the bulls leave. In some species the young are weaned when not much more than one month old. Others, however, are dependent upon the mother for many months and may even nurse when over a year old. Seal milk is very rich in fat but, unlike that of other mammals, is lacking in sugar. This is one of the reasons why it is so difficult to raise young seals in captivity. They become ill on cow's milk.

Seals and sea lions have enemies other than man. One of their great natural enemies is the killer whale, whose principal food consists of seal-like animals. Sharks may kill pinnipeds in certain regions, and the leopard seal of the Antarctic is a killer of other seals.

The aardvarks.   These are among the strangest mammals in the world. They differ so much from any other living members of the class that they constitute a separate order known as the Tubulidentata. The several rather closely related species of aardvarks are distributed widely over various parts of Africa south of the Sahara Desert region.

The head of an aardvark is elongate, with the snout proportionately longer than that of a pig. The ears are large, like those of many deer and antelope. The body, which may reach a total length from snout to tail of as much as six feet, is often very sparsely haired. The legs are short and stocky, and the feet are armed with very powerful claws.

(Above) A subadult male
elephant seal (*Mirounga an-
gustirostris*) beginning to develop a proboscis. R. T. ORR

(Right) An elephant seal
bull. R. T. ORR

Two large Steller sea lion (*Eumetopias jubata*) bulls engaged in serious combat over a harem.
R. T. ORR

These animals are great diggers and can penetrate very hard soil with remarkable rapidity. Their food consists largely of termites, which they secure by tearing the huge nests of these insects to pieces with their front limbs. Occasionally they will live under old termite mounds.

The name Tubulidentata is based on the peculiar structure of the aardvark's teeth, which lack an external covering of enamel. Each tooth consists of a series of parallel tubes of dentine.

The elephants.   Indian and African elephants are the sole survivors of the order Proboscidia. Before and even during parts of the Pleistocene epoch, when successive periods of glaciation occurred over areas of the Northern

Steller sea lion bulls in the center surrounded by cows in a harem area. R. T. ORR

Hemisphere, there were a number of different kinds of elephant-like animals in North America, Europe, and Asia. Some were abundant in what is presently the Arctic. Numerous tusks as well as other skeletal remains are found in Alaska, and frozen carcasses with the flesh and skin intact have been discovered in glacial ice in Siberia.

As far as size is concerned the African elephant is the largest living land mammal. The Indian elephant is considerably smaller and occupies the position of third behind its larger African relative and the African white rhinoceros. Elephants have a number of well-known structural characters that set them off from other mammals, but the most unique is the elongated nose, which forms a long trunk, or proboscis. This not only serves for respiratory purposes but is used as a tool in gathering food and even to spray water over the body while bathing.

Elephants are social animals and usually travel in groups in a nomadic manner. Among Indian elephants the leader may be an older female. In disposition the African and Indian elephants are quite different. The former is difficult to tame, and today is used for domestic work in only a few parts of Africa. The Indian elephant, on the other hand, while not truly domesticated in the sense that it will breed well in captivity, has been used by man for centuries. We read in history that Hannibal used elephants to cross the Alps and defeat the Romans in the third century B.C.

Female Indian elephants and, less rarely, African elephants are exhibited in zoos, but the males are generally regarded as too treacherous for this

An African elephant along the Nile below Murchison Falls. EDWARD S. ROSS

purpose. Nevertheless, there are a number of records of famous captive males.

The hyraxes, or coneys. These little animals of Africa and western Asia belong to the order Hyracoidea. They are about the size of a hare, and, because of the name "coney," which goes back to biblical times, have been confused with rabbits in the literature. Though they bear a superficial resemblance to lagomorphs and rodents, their true relationship brings them much closer to elephants and sea cows.

Hyraxes have four toes on the front feet and three on the hind feet. The nails on the feet are hooflike in form and enclose a thick central pad, which can be raised so as to produce a sort of vacuum cup. This enables them to climb very steep rocks without falling. Their ears are moderately small, and the body fur is coarse. A tail is essentially lacking.

There are two main groups of species in the order—the dassies and the tree hyraxes. The dassies occur in isolated, rocky, mountainous parts of southwestern Asia and in similar situations throughout Africa to the southern tip of that continent. The tree hyraxes of Africa are forest inhabitants spending most of their lives up in trees, where they live in holes or in dense clumps of epiphytic growths that are so characteristic of tropical forests.

Hyraxes are somewhat omnivorous. Their principal food consists of vegetation and insects, which they secure in the evening and early morning hours. They are shy and retiring, but have shrill voices, which are often heard even when the animals themselves cannot be seen.

The manatees and dugongs. Members of the order Sirenia are frequently referred to as sea cows. They might at first glance be confused with seal-like animals, but they are in no way related to them. They are rather large aquatic mammals whose front limbs are modified into flippers and whose hind limbs, like those of whales, are missing. The tail is expanded into a very broad, horizontal, paddle-like structure. Scientists are of the opinion that sirenians are distantly related to elephants and hyraxes because of certain structural characters.

The manatees occur along the tropical shores of the Atlantic Ocean as well as the mouths and lower stretches of the larger rivers, from Florida south to the Amazon River and along the west coast of Africa. They may occur in fresh, brackish, or salt water. Although they do not frequent the open sea like the dugong, they may be found around protected coral islands many miles from continental shores. Manatees are sluggish animals and live entirely on aquatic vegetation.

The dugong, while it is occasionally found at the mouths of larger rivers and in coastal waters, is quite marine in habitat, occurring all around the Indian Ocean, from Africa to Australia, as well as in the western Pacific Ocean. In parts of Asia these big, slow-moving, harmless animals are considered choice items of food and their meat is sold in the markets. This is responsible for their present scarcity throughout much of their range.

Some years ago we received a live dugong from the Coral Sea at the Steinhart Aquarium. It was given the name Eugenie in honor of a well-

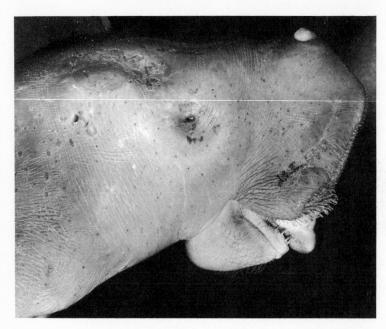

A portrait of "Eugenie" the dugong (*Dugong dugong*). There is little resemblance here to a mermaid. R. T. ORR

known woman oceanographer. Eugenie, being the only dugong in captivity, rapidly became famous and was pictured in one of our national weekly magazines in various poses. A friend of mine, who was an authority on sirenians at the American Museum of Natural History, soon wrote me that he had seen pictures of our new acquisition and that Eugenie was not a lady but should be renamed Gene. We ultimately learned a great deal about dugong anatomy.

A third type of sirenian existed in the north Pacific Ocean until the latter part of the eighteenth century. This huge creature, known as Steller's sea cow, was said to attain a length of thirty feet and weighed several tons. The early sealers and whalers, however, so prized its flesh that it was completely exterminated.

Sirenians have played a part in folklore of the sea for many centuries. They are believed to have been responsible for the legend of mermaids, because of their habit of raising the front part of the body vertically out of the water. Females holding young against their breast with their flippers may have vaguely resembled human females when seen by seafaring men at a distance. The face of a sirenian when viewed at close range, however, is far from human in any respect.

The odd-toed hoofed animals. These are hoofed mammals whose functional toes are reduced to three or one. They are known as the Perissodactyla and comprise the horses, the tapirs, and the rhinoceroses. Once widespread and abundant, the perissodactyls today are represented in the world by a very few species.

In prehistoric times horselike animals were common in North America, but presently they are found in the wild only in parts of Asia and Africa. The domesticated horse is believed to be a descendant of Przewalski's wild horse of Asia, a species now known only from remote parts of Mongolia and Siberia. Other living horselike animals are the onager of Asia, the two kinds of African zebras, and the wild asses of Asia, the latter having given rise to the domestic donkey.

All these horselike animals have relatively large bodies, elongated heads, molariform teeth adapted to grinding coarse vegetation as well as sharp cutting teeth in the upper and lower jaws, manes along the back of the neck, short tails covered with very long hairs, and extremely specialized limbs. Their limbs show a marked reduction in the number of bones present in contrast to those of most other mammals. The end of the limb consists of a single functional toe, whose nail is modified as a hoof on which the weight of the body rests.

The zebras are among the most interesting and, at present, most abundant of the wild horses. They are confined to Africa and constitute a very important source of food for the lion. Their bodies are variously striped in black and white, black and cream, or reddish-tan and white. Zebras show great variation in striping, both individually and geographically. It is probable that only two species exist in Africa today. These are the widespread Burchell's or common zebra and Grevy's zebra, a more restricted species with a larger head and much narrower stripes than the former.

The tapirs, like the rhinoceroses, possess three functional toes on each foot. The most conspicuous feature of these animals is their elongate, proboscis-like nose. The distribution of tapirs in the world is just about as strange as the shape of their nose. One species occurs in southwestern Asia, and three other species occur in parts of Central and South America. This is an indication that tapirs once occurred in North America and over much of Asia, a former distribution confirmed by the fossil record.

Tapirs are forest-dwelling animals and largely nocturnal. Their food consists of various kinds of vegetation ranging from water plants to the leaves of trees. The Malayan tapir is strikingly colored. Its short fur is black except on the back, sides, and flanks, which are white, thus producing a singularly disruptive color pattern that makes the animal inconspicuous in its native jungle habitat. The American species lack such contrasting coloration, being dark brown for the most part.

Several species of rhinoceroses are found in parts of Africa and Asia

The common zebra (*Equus burchelli*) is of widespread occurrence throughout much of eastern and southern Africa. Courtesy SAN FRANCISCO ZOOLOGICAL SOCIETY

The African black rhinoceros (*Diceros bicornis*) has a somewhat prehensile upper lip. Courtesy
SAN FRANCISCO ZOOLOGICAL SOCIETY

today. These strange, prehistoric-appearing animals have thick, mostly hairless, gray hides that are thrown into folds over various parts of the body. Their tails are short and piglike and their eyes are small. There may be either one or two hornlike structures on the front of the head. These so-called horns are really derived from matted hair and are not comparable to the true horns of certain artiodactyls.

The second largest land mammal in the world is the African white or square-lipped rhinoceros. This species, like the African black rhinoceros, has two horns. There are two species in Asia that possess but a single horn. The largest is the great Indian rhinoceros of Nepal, Assam, and Bengal. There are also other species in Asia with two horns.

The square-lipped or white rhinoceros (*Ceratotherium simum*) is becoming one of the rarer mammals in Africa. Courtesy SAN FRANCISCO ZOOLOGICAL SOCIETY

Rhinos in general are grazing animals. They may be found singly or in small groups. Their sense of sight is poor as contrasted with that of many other hoofed animals. They are extremely powerful and if aroused can prove formidable opponents for the largest carnivores.

The even-toed hoofed animals. The hoofed mammals with two or four toes on each foot are grouped together in the order Artiodactyla. It is a large and widespread one and of great economic importance to man. Some of the better-known representatives are pigs, hippopotamuses, deer, camels, giraffes, antelopes, cattle, sheep, and goats. Artiodactyls show great range in size as well as diversity in form. Some, like the chevrotains of Asia, are no larger than a rabbit, while the opposite extreme is shown by the giraffe, the water buffalo, and the bison.

Man has depended upon members of this order for food and clothing since before the dawn of history. Some species have been under domestication for thousands of years. Others have long been looked upon as game, and even today provide sport for millions of hunters annually.

The piglike mammals are divided into two families. The first contains the various Old World pigs, including the wild boar of Europe, Asia, and Africa, the bush-hogs, warthogs, and the babirusa of the East Indies. The tusks in the jaws of all these pigs tend to curve upward. The second family comprises New World pigs which are called peccaries. These gregarious little animals range from southern United States south to South America. The tusks of the upper jaw are always directed downward, unlike those of their Old World relatives.

Piglike animals have hair in the form of coarse bristles. Their tails are short and slender. Their muzzles are formed into a snout and flattened at the end where the nostrils are located. This snout is important in rooting through the ground in search of roots and various kinds of animal life.

The common hippopotamus (*Hippopotamus amphibius*) is a semi-aquatic inhabitant of tropical Africa. Courtesy SAN FRANCISCO ZOOLOGICAL SOCIETY

Pigs are omnivorous. They are also very dangerous if provoked. Peccaries often travel in packs and have been known at times to attack human beings.

There are two species of hippopotamuses, both of which are confined to the African continent. The common hippopotamus occurs in the rivers and lakes of tropical Africa, where it lives on aquatic vegetation. Despite its herbivorous habits this giant water mammal is considered to be extremely dangerous. Its unpredictable behavior and huge jaws are responsible for many human deaths each year. Another species, a much smaller one, is the pygmy hippopotamus, which occurs in a few parts of tropical West Africa.

Members of the camel family were once abundant in North America. They are absent there now, but their descendants are represented in the world today by the bactrian, or two-humped, camel of Asia; the dromedary, or one-humped, camel of Africa and southwestern Asia; and the llamas of South America. Camels are desert mammals, well known for their ability to go for considerable periods of time without water, although this has often been exaggerated. They have been kept by man for domestic use for some thousands of years, but they still have surly dispositions. It is questionable if any truly wild camels exist today.

Two kinds of wild llamas are found in South America—the guanaco and the vicuña. Both species are inhabitants of the higher parts of the Andes. The guanaco has been domesticated for centuries. The llama and the alpaca are derivatives of the wild stock. The wool of these high mountain animals has long been used by the native peoples of South America for clothing, and llamas are still employed as beasts of burden.

The most primitive deerlike mammals are the chevrotains, which are small antlerless inhabitants of parts of southeastern Asia and Africa. True deer are absent from Africa, except in the extreme northern part, but are abundant in Europe, Asia, and the Americas. The males of all the large deer of the world have antlers on the head. These structures are composed of bone and are shed each year, generally in late winter, and grown anew the following spring. This is true even of the enormous antlers of the moose. The only female deer to bear antlers are the caribou, or reindeer as the domesticated animals are called.

Members of the deer family are the most important big game animals in North America. Although the ranges of the wapiti, or American elk, and the moose are much restricted now, the white-tailed deer of eastern North

The llama (*Lama*) is one of the two domesticated South American camel-like animals. EDWARD S. ROSS

America and the mule deer of the West have survived well despite intensive hunting each year. The larger animals have been preserved in some of our national parks. Anyone who visits Glacier or Yellowstone National Parks or the Jackson Hole country in Wyoming will soon become familiar with moose and elk. It is not uncommon to meet these animals along the trails. Like many others I have had a number of such experiences and made it a practice to give them the right-of-way. You really do not appreciate the great height of a moose until you have had close contact with one.

Back in the mid-thirties I spent two months studying Roosevelt elk along a part of the Pacific coast and became impressed with the individuality of particular bulls of this species. In the area west of Prairie Creek in northwestern California I came to know one notably large male that was named Tusko by the local residents. Tusko was not afraid of anyone and would permit me to approach quite close. However, he had an intense dislike for a miner who lived in the region and would chase him every time he saw

A mule deer (*Odocoileus hemionus*) doe. EDWARD S. ROSS

him. According to the story that was given me, the miner had thrown some dishwater out of the back door of his cabin one evening and it had inadvertently landed on Tusko, who apparently never forgave this act.

The giraffe and the okapi are two strange related artiodactyls found in Africa. The giraffe, with its long neck and great height is adapted to feeding on the upper levels of leaves, where it has no competition from other browsing animals. The okapi, unlike the giraffe, is a shy denison of the dense tropical forests of central Africa. It is no larger than many antelope. The body is almost maroon in color, with white horizontal stripes on the legs. The okapi, because of its extreme shyness and the inaccessibility of the areas in which it lives, is one of the most recently discovered large mammals. It was unknown in the nineteenth century.

In the prairie grasslands of North America there is a unique antelope-

Nilgai (*Boselaphus*) are Asiatic bovines. Only the males bear horns. Courtesy SAN FRANCISCO ZOOLOGICAL SOCIETY

The Asiatic buffalo (*Bubalis bubalis*), unlike the buffaloes of Africa, has been domesticated for centuries. Courtesy SAN FRANCISCO ZOOLOGICAL SOCIETY

like animal known as the pronghorn. It belongs to a separate family by itself. The outer sheath of the horn in these animals has two prongs and is shed periodically.

The true antelopes are primarily inhabitants of Asia and Africa, especially Africa, where numerous species occur. A few of the better-known kinds are the waterbucks, the blackbucks, the gnus, the impalas, and the gazelles. They formerly inhabited the forests, the plains, and the deserts of Africa in seemingly untold millions, but are now being eliminated in many parts of that continent by the activities of man. Closely related to the antelopes are the large bovine animals represented in North America by the bison and musk-oxen; in Asia by the various kinds of wild cattle and oxen, the yak, and the water buffalo; and in Africa by the Cape buffalo.

The goat- and sheeplike animals are found in North America, Europe, Asia, and extreme northern Africa. In North America the musk-ox, the mountain goat, and the several kinds of native sheep belong in this group. The best-known European species are the chamois and ibex of the high mountains. In Asia there is a multitude of goat- and sheeplike artiodactyls. Some occur on the steppes, others in desert areas, and certain species, such as the takin, whose beautiful coat is thought possibly to be responsible for the legend of the Golden Fleece, are found only in the remote parts of the eastern Himalayas in far western China, Tibet, northern Burma, and Assam.

AFTERWORD

While this book is meant to serve as an introduction to the major groups of animals present in the world today, it is hoped that it will also stimulate further interest in living things and possibly influence some of the younger readers to enter the realm of natural science.

There are still many species to be discovered, especially among the invertebrate organisms. There is also a vast list of living creatures about whose habits we know little or nothing. Some of the smaller species of whales have never been seen alive and are known only from carcasses that have washed ashore. There are birds whose populations probably number in the millions but whose nests and eggs have yet to be found.

In addition to research on animals themselves, studies of their environment and its management must be made if we are to save certain species for the enjoyment of future generations. Animals such as the grizzly bear, the orangutan, the whooping crane, and the California condor are doomed to extinction before long unless some miracle of protection results in their increase. Wildlife conservation and the preservation of wilderness areas present a tremendous challenge to those of us who feel an obligation to pass on to others these natural heritages.

INDEX

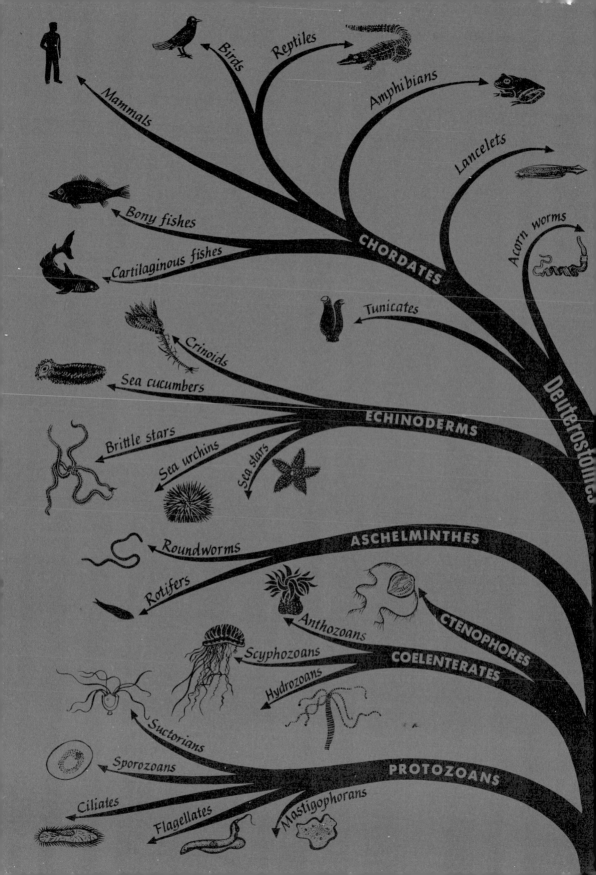

Birds

Reptiles

Mammals

Amphibians

Lancelets

Bony fishes

CHORDATES

Cartilaginous fishes

Acorn worms

Deuterostomes

Tunicates

Crinoids

Sea cucumbers

ECHINODERMS

Brittle stars

Sea urchins

Sea stars

Roundworms

ASCHELMINTHES

Rotifers

CTENOPHORES

Anthozoans

Scyphozoans

COELENTERATES

Hydrozoans

Suctorians

Sporozoans

PROTOZOANS

Ciliates

Flagellates

Mastigophorans